P9-DGD-254

Appropriate Technology Sourcebook

For tools and techniques that
use local skills, local resources,
and renewable sources of energy

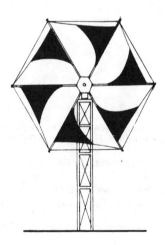

Ken Darrow and Rick Pam
November 1976

A Volunteers in Asia Publication

ABSTRACT

Appropriate Technology Sourcebook, second edition, November 1976, 304 pages.

A guide to practical plans and books for village and small community technology. Critical reviews of selected publications on alternative sources of energy, farm implements, shop tools,, agriculture, low-cost housing, health care, water supply, pedal power, philosophy of appropriate technology, and related subjects. Small-scale systems using local skills and resources are emphasized. Publications were chosen that provide enough practical information to be of significant help in understanding principles and in actually building the designs included. Entries selected on the basis of low price, clarity of presentation, easily understandable non-technical language, and unique subject matter. Materials and production techniques required are listed for all equipment plans. More than 375 publications from American and international sources. 250 illustrations. Price and address are given for each publication; some are also available in French or Spanish editions.

First Printing, November 1976,   6,000 copies
Second Printing, July 1977,   6,000 copies

Copyright © 1976, 1977
By Volunteers in Asia, Inc.
All rights reserved, including the right of
reproduction in whole or in part in any form.

Library of Congress Catalog No. 76-29526

International Standard Book No. 0-917704-00-2

First Printing, November 1976

Printed in U.S.A.

Additional copies of this book can be ordered from: Appropriate Technology Project, Volunteers in Asia, Box 4543, Stanford, California 94305, USA. Regular price is $4.00. For local groups in developing countries, the price is $2.00. For either group, discounts are available for purchases of more than 10 copies.

Contents

ACKNOWLEDGEMENT

We acknowledge with gratitude the inspiration and support provided by two friends:

Father Patrick Shaules of Taiwan, who offered support when the *Sourcebook* was only an idea and, through Operation Help, provided the financial means that enabled us to gather publications to be reviewed in the first edition;

Dr. W.P. Napitupulu, founder of Indonesia's domestic volunteer service who, through his support of appropriate technology efforts of his own volunteers and his understanding of the learning/working role of volunteers from abroad, provides the authors with much of their inspiration.

This second edition was made possible in large part due to the financial support of the following organizations:

United Methodist Committee on Relief
Lutheran World Relief
United Church Board for World Ministries
United Presbyterian Church
Maryknoll Fathers
Church World Service

To these organizations we extend our warmest thanks.

In addition, we are especially indebted to James MacCracken of CODEL, who since the first appearance of the *Sourcebook* in November 1975 has enthusiastically helped to get it into the hands of many people who could use it. He has been responsible for arranging the ecumenical funding from the above-mentioned groups. We are most appreciative of his invaluable help.

PREFACE

Preface

HOW TO USE THIS BOOK

The *Sourcebook* is intended to be used by anyone with a good English language ability, with the hope that interested people will be able to obtain whatever publications they feel are relevant. The equipment and techniques should be tested and adapted to fit local conditions. Only when it is determined that they are appropriate to these local conditions should they be spread, through the use of demonstrations and descriptive material in the local language.

This book was produced to inform people of different nationalities about some of the small-scale systems that have been successfully used. A parallel function within a country can be served when low-cost rural development catalogues showing a wide range of tools and techniques are distributed. Making people aware of what has been done elsewhere is an important step in the development of locally-appropriate technology, but it should never be forgotten that local adaptation, innovation and self-reliance is the goal.

WHY THE SOURCEBOOK?

This book represents the action component of our view of appropriate technology. It identifies existing plans for small-scale technology from all over the world, that can be used for local experimentation and adaptation *without* the need to import the equipment described. It represents a low cost method of information exchange from poor to poor, rich to poor, and increasingly from poor to rich, as people in the developed countries have begun to rediscover many of the things that they can in fact do for themselves. No computers and no experts are involved.

The intent of this book is not to suggest that appropriate technology consists only of technology; it is primarily an *approach*, and the technology arrived at is only the last step in the process. Part of the approach involves becoming aware of what other people in other places have done to solve similar problems. This is where the *Sourcebook* fits in.

We are a tiny group and intend to remain so, because that is the way we work best. The *Sourcebook* was born of conversations with Asians who complained of the inaccessibility of practical information on small-scale technology that they could adapt to fit the needs of rural development projects. The high price of the books they did know about and the scanty information about the contents of these books were discouraging—the price of a handful of books that might turn out to be irrelevant was equal to the salary of a staff member for a month. We checked around and discovered that no one had compiled a directory of do-it-yourself designs that didn't depend on industrialized materials. The *Whole Earth Catalog* is perhaps the closest thing to what we were thinking of, but its broad American-oriented focus overwhelms what it does contain that might be relevant to developing countries. (Sifting through the *Catalog* family of publications did lead to about 15% of the books we decided to include.)

Pat Shaules generously provided a grant for book purchases to get us started. We printed the 75-page first edition on a 10-year-old offset press and bound it by hand, which seemed very much in keeping with the spirit of the subject matter. We did this for three printings over 11 months (we had intended that first edition to last only 5 months). At the time this larger book is going to press, the first edition is being used in more than 75 countries. The extra time has allowed us to communicate with a wide variety of people involved in appropriate technology work, and make some important improvements in the *Sourcebook* format. We were also able to locate a much more substantial collection of materials to be reviewed; these are on the whole stronger than the original materials (which are included with some changes).

WHO WROTE THIS BOOK

Volunteers in Asia is a small group of young people, affiliated with three universities in California, USA. Some 30 people go to Asia each year at the request of Asian institutions, to live, work and study with Asians on their terms. Our work in Asia is done in a spirit of co-operation rather than problem-solving.

Two returned volunteers (who had worked in Indonesia) started the Appropriate Technology Project at VIA's home office in January 1975. Our living and working experiences in Asia had left us with an awareness of the many important values and models Asians have to offer us, a concern for the problems of developing countries, and a belief that while cooperative discussion is to be welcomed, it is inappropriate for foreigners to propose solutions. Great interest among Asian friends of VIA in the idea of appropriate technology had led us to seriously attempt to find a useful complementary role in that area. One of the very few roles which we decided foreigners could legitimately perform was to gather information *on* information. Specifically, we decided to attempt to identify published materials from all over the world that could be of use to those people creating an appropriate village technology.

There are three major sources for the printed materials we have reviewed here. One is the large number of small groups working on rural development projects in developing countries. Another is the growing network of international organizations that are deliberately doing research and development work around the concept of appropriate technology. The third is the small but vigorous alternative technology movement in the United States that is attempting to develop small-scale systems and renewable energy resources in a push towards self-reliance for small groups and communities. From this latter group we have attempted to identify the portion of the literature that *might* be useful in developing countries. The key is *adapting*, not *adopting*, the ideas contained in the materials from all three sources—for the fact that they were produced in a different context (and in English) limits their immediate applicability in most places.

It should be noted that everything reviewed here has been carefully examined by us, with the exception of about 5 publications which we have good reason to believe are quite valuable, but were unable to obtain ourselves before the press deadline; all of these are noted as such. All comments within quotation marks come from the publications reviewed—they represent what we feel are accurate claims as to the content of each publication or the intent of the authors. We have also included quotes that are valuable simply as information. Our reviews are an attempt to provide more of an idea of the content of each publication than can be determined from the titles on publications lists. This is deliberately a very selective list of what is available.

All of the reviews were written by people who have worked in a developing country, in cooperative projects with local people. The two of us involved full-time with the project were at one time volunteer English teachers with some local Indonesian organizations that had a legitimate need for the language. We both had an interest in village development and technology at the time we were there, backed up by academic and other work beforehand. Ken was able to return to Indonesia in the spring of 1976 after the appearance of the first *Sourcebook*, to visit appropriate village technology projects and discuss the concept with a large number of 'practitioners'. The English teaching experience has given us both an appreciation of the difficulties of the English language and the obstacles to understanding that technical terms can present. We have tried to write reviews in clear, easily understandable language wherever possible, though we admit that this has not always been successfully accomplished. Technical terms used are defined in the glossary.

This is a book written by non-experts for non-experts. The work on this book has been a period of intense self-education on these small-scale systems for the past 2 years. There are no experts at identifying potentially appropriate technology, and we certainly do not claim to have the 'final word' on any publications. We do hope the reader will find our judgement has been reasonably consistent. We believe that on the whole the publications we have chosen to review are of great potential value, both in this country and in developing countries. We have a huge pile of books that we decided not to include, because they were not clear enough, too expensive, or violated several of the principles of appropriate technology. Those publications we did review were selected from among literally thousands that we examined. Dozens of bibliographies and indexes were also carefully sifted for relevant information.

We generally used $10.00 as a rough upper price limit for books—anything more than this was considered too much to give the book a chance for a significant circulation. Exceptions were made for a few excellent reference books which might be purchased by an appropriate technology center. Each publication was checked for clarity, use of standard rather than technical English, and applicability to the conditions in rural areas of developing countries (where sophisticated components do not exist as 'scrap' in junkyards).

Much of the material listed here may already be known to you, the reader, or may cover technology that your country already effectively employs. We have simply tried to include things that might be useful in a wide variety of circumstances. We welcome your comments and suggestions.

While working on this second edition, we received a great deal of help from several people. Most significant was Thomas B. Fricke, who had worked in the past as a VIA village technology volunteer in Indonesia for 2 years. He produced virtually the entire Agriculture and Methane Gas sections and contributed some reviews in other sections.

For help on the health care section, we are particularly indebted to Lynne Coen, who suggested and reviewed many of the books we included. She had worked at a rural health care project that uses only villagers as primary health care workers (in the mountains of Sinaloa, Mexico). Lynne was a member of a team that visited some 40 village health care projects in Latin America. Dan Goodman, an old friend who was also part of the Sinaloa project contributed several reviews. Bill Bower, who had trained village health workers in the Sinaloa project and participated in the Latin America trip helped us with the introduction to the Health Care section.

Dick Stanley, formerly a staff member of VITA (Volunteers in Technical Assistance, based in Maryland) and recently doing appropriate technology work in Tanzania, provided great amounts of energy and enthusiasm along with good criticisms and suggestions, particularly with respect to the Water Supply section.

We are also indebted to a number of VIA volunteers, the regular VIA staff, and numerous friends. We remain responsible for any errors.

—Ken Darrow and Rick Pam

INTRODUCTION

Every machine that helps every individual has a place,
but there should be no place for machines
that concentrate power in a few hands
and turn the masses into machine-minders,
if indeed they do not make them unemployed.
—Gandhi

Shall we forever resign the pleasure
of construction to the carpenter?
...Where is this division of labor to end?
and what object does it finally serve?
No doubt another MAY also think for me;
but it is not therefore desirable that he should do so
to the exclusion of my thinking for myself.
—Thoreau

Introduction

"...valuable know-how as well as excellent equipment, fitting into the constraints and limitations of poverty and suitable for genuine development, exist all over the world—in the rich as well as in the poor countries. But it is scattered, hidden, often very poorly documented, and generally inaccessible to those in need, when it is most needed. Countless men and women 'in the field' are trying to solve problems for which solutions have already been found somewhere else; are embarking on experiments which have already been shown to be unfruitful; are trying to find methods of working and items of equipment which may be available, but they do not know where. At this level of know-how and technology there is an almost total lack of effective international communication."

—E.F. Schumacher, in the journal *Appropriate Technology*

This book represents an attempt to increase cross-cultural communication among non-experts about small-scale technologies that are potentially appropriate in a wide variety of circumstances. Our purpose is to present a selection of capital-saving, labor-using tools and techniques that *already* have proved to be of practical value.

It is not suggested that anyone adopt everything listed here. "Appropriate technology" is an approach, not a specific package of technology. It is our hope that there will be a few tools, a few techniques, and a few ideas here that deserve a closer look by any reader, that could be usefully adapted to his or her country's set of circumstances. These might be adapted to help create an appropriate technology for any one locality.

WHAT IS "APPROPRIATE TECHNOLOGY"?

"Appropriate technology" is a term that represents a particular view of society and technology. It suggests that technology is neither neutral nor does it evolve along a single path. It recognizes that different cultural and geographical groups will have different technologies that are appropriate to their circumstances; that technological self-determination is essential to cultural identity (and political independence). It suspects that the only wise technologies are those which seek to accomodate themselves to the biological environment within which they are used; it is called, among other things, 'environmentally appropriate technology.' It assumes that the purpose of economically productive activity is to produce what is determined by need, in an enjoyable, creative process; not what is determined by endless greed, in an alienating, repetitive production process. It stresses that every society has a technological tradition and that new technologies must grow out of this tradition. And it presumes that the only development that makes sense is development of the people and their skills, by the people and for the people.

The term "appropriate technology" implies that there is such a thing as *inappropriate technology.* As suggested above, there is a need to develop appropriate technologies not only among those people on the planet who have too little, but equally among those people that have so much that they are extraordinarily wasteful. It is significant that appropriate technology thus is not one more fashionable remedy to be recommended to the people of poor countries by the people of rich countries.   Not only are many of the most committed advocates of appropriate technology members of rich countries who are working for a more human-scale technology to fit their own conditions, but the very origins of the movement come from the Gandhian tradition of local production for local needs.

CRITERIA

The tools and techniques found in this book share the following characteristics:

1) low in capital costs;

2) use local materials whenever possible;

3) create jobs, employing local skills and labor;

4) are small enough in scale to be affordable by a small group of farmers;

5) can be understood, controlled and maintained by villagers wherever possible, without a high level of Western-style education;

6) can be produced out of a small metal-working shop, if not in a village itself;

7) suppose that people can and will work together to collectively bring improvements to their communities, recognizing that in most of the world important decisions are made by groups rather than by individuals;

8) involve decentralized renewable energy sources, such as wind power, solar energy, water power, methane gas, animal power, and pedal-power (such as in that highly efficient machine, the bicycle);

9) make technology understandable to the people who are using it and thus suggest ideas that could be used in further innovations;

10) are flexible so that they can continue to be used or adapted to fit changing circumstances;

11) do not involve patents, royalties, consultant fees, import duties, shipping charges, or financial wizards; practical plans can be obtained free or at low cost and no further payment is involved.

APPROPRIATE TECHNOLOGY IN DEVELOPMENT

Sor.ie of the reasoning that underlies the concept of appropriate technology might be summarized as follows:

1) it permits local needs to be met more effectively, because local people are involved in identifying and working to address these needs;

2) it means the development of tools that extend human labor and skills, rather than machines that replace human labor and eliminate human skills; there is not an attempt to eliminate the human element but to make it both more productive and more creative;

3) it represents a comprehendible and controllable scale of activities, organization and mistakes, at which people without sophisticated management training can work together and understand what they are doing;

4) it allows a more economical operation by minimizing the transport of goods in an era of expensive energy, allowing greater interaction of local industry and permitting greater use of local resources—both human and material;

5) it makes unnecessary many expensive or unavailable finance, transportation, education, advertising, management, and energy services; and avoids the loss of local control that use of such outside services implies;

6) it helps to establish a self-sustaining and expanding reservoir of skills in the

community which begins from already existing skills;

7) it tends towards decentralization of production, thus permitting the full benefits of work to remain within a community; this also allows control to remain within the community;

8) it provides a region with a cushion against the effects of outside economic changes (e.g., the collapse of the world sugar market or the sudden unavailability of fertilizer);

9) it helps to reduce economic, social, and political dependency between individuals, between regions, and between nations, by recognizing that people can and will do things for themselves if the obstacles to this are removed;

10) it is in harmony with the cultural traditions of the area; this does not mean that it is stagnant, but that it evolves along with the culture, and does not contradict values the people believe to be important; the technology is adapted to fit the culture rather than the culture being forced to adapt to fit the technology.*

Taken together, these ideas mean that the maximum amount of control and initiative should be invested in the people affected, at the village or small community level. The role of the outsider is limited to that of catalyst, who helps to motivate villagers to collectively address their problems and who helps to provide some technical support for whatever the villagers decide they would like to do. Creativity and ingenuity are encouraged—people who have been self-reliant for centuries are aided in their efforts to improve their living conditions, agricultural production, and health through techniques and equipment that they can understand, build, and repair themselves—and so remain self-reliant. These same people should become the new inventors and initiators of new forms of appropriate technology in the future—appropriate to their own local conditions.

This view implies a participatory technology development process, and demands a horizontal communication network that will enable villagers in one corner of the country to learn what other villagers elsewhere have invented to handle common problems. Such an information network seems to work in China, and is being tried in Indonesia, Papua New Guinea, and India, among other places, where catalogues of village technologies are being circulated. A parallel function is being served by the Sourcebook—communication across national boundaries among small groups and individuals who are experimenting with appropriate technology.

Another essential complementary effort must be the reorientation of the schools away from subject matter left over from colonial curriculums of use only to the few who progress to each new level. Education must be relevant to the daily life of the community. The technical schools must shift their training away from the operation of imported machinery towards the creation of an inventive capacity in their students that can make use of local resources, local skills, and renewable sources of energy.

The widespread adaptation and development of appropriate technology would in itself probably do little to affect the domestic political problems that developing countries face. (It might have a considerable effect on foreign policy considerations with respect to equipment imports, monetary policy, political concessions in return for aid, and other matters—but this depends on the structure of the political and economic system and at what level the development of local self-reliance begins to conflict with other political interests.) The need for real land reform, for example, cannot be eliminated simply by placing

*See Tom Bender in *Sharing Smaller Pies* on many of the criteria listed on these 2 pages.

techniques and equipment in the hands of the villagers. On the other hand, the development of appropriate technology is probably a necessary part of meaningful land reform—if villagers cannot afford the equipment used in agriculture, their new land will soon be owned by someone else. The fact that appropriate technology depends so heavily on an organized, self-reliant community means that where it is successful it is likely to evolve along with the political power of the villages.

The criteria we have mentioned represent an emerging consensus in response to the many criticisms that development efforts have received. We have made many assumptions here, e.g., that some development is needed in most rural areas of developing countries. (Some people assume that all development is good, while others assume that all development is bad—that people should be left alone.) The commonly-held view that most peasants are desperately poor is sufficiently true that some rural development help is needed. On the other hand, the opposing view of the contented peasant living close to the natural rhythms of life is also sufficiently true that it cannot be ignored. The best way to ensure that development addresses the felt needs but does not destroy what the people believe to be of value, is to help people to develop themselves in the ways that they choose.

We do not agree with the assumption that development must lead along the same path for all societies. Indeed, the very relevance of this book to North Americans is that it helps to see some paths other than the one our society is currently on. One of the challenges facing us is to find a path along which technology can once again have a human scale.

It is significant that while appropriate technology in the United States will necessarily take different forms than in developing countries, there will be a great deal more overlap than in the past. This will be particularly true with respect to the use of small-scale systems that harness alternative sources of energy. American appropriate technologists will begin to regain the ability to use tools and shape their working and living environments. This is an ability that most people in the rural areas of developing countries have not lost, and in that sense we, not they, are underdeveloped. It is a primary assumption of the authors that these skills can be developed further among both groups.

There are engineers and other highly-trained professionals in Asia, Africa, and Latin America for whom the kind of technology we have been discussing may seem less exciting than nuclear power plants or communications satellites. To these people we ask the question: "Who is going to design a windgenerator that is truly adapted to the conditions in your country?" The alternative technology movements in England and the U.S. are indeed using 'locally available materials' such as scrap auto parts and surplus military aircraft generators. These are available resources, and thus in some sense appropriate technology in these countries, but certainly not in other countries where such parts are not readily available. Other subjects which almost certainly will not be addressed by any organizations within the rich countries include the development of: a truly low-cost methane (bio-gas) digester for the poor farmer; safe, practical, low-cost solar cookers; pedal-powered equipment to drive shop tools; small-scale water wheels to power threshers, hullers, mills and shop tools; and small rough terrain vehicles with low horsepower engines.

There is a need for such people to become involved in the establishment of regional appropriate technology centers:

> "The most important way of communicating data on low-cost technologies is through the development of indigenous 'knowledge centers' in the developing countries themselves. It is only through such centers that needs and resources

can be properly identified, and the knowledge and practice of appropriate technologies widely disseminated.''

—from the journal *Appropriate Technology*

Some Thoughts on the Appropriate Technology Movement

AN ILLUSION OF CONSENSUS

The term 'appropriate technology' appears to be at the point of two important thresholds. The first is into general acceptance by development professionals as a legitimate idea. The second is the beginning of a decline in the integrity of the term, the signs of which are already evident.

The trouble with the term 'intermediate technology', it has been argued, is that it seems to imply that the technology is somehow inferior to the existing 'modern' technology. 'Intermediate' also says nothing about the *process* by which the technology is to be developed, who is to control it, how it relates to social and cultural factors, and what effects it will have on the natural environment. 'Appropriate technology' seems to include a concern for all of these; yet just like 'alternative technology' it depends on the sensitivity of the user to communicate the full connotations, without which both terms are almost meaningless. Just recently some visitors wanted to discuss ''alternative technologies—solar and nuclear''! Nuclear power is certainly an alternative to other power sources, but it decidedly is *not* an 'alternative technology' in the sense in which that word has come to be understood! Peter Harper, an editor of *Undercurrents* magazine (see review among PERIODICALS), made the point about terminology quite well: *''the meaning becomes established by convention within the community that uses it...the term 'alternative technology' has acquired an 'illicit' content narrower than a strict interpretation would call for...which seems to be conditioned by the connotations of the word 'alternative' in the counter-culture of the West: not controlled by dominant institutions, cheap, improvisatory, personalized, accessible to amateurs.* In this book we are using the term 'appropriate technology' to include social, political, cultural and environmental elements that are essential in determining 'appropriateness.'

The appropriate technology movement is now experiencing a false consensus that is directly related to the discrepancy between the apparent meaning suggested by the word 'appropriate' and the full connotations of the term as used by a part of the movement. The term 'appropriate technology' has been repeated and used and invoked in article after article, and the essential connotations of the term have been increasingly eroded and ignored during this process. Curiously, this seems to be because the concept did not have time to mature properly so that its implications could be identified and appreciated, before it began to come into wider use (often as an equivalent to 'intermediate technology'). The concept of 'intermediate technology' has emerged and run its course, and has now given way to the concept of 'appropriate technology', which is different is some important ways. Unfortunately, there has been no single book like *Small is Beautiful* to fully articulate this more evolved concept (Tom Bender's *Sharing Smaller Pies*, Nicolas Jequier's Part 1 of *Appropriate*

Technology: Problems and Promises, and *A Handbook on Appropriate Technology* do this quite well, but none of these has yet had a circulation comparable to *Small is Beautiful*).

The consequences of this false consensus are rather alarming. While many people who consider themselves part of the appropriate technology movement are focusing their energies on enthusiastically recruiting others, some very critical events are already beginning to take place relatively unnoticed. A representative from a major international organization visited us recently, and had this to say: His organization intends to get technically sophisticated engineers and social scientists to visit the rural areas of developing countries and design technology to fit these circumstances. Stainless-steel small-scale machines would then be produced in American factories and exported to these countries. It is rather unnerving to hear this described as 'appropriate technology.' It is just a formula for continued dependency.

It is very possible that some great mistakes will be made due to this kind of thinking, all in the name of appropriate technology. The failure of any effort conceived along these lines is assured; the introduction of high-technology small-scale machines has been tried for years by other groups, but without being called 'appropriate technology.' This is probably best illustrated by the enormous number of small-scale water supply systems built with industrialized products and installed in small village communities. Most of these have failed to successfully operate for long, because local social and cultural practices have been neglected, local people have not been trained in maintenance, and the pumps have required a highly skilled technician with a sophisticated workshop for repairs. In fact, the number of new water pumps rusting in government stockpiles, and outside the homes of local officials who obtained them but did not distribute them, is shocking.

To return to the erosion of the integrity of the term 'appropriate technology,' we can cite some other instructive examples. The most extreme of these is that some influential people are now simply claiming that high technology is the most appropriate technology, thereby begging the questions involved (and obviously ignoring whatever consensus does exist about the criteria for appropriate technology). Another noticeable example is the fact that organizations all over the United States and the world are rewriting their histories and claiming that appropriate technology is of course what they have been doing all along.

Some groups undoubtedly *had* been doing appropriate technology work for a long time before the term became fashionable. But for most organizations, the particular set of concerns that define this approach have never before been seen as a related package. For example, only recently have many people begun to think of AT and self-reliance as essential to each other. If village-level work is to be redefined as AT work—without a careful look at this whole set of ideas—only a semantic shift will occur. Most of what is written about American volunteers, for example, discusses at length the successful technologies they have introduced. But rarely is there mention of local participation in innovation, or attempts by volunteers to encourage or support such innovation. Instead, these Americans are presented as the only innovators, bringing oil-drum gadgetry to what are portrayed as people with no knowledge, skills, or technological history. This attitude has hurt many development efforts in the past—villagers have in effect been told that they have no skills that are relevant to 'modern' life. Under such circumstances, at best the local people many reproduce something useful that the outsider has introduced; but the ability of local people to solve their own problems hasn't been increased at all. The spirit of the AT movement is lacking here; also missing is a full appreciation of questions of who controls, adapts, and uses technology. Appropriate technology includes all these things; it must not be allowed to become synonymous with oil-drum technology.

APPROPRIATE TECHNOLOGY AS A CULTURAL REVOLUTION

Appropriate technology is especially attractive because it seems to solve a number of problems at once. Because it involves self-reliance and local production for local needs, on a national level this approach can remove from the list of obstacles to development many of the inequities of an international system that is dominated by the expensive technology and economic power of the rich countries. At the same time, the lack of a well-developed infrastructure and the shortage of highly-trained manpower to run large industrial operations become much less important when people are allowed and encouraged to develop themselves wherever they are. A whole array of problems can potentially be solved at once.

It is precisely for these reasons that the appropriate technology concept is spreading in popularity so rapidly. Those who believe in small entrepreneurial capitalism, decentralist Marxism, European socialism, African communalism, and Buddhism can all find much of value in the ideas underlying appropriate technology. Different people are attracted to it because it seems to address so many fundamental problems so directly. The question becomes "Will these people discover the full implications of appropriate technology principles? Or will they see only the part of the appropriate technology philosophy that directly affects their concerns, and ignore the rest?"

Nicolas Jequier* has described the soaring popularity of the appropriate technology approach as evidence of a 'cultural revolution' in development thinking. The elements of self-reliance, local initiative, and local control that are essential parts of this approach have far-reaching implications when they are logically applied to the development structure as it now exists. As with any cultural revolution, this one threatens to turn the whole organizational structure upside-down, and shake up the old ways of doing things.

The initial reaction from development professionals has been varied. Some seem to be welcoming appropriate technology as the new panacea that will cure all the ills identified in development efforts so far. Others seem to view it as requiring only a slight adjustment in the emphasis of their efforts—rather like adding one more person to an already crowded bus. Still others find the accompanying philosophy of self-reliance in harmony with what they have been doing all along.

Appropriate Technology, while not a panacea by any means, is an unusually broad spectrum medicine—as noted above, it addresses so many parts of the development process that virtually everyone can find something valid in it. But the appropriate technology philosophy not only treats many of the ills of the dominant approaches to development, it also threatens to dramatically change the relationship between the 'doctor' and the 'patient.' The role of large organizations is fundamentally challenged, and the kinds of research and researchers required are radically different. Much of the development-aid process as presently conceived is called into question.

Some people have suggested that the way in which a restructuring of development efforts can best be handled is in a shift in emphasis away from 'hardware' (equipment) to 'software' (e.g., organizational systems, data gathering techniques, motivational strategies, 'institution building'). If we understand appropriate technology to be an approach rather than a specific

---

*See *Appropriate Technology: Problems and Promises*, reviewed on page 31.

package of technology, we are in fact agreeing that the hardware is of secondary importance. However, 'software' can be equally as capital-intensive as hardware, and equally inappropriate.

In the wake of a cultural revolution, the game must change considerably—the field, the players, and the goals will no longer be the same. Not only the *content* but the *relationship* of rich country research to poor country development must be a very different one. Given the importance of initiative, creativity, and adaptiveness on the part of local people and their role in judging 'appropriateness', there will be much less of a place for the results of capital-intensive research by foreign scholars. Local research will be much less capital-intensive and will be more closely linked to action in local programs. As knowledge is demystified, there will be no room for jargon such as the word 'software' itself, a term borrowed from computer terminology which obscures more than it reveals when applied to development issues. Indeed, one of the prime principles of appropriate technology is the demystification of knowledge and the triumph of the common man over the experts. Research will be valued to the extent that it is understandable and usable to the large number of appropriate technology practitioners.

APPROPRIATE TECHNOLOGY AND PLAIN SPEECH

There are some interesting models of how a network of plain speaking appropriate technologists can communicate with each other. There are a number of such networks in the U.S. and U.K., particularly doing experiments with alternative sources of energy. It is a relatively common thing for small newsletters to spring up among such people, and it is interesting to look at their contents, particularly at the way they use language.

The English 'radical technologists' in particular seem to have begun to address the problem of jargon (specialized vocabulary). Conventional scientists and researchers are always creating new terms which do two things: serve as a shorthand notation for a useful concept and (usually unintentionally) keep the uninitiated from understanding what's being discussed. The radical technologists have the same need to create terms to indicate entire concepts, but what they have started to do is to use common English words and phrases, so as to create a jargon that is at once useful and understandable to all. Thus we have sentences like this: "*What I shall call 'clever ideas' are otherwise known as Doing More With Less and boil down ultimately to Good Design.*" After reading this, who needs phrases like 'optimum input utilization' anymore?

In the United States, Peter Van Dresser has identified a phenomenon that he has labeled the 'Clothes Line Paradox.'* This kind of language use is effective and easy to understand.

The determination of what is appropriate technology cannot be left solely to the engineers, because it is really a multi-disciplinary problem that demands the participation of people who can see the many different elements that need to be considered:

> "*Above all appropriate technology demands fundamental thinking...the most significant contributions will come from those who can ask basic questions about the purpose of a technology and the way in which it should be used.*"
> —M.M. Hoda in *Appropriate Technology and Research Projects*

---

*'Clothes Line Paradox'—this refers to the fact that solar energy is never figured into the national energy use statistics; if you switch from an outdoor solar clothes line to an indoor clothes drier, the recorded energy use goes from zero to some positive figure. If you switch back to an outdoor clothes line, you suddenly drop out of the statistics once again. Statistics thus never adequately show the importance of solar energy use.

*"One of the central problems about terminology use in developing countries
is that issues are raised which seem to require the use of language in relatively
unusual ways. Most obviously, it seems more urgent in developing countries
than in developed countries to have technology issues discussed by
non-technologists."*

—Choice and Adaptation of Technology in Developing Countries (OECD, 1974)

This is provocative; we would go a bit further and suggest that for the
development of appropriate technology *anywhere* it is important to have
technology issues discussed by non-technologists.

In general, it seems we can all appreciate the first principle of 'appropriate'
language: jargon should be used only when absolutely necessary, and it should
be both reasonably obvious in meaning and retain a sense of humor and human
scale.

APPROPRIATE VILLAGE TECHNOLOGISTS: THE NEW GENERALISTS

There is a particular group of people in developing countries who need to
have a larger role in the dialogue about technology issues. These are people
working in small rural development efforts, often without the support of the
government or outside agencies.

Up to 80 or 90% of the population in most developing countries lives in rural
villages. Probably 50% of the people who do live in the urban areas wouldn't
be there if they hadn't fled the stifling lack of opportunities that characterizes
many rural areas. Thus a rural based, appropriate village technology would
seem to directly concern some 90-95% of the population. An important voice in
the dialogue about village technology can and should be provided by educated
people working at the local level in small projects. However, many of the
members of groups doing extension work seem hesitant to get involved in
experiments with the technology they are disseminating, because this is seen
as the province of engineers. But the development of appropriate technology is
not solely a question of engineering design—it involves a wide range of considerations that engineers have not been trained to include in their calculations.

Appropriate technology cuts across traditional lines of expertise, and must
rely heavily on intuition and experience where the data is simply not available
for the conventional scientific approach. The small-scale systems covered in
this book are not particularly difficult to understand. Village problems do not
require the importation of licensed technology, the intervention of multi-
national corporations, or the use of computer print-outs for their solutions.
These problems are centered around basic needs such as water supply,
adequate housing, increased agricultural production as a means to improved
nutrition, better methods for food and crop storage, and fuel supplies. Many of
the people of generalist backgrounds who are presently involved in running
small village development projects are quite capable of understanding and
effectively using most of what is included in the *Sourcebook* on these subjects,
without any further training. There is a clear need for people like this to begin
to think of themselves as 'village technologists' who can keep the villages
aware of what has been done elsewhere.

Quite often a friend in a developing country sees what we are doing and says
"Great! Can you send me someone who can build these things?" In fact, these
friends and the people they work with are quite capable of building and
operating most of these systems themselves, although sometimes they will
need some technical help and advice. However, in most cases the technical
knowledge they need can be found among their countrymen; it is just a matter
of finding out which person can help them.

An unusual but true example can illustrate how far this approach can take people. We have visited a village in northern Bali where the people have been very active in their own self-help projects for many years. Recently, they asked an engineer in a nearby town if it was true that electricity could be produced by harnessing a small stream. They ended up getting all the technical help they needed to design a small water-turbine system, which they proceeded to build and pay for themselves using money from the sale of coffee. They had to buy the generator and they had the simple Banki turbine made in a large city, but the dam construction, the turbine installation, the wiring throughout the village, and all the rest were done by the villagers themselves. This is a dramatic example, which admittedly could not have been completed without the coffee revenues. The point is that remarkable things are possible when villagers are organized and begin to believe that they can work to develop their own village.

If a village can mobilize itself to find needed technical help, it should be possible for better educated members of small organizations in developing countries to find similar technical help within their own countries.

PEOPLE'S PARTICIPATION

Nicolas Jequier identifies the major practicing group of appropriate technologists as the millions of craftsmen around the world, who quietly and individually innovate and over time create the most appropriate technology. It is almost by definition appropriate, because it has evolved within the existing resource, skill and cultural context.

The theme of people's participation runs through most of what has been said about appropriate technology. This comes in part from a philosophy which measures development in terms of the people's skills and their ability to solve their own problems. Self-determination and local control can only come through this. Outsiders cannot develop people—they can only remove obstacles and provide access to resources and information that people can use to develop themselves.

People's participation also makes a great deal of sense from a technical standpoint, as described in the following quotes:

> "It is clear that much of the technological power in the developing countries may take forms other than the expenditure of R&D (research and development) resources on highly sophisticated, capital-intensive and skill-intensive research establishments or on the creation of multi-headed scientific elites. Popular participation, i.e., the mobilization of people now struggling for survival beyond the fringes of modern technology and often showing considerable ingenuity in doing so, should play a much larger role. This applies particularly to the small farmer."

> —Hans Singer, Institute of Development Studies in Brighton, England

> "Detailed technological information in terms of local labor conditions, and the resource situation, transport facilities, etc., may well be more easily accessible to the man on the spot, but does he really know very much about the potentially relevant techniques used in other economies but not yet locally? Certainly, if he learns more about the experiences of other countries, he may well be in a better position than the man at the center to judge the local technological possibilities in the light of rural conditions."

> —Amartya Sen, in Technology and Employment in Industry

THE HORIZONTAL DIFFUSION OF INNOVATIONS

If the real innovation is going to take place from the bottom up, this leaves a rather different role for those people traditionally involved in the field of 'diffusion of innovations.' Some innovations will still need technical back-up as they spread, and effective communications techniques to demonstrate their usefulness. It will now be the villagers, however, who are telling the extension agent how to do things!

The scientific study of the diffusion of innovations has concentrated on spreading a particular innovation as widely as possible with little attention given to its appropriateness and a great deal of attention given to how to *overcome* peasant resistance. The attitude has been that the extension worker 'knows best,' and the emphasis has been on how to convince the farmer that the extension worker is right. Only rarely in this literature does one find suggestions that one should attempt to understand the farmer's perspective and cooperate with him. This should be turned around, and the extension agent should work with the peasants to try to identify what might be appropriate. He should *listen* to the peasants when they are resistant to an innovation, because there is probably a very good reason for this. The extension worker will probably know more about what has been tried in other areas, but the villagers will know more about what local skills and resources are available. Neither group can really know whether a particular idea from outside can be effectively combined with these local skills and resources until it is tried; and the extension worker should not pretend to know that something will work (which has too often happened in the past).

THE ROLE OF THE CATALYST IN THE DEVELOPMENT OF LOCALLY APPROPRIATE TECHNOLOGY

> "A student who can weave his technology into the fabric of society can claim to have had a liberal education. A student who cannot weave his technology into the fabric of society cannot even claim to be a good technologist."
> —Sir Eric Ashby, quoted in Lectures on Socially Appropriate Technology

> "Catalysts...must realize their own behavior, beliefs, and attitudes are not universal—rather, they must be able to understand and accept the values and behavior patterns which exist in the area where they are working. Thus, it is not enough to be technically competent."
> —A Handbook on Appropriate Technology

> "As Westerners and as technologists we have a role to play, but we must be self-critical about our own society before we have the wisdom and insight to be of any real value."
> —Harry Dickinson, in Lectures on Socially Appropriate Technology

These three people have identified some of the most important considerations for an outsider going to work on the development of locally appropriate technology. Because the expensive high technology of the rich countries cannot really even be considered appropriate in the rich countries (due to high levels of unemployment, poor quality of goods, environmental destruction, lack of control at the local level, wanton energy wastage, and a host of other reasons) it is hard to imagine that a person who is unaware and uncritical of this in his or her own country will be sensitive to the same kind of questions while working in a developing country.

A village technologist or engineer who thinks that technology is neutral and that cultural practices must change to fit the technology is also not likely to be of much help in the development of technology appropriate to local culture and beliefs. He denies that this is possible, and seeks to convince the 'backward' people with different beliefs that *they* should change their beliefs and 'enter the modern world.'

In fact, it seems most likely that such a person would have to view intermediate technology as simply a stepping stone to high technology. This view of a uni-directional inevitable path in the development of technology is precisely one of the things that appropriate technologists have been challenging. They argue that while technical knowledge is absolute and not a matter of choice, the particular way this technical knowledge appears in the form of technology can be entirely a matter of choice. They conclude that societies should be able to develop their people and their tools in novel ways that are compatible with their views of the world. Schumacher touches on this point in the essay "Buddhist Economics" that appears in *Small is Beautiful*.

> "The modern economist...is used to measuring the standard of living by the amount of annual consumption, assuming all the time that a man who consumes more is better off than a man who consumes less. A Buddhist economist would consider this approach excessively irrational: since consumption is merely a means to human well-being, the aim should be to obtain the maximum of well-being with the minimum of consumption."

The point here is that so-called 'modern' technology and the engineering and economics that accompany it are not neutral, but are the products of a set of very distinct assumptions and ideological choices. In particular, we live by the assumption that more is better, and that endless growth is both possible and desirable. We assume that if people have more to consume but lose control over their work they will be happier than if they have less to consume but control the work that they do. It is the responsibility of people in the rich countries who disagree with this philosophy to try to change it. Regardless of one's personal opinion on this question, one must at least recognize the assumptions that underly our technology, and try to help other peoples with other belief systems develop technologies that are not in opposition to their beliefs.

Foreigners are often both unaware of their own culturally-bound beliefs and unnecessarily critical of the beliefs of local people. The 'image of limited good' is often used as an example of an irrational belief frequently found in villages. The essence of this belief is that anything that benefits one person does so at the expense of another. Westerners tend to ridicule this idea. Environmentalists, however, are probably quite aware of the element of truth contained in this belief—they know that many technical 'advances' bring with them negative environmental results. In this light, the villagers appear to be not so irrational after all. As we see it, the 'image of limited good' (which can admittedly get in the way of needed development work) is no more irrational than the ideology of unlimited growth and affluence.

Apart from respect for local beliefs, the way in which an outsider goes about being an appropriate technology catalyst deserves some consideration. The following note from *A Handbook on Appropriate Technology* provides some useful insights:

> "One of the most important factors which determines whether a new technology will be successful or not is the extent of real community participation in its conception and development. It is very important that the appropriate technology catalyst work with the local leaders and community members

during the entire process of introducing a technology, from its conception to its installation and use. This involves more input from the community than merely casual labor. It means that the technology must be understood by all and controllable at the local level. Only if the population is really involved will there be sufficient awareness to capitalize on the new knowledge and generalize it to other situations...(Success should not be judged by the extent to which the community adapts to the new technology, but)...by the extent to which the community becomes more self-reliant and more able to solve its own problems in the future.''

NO-COST TECHNOLOGY

One of the prime considerations in the development of appropriate village technology is to find ways in which people can invest just their unemployed labor to produce something more than what they now have. If these people are not fully participating in a market economy (which is commonly the case), it is not a question of what manipulations an economist can suggest to maximize the yield on their time and capital; capital in this case is not easily measured because it is in the land and the trees and the bamboo. Conventional economic analysis has little to say in such a situation because such capital is generally ignored. In the *Sourcebook*, for example, there are five or six books that demonstrate that a windmill for pumping water could be built with absolutely zero cash investment. If there is a normal amount of wind in an area that needs some irrigation of small plots, industrialized gas-powered pumps, even if cheap, should not be able to compete with 'no-cost' windmills (even low-lift pumps can be made of wood!). This is just one example of the kind of appropriate village technology that uses local skills for production, local materials, and results in significant benefits to the entire population, despite the fact that it cannot enter the conventional economist's balance sheet. One of the things that appropriate technology seeks to do is precisely this—to find ways to mobilize 'hidden' resources that the money economy does not recognize or cannot mobilize.

APPROPRIATE TECHNOLOGY AND SOCIAL JUSTICE

Small-scale appropriate technologies have some notable characteristics which contribute to social justice, in addition to those we have already mentioned. While the introduction and development of these systems will always require some political support,

''...the most interesting feature is that there seem to be inherent limits to the extent to which (such technologies) can be alienated and turned into commodities or controlled by experts. Since they necessarily require care and involvement from their users, they cannot be mechanized, marketed, or merely consumed. As Illich might say, they are 'structurally convivial'!''

—*Radical Technology*

A pedal-powered rice thresher might have this effect if introduced into an area that ordinarily employs only two technologies for rice threshing: hand beating and motorized threshing using expensive imported equipment owned by the rich farmers. The pedal thresher, if easy to make out of locally available materials, may be affordable by the poorest farmers. It would allow them to step up from hand threshing without being forced to pay a share of their crop for motorized threshing. The rich farmers would no longer be able to collect a 'tax' on other people's crops simply because they own the only machines.

It would be a mistake to assume that small-scale appropriate technologies by themselves will lead to social justice, but they do make this an easier transition.

IMPORTED EQUIPMENT

As part of an appropriate technology research and development effort, it may be useful to import a few machines from other countries. These machines would then be disassembled to provide ideas for locally produced versions if they otherwise seem to be appropriate. If imported equipment is seen as a way to supply basic equipment needs, however, many of the old problems of technological dependency will still remain:

> "It is not particularly exciting to know that there are groups in the economically more advanced countries whose stock in trade is to peddle machines and equipment manufactured in their home countries for profit-making with industrialists in the developing world. Invariably such groups continue to indulge in self-glorification in international conferences and seminars with regard to technological cooperation and technological transfer to the Third World. It is as if all a country needs in industrialization is to indefinitely continue to import all its requirements in terms of machines and equipment."
>
> —Emmanuel Nwosu, in an article entitled "Some Problems of Appropriate Technology and Technological Transfer" in the African Journal of the Institute of Developing Economies

> "There is a danger that a too narrowly defined appropriate technology might become a way of promoting the export of cheap equipment from the industrialized countries to the developing areas of the world. The latter might become dependent on this equipment and yet remain unable to produce it themselves.
>
> ...Development organizations might promote the purchase of such items in their programs. For example, a tool may be made simpler with some of the labor-saving devices removed, and exported as an example of appropriate technology. If the technique and know-how for production of the tool remain in the industrialized country, the recipient country still remains simply a market place for the products of the rich. The creativity which could have been stimulated in the developing areas to solve their own problems and generate indigenous production would be stifled. In addition, there would usually be very little the importing country could do to influence the price of these tools.
>
> The appropriate technology approach, however...emphasizes that a community should use imported techniques only if they can be understood and reproduced locally. This is based on the belief that the faith of the people in their own capabilities is the basis for all development and progress. The idea of self-reliance is a central part of the concept of appropriate technology. The creative ingenuity of people to devise appropriate solutions in response to their needs and requirements should be encouraged rather than suppressed."
>
> —A Handbook on Appropriate Technology

THE ROLE OF AID ORGANIZATIONS
IN THE APPROPRIATE TECHNOLOGY MOVEMENT

It is very difficult to see how 'development from below' can be directly aided by large organizations in which initiative comes from the top. The problem is that the question of scale is a fundamental one in appropriate technology—not just the technology but the organizations involved must be of a 'human scale.' What we have seen of the preliminary activities of large groups entering this field leads us to be skeptical about what they can accomplish in a movement primarily concerned with self-reliance and technology appropriate to local circumstances.

Identifying precisely what roles are legitimate for foreign aid agencies is not an easy task. It seems useful to begin with an appreciation of these words of Julius Nyerere, President of Tanzania:

> *"Implicit in the conventional concept of aid is that internal problems can be remedied by the transfer of goods, services, or knowledge from external sources; in true development, internal problems call up internal remedies."*

If we seriously ask whether any particular country has the technical capacity to develop village technology appropriate to its needs, in most cases we will find that it does. The media and extension workers can play an important role in making people aware of how others have solved similar problems, for surely no one village need reinvent everything it requires. Yet the choice of what should be developed must remain with the villagers. In some cases, such as the design and operation of methane digesters or small-scale systems for the generation of electricity, outside help will be needed, but only with the assumption that the local people are capable of choosing, understanding, and maintaining these systems. Expatriates may have a legitimate role in helping to develop this kind of expertise within the country, but they should be able to quickly work themselves out of their jobs.

When it comes to the question of who should be doing research work on appropriate technology, the answer would appear to be that whatever *can* be done within the country *should* be done there. Unfortunately, the tendency so far has been to take technical problems to the people with expertise in rich countries, while failing to recognize that a lack of familiarity with local customs and resources make it unlikely that these people can find appropriate solutions. By going first to these foreigners an opportunity is missed to bring indigenous trained scientists and engineers into the appropriate technology development process and further stimulate a capacity for 'internal remedies.'

Ken Darrow
October 1976

PUBLISHERS, SOURCES,
and BOOKSTORES

Publishers, Sources, and Bookstores

Prices

The prices listed in this sourcebook are intended as **approximations** of the prices you will have to pay. Fluctuations in the international money markets, rising postal rates, and inflation mean that it is impossible to provide completely accurate price information. 95% of the prices listed in this sourcebook are prices we actually paid for these materials between November 1975 and September 1976, or updated prices on materials we had gathered before November 1975. We occasionally received price information from other sources. The books we purchased from American suppliers did not include overseas surface mail postage in the prices listed. For many of the publications listed as 'free' there will probably be a small charge for postage; and for the most popular ones, the source will probably have to charge a small fee to cover reprinting costs. We suggest trading your publications to other groups, particularly when a publication is listed as 'free.'

Because prices will undoubtedly continue to rise, we recommend sending an AIRMAIL letter to inquire about current prices and shipping costs. The Whole Earth Truck Store, for example, will reply to your letter and include an order form. After you have sent in the correct payment, they will send the materials by surface mail (6-10 weeks delivery). We recommend surface mail because airmail postage often doubles the cost of a book.

Addresses

In most cases, the ordering address has been included with the title of the publication. For organizations that have multiple publications listed, we have used an abbreviated name only. Those addresses are:

BRACE—Brace Research Institute. This group has developed some of the most innovative village and small community equipment. Their particular focus is on water supply for arid regions. For their publications write to Publications Dept., Brace Research Institute, MacDonald College of McGill University, Ste. Anne de Bellevue, Quebec H0A 1C0, Canada.

CoSIRA—Council for Small Industries in Rural Areas. Their primary interest is in small industries in England, but the publications we've reviewed would be relevant anywhere. Information Section, Council for Small Industries in Rural Areas, P.O. Box 717, 35 Camp Road, Wimbledon Common, London SW19 4UP, England.

DTWS—Department of Transport, Works and Supply. This group in Papua New Guinea has a limited number of the publications we've reviewed that are available free of charge, but they will very likely have to charge at least a small fee to cover postage, and possibly a small fee for each publication if they have to reprint. Department of Transport, Works and Supply (Technical Bulletins), P.O. Box 1108, Boroko, Papua New Guinea.

FAO—Distribution and Sales Section, Food and Agriculture Organization of the United Nations, Via delle Termi de Caracalla, 00100 Rome, Italy.

ITDG—Intermediate Technology Development Group. They are doing a large amount of research and development, and have been actively helping in the establishment of national intermediate technology centers in a number of developing countries. They have the largest publications list on intermediate technology. Write to them and ask for their latest one. For their publications write to: Intermediate Technology Publications, 9 King St., Covent Garden, London WC2E 8HN, England. (The main office of the organization has recently also moved to this address.) In the United States, you can order ITDG publications directly from their American distributor at the following address: International Scholarly Book Services, P.O. Box 555, Forest Grove, Oregon 97116.

META—Metastasis. These people have a wide range of appropriate technology books for sale, including many of those reviewed in the Sourcebook. They operated a book ordering center at the UN Habitat conference Metastasis, P.O. Box 128, Marblemount, Washington 98267, USA.

Mother Earth News—Their book-selling address is Mother's Bookshelf, Box 70, Hendersonville, North Carolina 28739, USA.

NTIS—National Technical Information Service, an organization created by the U.S. Government. They reprint many of the publications other government organizations have originally produced, but the prices are generally quite high. They add a $2.50 handling charge for foreign orders; this is on the entire order, not on each individual book. Be sure to include the Accession Number of each book you are ordering. National Technical Information Service, Springfield, Virginia 22161, USA.

TALC—Teaching Aids at Low Cost. An excellent source of low-cost books and teaching slides in the health care field, especially for auxiliaries. Over 30 different sets of teaching slides. They have just added a number of new books to their publications list, which we were not able to review in time for this edition. Administration, packing and postal charges on every order are 30 pence minimum; for orders over ₤3.00 (US$6.00) add 10%. If paying in currency other than Sterling, add 50 pence. Registration fee if considered necessary: 45 pence (about $0.90). Teaching Aids at Low Cost, Institute of Child Health, 30 Guilford St., London WC1N 1EH, England.

TOOL—The TOOL Foundation, for Technical Development in Developing Countries, has members on a large number of university campuses in the Netherlands. They offer publications in both Dutch and English, including some Dutch only publications that we have not reviewed. They also publish a newsletter in Dutch for people in developing countries. Their new (October

1976) address is: Stichting TOOL, Mauritskade 61a, Amsterdam, The Netherlands.

VITA—Volunteers in Technical Assistance. They have some volunteers in the field, and a much larger network of people who handle technical problems by mail. Their **Village Technology Handbook** and other plans are excellent. They accept UNESCO coupons in payment. Publications, Volunteers in Technical Assistance, 3706 Rhode Island Ave., Mt. Rainier, Maryland 20822, USA.

WETS—Whole Earth Truck Store, 558 Santa Cruz Ave., Menlo Park, California 94025, USA. They have a book price list, updated every 6 months, available for $1.00. For overseas orders, they add 10% to cover postage and insurance. See notes on the Whole Earth Catalog family of publications on page 51.

Whole Earth Access Company—This organization offers the advantage of a single source for about 100 of the publications reviewed in the Sourcebook; ask for their special Sourcebook booklist. They are offering quantity discounts for orders totaling more than $25.00. Whole Earth Access Company Books, 2466 Shattuck Ave., Berkeley, California 94704, USA.

PHILOSOPHY OF
APPROPRIATE TECHNOLOGY

Philosophy of
Appropriate Technology

The books in this section complement each other well, and together contribute to a philosophy and definition of appropriate technology. Many of the thoughts presented in the introductory remarks have come from these sources.

We have not included any books which primarily address the related issues of environmental destruction, resource depletion, economic and technological dependency, and a multitude of others. Such issues are central to the philosophy of appropriate technology, and many of the authors refer to these and assume that the reader already has a familiarity with these subjects. The books included here are more narrowly concerned with technology by and for the people, and how this technology might be developed.

Other introductory or general books have been included in the sections in which they are most relevant. Thus Hassan Fathy's **Architecture for the Poor** and Erik Eckholm's **Losing Ground** are to be found in the ARCHITECTURE and AGRICULTURE sections respectively.

Small is Beautiful, book, 297 pages, E.F. Schumacher, 1973, Ł1.80 or US$4.15 surface mail from ITDG; or $2.45 plus postage from WETS.

This book is a common-sense introduction, presented in plain terms, to some of the theory that underlies "intermediate" or "appropriate" technology for both the industrialized and the developing worlds. The book has had a major impact on the current thinking in the development field. Schumacher (founder of the Intermediate Technology Development Group) writes in an almost poetic style—surprising for an economist. Most of his career has been spent in England and the developing countries.

For Schumacher, solutions to the world's problems must embody the four qualities of smallness, simplicity, capital-saving, and non-violence. To that end he is a leading advocate of "appropriate technology" as a partial answer to global problems of food and energy shortages, alienation, and poverty. In the developing countries, designed particularly to suit agricultural conditions that are different from those in the industrialized countries, this technology is vastly superior to the primitive forms of the past. Yet it is at once simpler, cheaper, and all but independent of the energy requirements of today's super-technology of the rich. "One can also call it 'self-help' or 'people's technology'," says Schumacher.

"The task, then, is to bring into existence millions of new workplaces in the rural areas and small towns. That modern industry, as it has arisen in the developed countries, cannot possibly fulfill this task should be perfectly obvious. It has arisen in societies which are rich in capital and short of labor and therefore cannot possibly be appropriate for societies short of capital and rich in labor. The real task may be formulated in four propositions:

1) Workplaces have to be created in the areas where the people are living now, and not primarily in metropolitan areas into which they tend to migrate.

2) These workplaces must be, on the average, cheap enough so that they can be created in large numbers without this calling for an unattainable level of capital formation and imports.

3) The production methods employed must be relatively simple, so that the demands for high skills are minimized, not only in the production process itself but also in matters of organization, raw material supply, financing, marketing, and so forth.

4) Production should be mainly from local materials and mainly for local use.''

Schumacher on technological complexity: ''Any third-rate engineer can make a machine or a process more complex; afterwards, it takes a first-rate engineer to make it simple again.''

An excellent book.

Appropriate Technology: Problems and Promises, book, 344 pages, edited by Nicolas Jequier, 1976, $12.50 from OECD Publications, 2 rue Andre Pascal, 75775 Paris CEDEX 16, France; or Part I only (100 pages) available in a special reprinted edition by the Appropriate Technology Project, for sale only in the U.S. and in developing nations (not to people in the 23 industrialized member nations of OECD). $2.50 in U.S., $2.00 in developing nations, surface mail from AT Project, Volunteers in Asia, Box 4543, Stanford, California 94305, USA.

This book is the most significant publication on the subject of appropriate technology since Schumacher's **Small is Beautiful** appeared in 1973. It is edited by Nicolas Jequier of the association of industrialized nations called the Organization for Economic Cooperation and Development (OECD)—a group one might not expect to produce such a book. The editor emerges as the most significant contributor, providing a brilliant 100-page overview of the major policy issues that confront appropriate technology advocates. 19 articles by participants in the 1974 OECD conference on low-cost technology give a backdrop of some of the efforts and perspectives currently found among practitioners in the appropriate technology movement.

Under another editor, this book would simply be a very good collection of articles, providing a sample of the viewpoints of the larger groups that have been involved for several years in the development of appropriate technology. We welcome it as such and recommend it. But the surprise is that Jequier's introductory Part I is possibly more valuable than the articles it is intended to introduce.

Jequier describes appropriate technology as a cultural revolution in the field of development, and spells out implications that virtually no one else is writing about; identifies local people as the primary innovators of appropriate technology; points to the danger that appropriate technology research will be carried out mostly by groups from the rich countries, thereby stifling the development of research groups with this focus from within the developing countries and leading to the same technological dependency that currently exists; discusses the political implications of appropriate technology; poses questions for national government policy and for aid policy; contrasts decentralized with centralized research on appropriate technology; and explores many other 'problems and promises' of the appropriate technology movement. In short, Jequier is among the first to try to identify the disagreements and problem areas facing appropriate technology enthusiasts; he draws up an agenda for discussion and action.

Now that appropriate technology is clearly on its way to becoming a permanent part of development thinking, it is important that: 1) practitioners define more clearly exactly what they mean by 'appropriate technology'; 2) differences among these practitioners are recognized and debated rather than ignored; and 3) the implications of appropriate technology as a cultural revolution within the field of development be recognized so that it can be completed.

Highly recommended. It is unfortunate that the very high price will probably limit the distribution of the book. As noted above, we have received permission to offer a lower-cost reprint of Jequier's Part I, to anyone in a developing nation or non-OECD member nation.

A Handbook on Appropriate Technology, 200 pages, by Brace Research Institute and the Canadian Hunger Foundation, 1976, $7.50 in Canada, Europe, U.S. and Japan; one copy free to concerned groups from developing countries and additional copies $2.50 to these groups; from Canadian Hunger Foundation, 75 Sparks St., Ottawa, Ontario K1P 5A5, Canada.

This handbook combines many aspects of appropriate technology (AT) in one volume. "Presents a synthesis of the theory and concepts of AT. Describes specific examples of existing projects which have been undertaken with these concepts in mind. Introduces a variety of technologies, and lists individuals and groups who are working in the field of AT."

There is a short, readable introduction to the rationale for appropriate technology. Emphasizes that sociocultural, economic, political and ecological factors should be taken into consideration. Stresses the complementary role of credit and marketing factors.

The 12 Case Studies form one of the strongest sections in the handbook. Most articles are complete with photos, drawings, and further references. Includes: village-scale iron foundry in Afghanistan; well-drilling bit rebuilding in India; solar distillation in Haiti; solar crop dryers in Colombia; small-scale bio-gas plants in India (see separate review, page 185); smokeless stoves for fuel conservation in Ghana; pedal thresher and hand weeder in Bangladesh; group credit in community development in the Dominican Republic; and ferro-cement boat building in Bangladesh. 58 pages.

A 45-entry glossary provides definitions for some common technical terms. The 32-page catalog of tools is intended as a source of ideas. Single drawings or photo of each. Complete plans for many of these are available elsewhere as part of ITDG's Agricultural Green Leaflets (see pages 104-12), or Brace Research Institute leaflets (listed under topic area in the **Sourcebook**). The remainder are mostly drawings of commercially available equipment for which plans are not available.

There is a 250-entry bibliography listing books, papers and articles. These are primarily theoretical/academic, although some attempt to include practical publications has been made. No annotations, addresses, or prices.

This is followed by a list of some 80 groups that are in some way involved with AT; single paragraph descriptions of some of them. Next comes a list of 140 individuals involved in AT. Both lists are admittedly incomplete, yet valuable.

Lastly there is more text, covering these topics: the need for an alternative approach to development, elements of the AT approach, response to some criticisms of AT, ecological awareness and AT, and the introduction of AT into a community. 32 pages. This excellent section contains a broader critique of current development approaches than usual. A welcome discussion of the implications of AT in terms of national policy.

"The only situation in which tools, technologies, or know-how from the industrialized parts of the world should enter a developing area is when they assist in activating and promoting local initiative, local understanding and local know-how, so that the responsibility for the technology can be assumed by the local people. This responsibility in part means the capability to reproduce the technology in a form adapted by the indigenous populations to suit their conditions and needs."

Tools for Conviviality, book, 119 pages, Ivan Illich, 1973, $1.25 from WETS.

Illich used the unfamiliar term 'convivial' in a special way—"as a technical term to designate a modern society of responsibly limited tools...People need new tools to work with rather than tools that 'work' for them. They need technology to make the most of the energy and imagination each has...A convivial society should be designed to allow all its members the most autonomous action by means of tools least controlled by others. People feel joy, as opposed to mere pleasure, to the extent that their activities are creative... We must recognize the nature of desirable limits to specialization and output...Common tools would be incomparably more efficient than primitive, and more widely distributed than industrial devices."

The language used in this book is often rather difficult; while the subject matter is theoretical and philosophical. Illich makes a significant contribution to the development of a philosophy of appropriate technology that would be applicable to both rich and poor countries. The book is a critique of the system of industrialization which destroys people's capacity to do things for themselves. Illich sees 'conviviality' as one of the primary treasures still remaining in small communities of developing countries, that has already been tragically lost in the industrialized countries.

Illich comments on the housing industry in Latin America: "Components for new houses and utilities could be made very cheaply and designed for self-assembly. People could build more durable, more comfortable, and more sanitary dwellings as well as learn about new materials and systems. But instead of supporting the ability of people to shape their own environment, the government deposits in these shanty-towns public utilities designed for people who live in standard modern houses. The presence of a new school, a paved road, and a glass and steel police station defines the professionally built house as the functional unit, and stamps the self-built home a shanty." (See review of **The Ecol Operation** on page 221 for more on the idea of housing components designed for self-assembly.)

Lectures on Socially Appropriate Technology, book, 235 pages, edited by R. Congdon, 1975, $6.00 from TOOL.

Most of these lectures were originally given by members of the British Intermediate Technology Development Group to a university audience in The Netherlands. 'Socially' appropriate technology is the subject, on the assumption that "all development must be for the benefit of as large a section of the population as possible, and not remain the privilege of a small elite."

The 12 lectures provide a range of insights into the nature and definition of appropriate technology, from the perspectives of members of ITDG. George McRobie's lecture, "Approach for Appropriate Technologists," gives a good overview of the rationale and work of ITDG; he writes very much like Schumacher—not surprisingly as the two have known each other for many years. S.B. Watt's lecture on choosing water technologies is illustrative of some of the best thinking from that group (e.g., "the professionals have become colonials in the sense that they have taken possession of the knowledge of technology—a knowledge that all people should possess to be able to change their own lives.") Other subjects include agricultural tools, building, energy, chemicals, education, industrial liaison, social criteria for appropriate technology and production systems.

Probably the most practical item here is S. Wilson's 18-page article on pedal-power, which represents a good overview of the potential in that area. A number of designs are discussed, and 20 photos are included. This is the best treatment of pedal-power that we know of (we decided to include a separate review of it on page 191).

Harry Dickinson's concluding piece entitled "The Transfer of Knowledge and the Adoption of Technologies" should be **required reading** for any person going overseas to do appropriate technology work. "As Westerners and as technologists we have a role to play but we must be self-critical about our own society before we have the wisdom and insight to be of any real value."

An excellent book, liberally sprinkled with British humor and understatement.

Alternative Technology and the Politics of Technical Change, book, 204 pages, David Dickson, 1974, $1.50 paperback from William Collins & Sons Ltd., 14 St. James Place, London FW1A 1PS, England; or $7.95 hardbound from Universe Books, 381 Park Avenue South, New York, N.Y. 10016, USA.

Dickson examines the 'modern' technology of the industrialized countries and concludes that "technology, originally developed as a means of raising man above a life of poverty, drudgery and ill health, now shows its other face as a major threat to sanity and survival."

The book includes a summary of the basic principles of 'alternative' or 'utopian' technology (involving community production and social organization), the characteristics that distinguish it from the dominant technology, and its relationships to the individual, the community, and the environment.

Throughout the book, the author argues that the development of modern industrialized technology has been a reflection of and a reinforcement to existing dominant political interests.

There is a chapter on intermediate technology and the Third World, providing a critique of the view that intermediate technology has no political component. "Political changes will neither flow automatically from, nor be determined by, the technology. They must be introduced separately as part of the general political struggle for emancipation. Truly appropriate technology can only come from the demands of the people by whom and for whom it is to be used, once they have successfully realized their own political and economic strength."

Radical Technology, book, 304 pages, by Godfrey Boyle, Peter Harper and the editors of Undercurrents magazine, 1976, $5.95 from WETS; or £3.50 surface mail from Undercurrents Books, 11 Shadwell, Uley, Gloucestershire, GL11 5BW, England.

"Radical Technology is a large format, extensively illustrated collection of original articles concerning the reorganization of technology along more humane, rational and ecologically sound lines. The many facets of such a reorganization are reflected in the wide variety of contributions to the book. They cover both the 'hardware'—the machines and technical methods themselves—and the 'software'—the social and political structures, the way people relate to each other and to their environment, and how they feel about it all."

WOOdEn JocKEY
PulIEY uSing
bicyclE hub

bEnch grindEr
uSing bicyclE whEEl hub.
Could fit on trEAdLE SEWing mAchinE.

Radical Technology is a book packed with information and ideas. Well-written and thoughtful, its 304 dense pages give a remarkably thorough treatment of what for many is the logical application of the concept of appropriate technology to the developed countries. Thus, while coming from a different perspective, it does cover nicely (though briefly) such topics as bio-dynamic agriculture, composting, agribusiness, hydroponics, solar energy, water power, metal-working, and transport, along with the more expensive intermediate technologies of printing and communications. Essays alternate with factual presentations.

Outstanding sections: On **autonomy**, its limits and possibilities. There is a good overview of wind power designs. A 5-page essay by Jimoh Omo-Fadakah of Tanzania entitled "Escape Route for the Poor" is excellent. The running commentary through the 30-page bibliography is delightful—the best biblio-graphy for de-developing and de-centralizing the rich countries we've seen.

Unquestionably the sudden popularity of appropriate technology stems at least in part from the energy/environmental/cultural crisis in the West. This book provides a good overview of some of the thinking going on in the West in response to the multi-crisis.

"Radical Technology encompasses much that is meant by 'alternative technology' but sees these new, liberating tools, techniques and sources of energy as part of a restructured social order, and aims to place them directly in the hands of the community."

Design for the Real World, book, 375 pages, Victor Papanek, 1972, $2.95 from Bantam Books, 666 Fifth Ave., New York, NY 10019 USA; or WETS.

The author is a UNESCO International Design Expert and former Dean of the School of Design at the California Institute of the Arts. His basic thesis is that designers should design for **use** and address real human needs. Instead, today most design is for style and planned obsolescence. Papanek attacks the wasteful, irresponsible use of design in the industrialized world, and provides hundreds of examples of inexpensive, long-lasting, highly-useful products that he and others have "designed for the real world." He is opposed to patents, because he feels ideas should be made freely available.

Although most of the book is directed towards proposed changes in the industrialized world, the author frequently discusses innovative designs that address the needs of the developing world's villagers: a single-channel, cow-dung-powered radio that can be handmade for $0.09; a rough-terrain, multi-purpose, low-slung bicycle transporter; a bicycle luggage carrier that folds down and can be used for generating electricity, running a lathe, and other things; a hand-cranked produce cooler that can be built for $6.00 by hand; irrigation pumps made of recycled tires; "fiber**grass**—using conventional chemical fiberglass catalysts, but substituting dried native grasses, hand-aligned, for the expensive fiberglass mats," and more. Construction details, however, are not given.

Papanek provides hundreds of ideas and a starting point for responsible, socially useful design. Many photos and illustrations.

Sharing Smaller Pies, leaflet, 38 pages, Tom Bender, 1975, $1.50 from RAIN magazine, 2270 N.W. Irving, Portland, Oregon 97210, USA.

This is the American response to **Small is Beautiful**.

"There is no longer any doubt that our age of affluence based upon depletion of our planet's non-renewable energy and material resources is at an end and that major changes must be made in every aspect of our lives."

"Medicine, architecture, law, education, transportation, social work, and civil engineering have all followed the path of increasingly professionalized, more restricted, and less beneficial application of their skills."

"We need skill-developing rather than labor-saving technologies."

This leaflet includes an excellent 6-page discussion of the meaning of appropriate technology for industrialized nations. A thoughtful look at what has gone wrong in America's high-technology society, and explanations of a new set of values which might help us move toward a society characterized by "stewardship not progress" and "enoughness not moreness."

Highly recommended.

Churches in Rural Development: Guidelines for Action, book, 138 pages, Peter Sartorius, 1975, $3.50 from CCPD, World Council of Churches, P.O. Box 66, 1211 Geneva 20, Switzerland.

This book is an effort to inform churches and church-related groups on "questions of rural development, and it proposes some guidelines for agricultural and forestry programmes...it is aimed to foster people's participation in a development process directed towards the attainment of social justice, self-reliance, and economic growth.''

A look at cooperatives, extension work, and a strategy for rural development based on appropriate technology and people's participation; problems with all of these are discussed. There are sensible criticisms of the Green Revolution approach. Included is a bibliography and list of international organizations which may offer some assistance with rural development projects.

Environmentally Appropriate Technology, book, 160 pages, Bruce McCallum, 1975, limited numbers of this edition are available free, and a new edition will be sold at cost (end of 1976), from Advanced Concepts Centre, Office of the Science Advisor, Dept. of the Environment, Ottawa, Ontario K1A OH3, Canada.

The subject of this book is environmentally-sound technology. It provides an overview of the present state of development of this kind of technology, and some ideas about how a 'conserver' society might use it. The perspective is that of an industrialized country (Canada). Covers large and some small-scale systems, but no real consideration is given to the do-it-yourself small-scale designs and the forms they might take in developing countries. Major topics are solar technology, improvements in wood-burning stoves, heat pumps, wind-generated electricity (many drawings and photos of different units), and housing in cold climates.

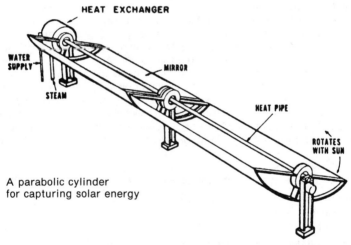

HEAT EXCHANGER

WATER SUPPLY

MIRROR

STEAM

HEAT PIPE

ROTATES WITH SUN

A parabolic cylinder
for capturing solar energy

China: Science Walks on Two Legs, book, 316 pages, by Science for the People, $1.75 from Avon Books, The Hearst Corporation, 959 Eighth Avenue, New York, N.Y. 10019, USA.

This report by an American delegation describes the role of science in China, specifically as it applies to agriculture, industry, research, medicine, and education. It is not a technical book, but rather an overview of Chinese social and political attitudes towards science.

At the heart of scientific practice in China is the belief that everyone should learn and use science—the ''summation of the laboring people's experience.'' The book discusses how students, scientists, and peasants work together to create a useful technology.

Emphasizing decentralization and self-reliance at all levels, the Chinese seek to maintain a balance between big and small technology, use local materials whenever possible, and attempt to utilize waste materials. For example, small-scale fertilizer plants are maintained throughout the countryside. Traditional knowledge is used along with more recent discoveries. Acupuncture is practiced by the same people who use some modern medical techniques. Health care is decentralized, with an emphasis on rural areas, neighborhood clinics, and preventive medicine.

This book makes good reading for anyone interested in developing different models for the use of science in society, especially to meet the needs of developing nations.

Technology and Employment in Industry, book, 324 pages, edited by A.S. Bhalla, 1975, 37.50 Swiss Francs (approximately US$15.00), from ILO Publications, International Labour Office, CH-1211 Geneva 22, Switzerland.

A collection of case studies: can making in Kenya, Tanzania and Thailand; jute processing in Kenya; textile manufacturing in the United Kingdom; sugar processing in India; manufacturing cement blocks in Kenya; running engineering industries in Colombia; metalworking in Mexico; and extracting and processing copper and aluminum in the United States, Zambia, Zaire, and Chile.

''The studies demonstrate quite clearly that substitution possibilities exist in industry in both core and ancillary operations. This conclusion, based on empirical evidence, is important, since it has often been assumed that there is no choice of techniques in manufacturing industry. Secondly, the range of available techniques can be widened by re-designing or copying older designs and blueprints with local engineering adaptations, or through local manufacture of equipment. Thirdly, quite often the use of capital-intensive techniques, where more labor-intensive ones could have been used equally efficiently, is due not to the fact that there are no other technical possibilities in industry— there are—but to imperfect knowledge and inappropriate selection systems.''

This book strays rather far from our focus on home-built and village level technology, but the conclusions are significant from the point of view of village industries and other small scale industries to which they may be linked.

FURTHER REFERENCES ON PHILOSOPHY OF APPROPRIATE TECHNOLOGY

Architecture for the Poor, see review on page 217.

Losing Ground, see review on page 76.

Forest Farming, see review on page 77.

Medical Care in Developing Countries, see review on page 243.

Pediatric Priorities in the Developing World, see review on page 243.

Doctors and Healers, see review on page 244.

Indigenous Building and the Third World, see review on page 218.

Shelter, see review on page 219.

Chawama Self-Help Housing Project, see review on page 236.

Towards Village Industry, see review on page 55.

PRACTICAL
REFERENCE BOOKS

Practical Reference Books

The books in this section cover a wide range of subjects important to appropriate technology practitioners. There are basically two kinds of books included here. There are books which are concerned with the principles of how equipment and processes work; these lead to a general understanding and are critical to the development of a capability to innovate effectively. The second category of books are those which are filled with plans for different kinds of equipment. These have been called 'cookbooks' because while they enable the user to make the equipment presented, they don't provide the kind of background understanding necessary if the user is to go beyond them.

We feel that these two kinds of books play essential complementary roles. The 'cookbooks' serve to illustrate the principles explained by the more general books, including the valuable function of demonstrating which principles are in fact more important in any given application. This is of particular importance to appropriate technologists, because so often what is needed is to adapt a machine, both in materials and in scale, to fit local circumstances. It is very valuable to have a practical working design to start from in this process.

In other sections of the Sourcebook this pattern is repeated; general reference books on the particular subject are complemented by books with plans that can be directly used.

In addition to the obviously relevant subject matter, these books have been chosen because they are easy to understand yet remain reasonably complete treatments of technical subjects. This is significant, because the development of appropriate technology demands more from generalists than from specialists. Two of the books in this section [the VITA **Village Technology Handbook** and **Other Homes and Garbage**) and one book that is reviewed in another section (the **Energy Primer**) we consider to be exceptionally valuable. Other reviews in the Sourcebook will commonly make references to these three books.

In addition, there are several examples of catalogs that represent an effective low-cost method for disseminating information. Perhaps the most valuable of these is **Liklik Buk**, a rural development catalog for Papua New Guinea. And of course the **Whole Earth Catalog** family of publications is the equivalent in the United States. There are also 3 books which are full of ideas for simple equipment and techniques to be used in science teaching in developing countries; these also have a great deal of information of general value. In a category by itself is another book entitled **Village Technology Handbook** by Rural Communications in England; this book is a guide to several hundred groups around the world that are actively doing work on appropriate technology subjects. The last book in this section, **Towards Village Industry**, provides some important insights for people working in the field, though it is actually a theoretical book rather than a practical book.

Village Technology Handbook, book, 387 pages, VITA, 1970, $9.00 (free if you live in the developing world and can't afford it), Spanish and French editions also available, from VITA.

"This handbook describes techniques and devices which can be made and used in villages. Hopefully the book will generate new ideas as well as pass on information which has already been tried."

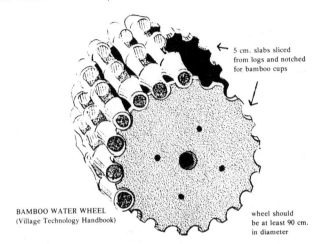

← 5 cm. slabs sliced from logs and notched for bamboo cups

BAMBOO WATER WHEEL
(Village Technology Handbook)

wheel should be at least 90 cm. in diameter

The book "was conceived by VITA volunteers in 1962 as a means of bridging the technical information gap which keeps the world's villages from learning from one another's experience. The book's aim is to gather in one publication information from many sources which has been found helpful in villages."

"In the 1970 edition, two earlier volumes are integrated into one book, the editing has been made more uniform, some new information has been added and the illustrations have been improved. The entire handbook has been checked for accuracy by VITA volunteer specialists."

Subjects covered include:

a) Developing water resources (including basic well-drilling or digging information, such as how to make a hand-operated earth boring machine).

b) Water lifting and transport (chain pump for irrigation, pipelines, hydraulic ram pump).

c) Water storage and water power.

d) Water purification (for example, sand filters).

e) Health and sanitation (principles of latrine building).

f) Agriculture (earth-moving devices for irrigation and road-building, underground irrigation using tiles, tile-making, grain drying, two-person bucket sprayer, back-pack crop duster).

g) Food processing and preservation (for example, iceless refrigerator).

h) Construction (concrete, bamboo, making glues).

i) Miscellaneous (solar water heater, hand-operated washing machines, soap-making, building a kiln for pottery, silk-screen printing, and winding a spring).

j) An appendix with conversion charts for English to metric units.

An extraordinarily valuable book. It always seems to have the information you're looking for when you can't find it in another place.

Highly recommended.

Other Homes and Garbage, book, 300 pages, J. Leckie, G. Masters, H. Whitehouse, L. Young, 1975, $9.95 from WETS.

This is an extremely practical book, dealing with "Designs for Self-Sufficient Living." It contains complete but simple and well-illustrated discussions of the theory of energy sources, alternative architecture and complete agricultural systems. A major step towards making technical knowledge understandable and accessible to people without technical training.

Topics include: alternative architecture, small-scale generation of electricity using wind power and water power, solar heating of houses and water, waste handling systems, water supply, agriculture and aquaculture. The solar section contains very useful charts, such as "coefficients of transmission" of heat for different materials in buildings, and proper solar collector positions for different latitudes. The chapter on waste systems includes methane digesters and other methods of waste disposal. The water supply chapter covers wells, solar distillation of water, pumps and water purification. The book is conceived as an easy-to-use textbook; each of the chapters includes many sample calculations to aid in reader understanding of how to solve practical problems.

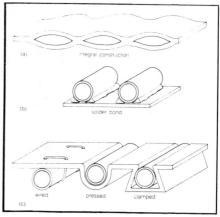

Figure 4.22 Various bonding schemes.

This book does not attempt to provide the reader with specific plans for projects. Throughout, the emphasis is on providing the reader with most of the necessary background information to design his or her **own** projects within the topic areas covered: "This book represents an attempt by engineers and other technically-trained people to communicate practical, useful technical information in an interesting format and in terms that are comprehensible to non-specialized people..." We think the authors do an excellent job of this.

Other Homes and Garbage differs from the **Energy Primer** in that the former does not cover **where** to obtain equipment and other books, but does cover the technical information in much greater detail. It

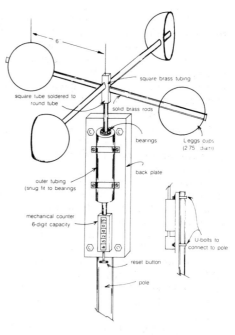

Figure 3.11 A do-it-yourself cup anemometer for measuring average wind speeds.

could be used as a textbook or reference book. Highly recommended. A good combination with the **Energy Primer** (see review page 130).

Appropriate Technology: Directory of Machines, Tools, Plants, Equipment, Processes, and Industries, book, 280 pages, first edition 1974, second edition 1977, Rp. 50 in India, US$10.00 plus postage abroad, from Appropriate Technology Development Association, Post Box 311, Gandhi Bhawan, Lucknow 226001, U.P., India.

A limited number of copies of the first edition were printed, but a new second edition is now available (which we haven't seen). Subjects range from agricultural tools to village industries and decentralized sources of energy.

"This directory is an attempt to bridge the 'knowledge gap' which keeps the Indian villages from learning from one another's experience. There are some very good tools and equipment devised in one corner of India, and there is no channel through which people in other parts of India can learn about them and benefit from them."

The first edition covers about 30 pieces of equipment from a variety of sources. There are descriptions, drawings, and construction information for all of these. For the following items the material included appears to be sufficient for construction: six agricultural handtools, hand crop duster, earth auger, hand seed drill, plant puller, chaff cutter, roller thresher (same design as ITDG's **Rasulia Thresher** on page 110), equipment for parboiling rice, equipment for making matches, forms for casting well rings, winch, latrine mold and casting, and the Quaker Arm Circumference stick for measuring the arms of children to identify malnutrition.

Some information, although not enough for construction, is also provided on the following equipment: single-spindle charkha (spinning wheel), equipment for red and white clay pottery, lime kiln, hand pump, low-cost microscope, solar water heater, household water filter unit (combines sand and charcoal filters), gobar gas (methane or bio-gas) plants, and designs for 1 and 2 room houses.

The first edition is remarkable, and the second edition promises to be of great interest to village technologists worldwide. Highly recommended.

Cloudburst 1 (A Handbook of Rural Skills and Technology), book, 126 pages, 1973, $4.95 from Cloudburst Press, Dept. C-1, Mayne Island, B.C., V0N 2J0 Canada (add $0.25 handling charge); or WETS.

"**Cloudburst** is a book born of people's experiences; people who are finding ways of living harmoniously with nature rather than exploiting it; people who are seeking to think small in a world overrun by big thinking; people who are forming lifestyles based on the economics of semi-sufficiency...It attempts to cover with depth some of the basic problems facing the growing movement of people seeking to decentralize society and repopulate the countryside. As such, it gets a lot of its impetus from days gone by, from the crafts/skills/technologies of the last 100 years which have been glossed over in our pursuit of 'high' technology...the use of low impact or intermediate technology and skills" is what this book is about.

There are 30 articles with plans, most of them quite practical. Many of them are reprints from other sources. Included are: pit privies (Mother Earth News, VITA, WHO), storing fruits and vegetables (includes 15 drawings of different storage ideas for temperate zone countries), poultry housing, harnessing the small stream (a 1947 Popular Science reprinted article with many plans (see page 156), the Michell water turbine (VITA), three articles on water wheel design including specific information on undershot and overshot water wheels (see page 158), a homemade windmill, a homemade forge, a treadle-powered wood-turning lathe (one of the best designs—see page 66), a solar dryer for produce (Brace), the smoke curing of fish (VITA), a cardboard smokehouse (VITA), how to salt fish (VITA), and a hand-operated wooden washing machine (VITA), plus a set of hints on a variety of subjects. The VITA and Brace designs are available separately from these organizations (see reviews of each in the appropriate sections of the **Sourcebook**); many of them are in the VITA **Village Technology Handbook**.

A large paperback with simple text and many dimensional drawings (English units). A good source of plans. Highly recommended.

Cloudburst 2, book, 128 pages, edited by Vic Marks, 1976, $4.95 from Cloudburst Press, Dept. C-2, Mayne Island, B.C., V0N 2J0 Canada (add $0.25 handling charge) or from WETS.

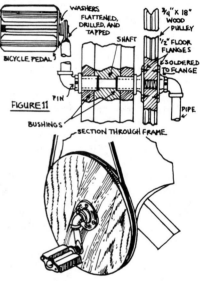

FIGURE 11

The pedal mechanism for a saw

Another useful appropriate technology handbook, full of ideas and designs appropriate to a wide range of circumstances. Aimed at the North American back-to-the-land movement, but relevant elsewhere; the first edition resulted in letters from all over the world.

Reprints from VITA, Popular Science and Popular Mechanics magazines and other publications, most of which are not available elsewhere. 31 articles plus a glossary of unfamiliar terms. Includes: BRAD's Solar Roof Plan for hot water heating (Great Britain); simple buildings and stoves, 3 articles on hydraulic rams, a pottery wheel and two kilns for firing pottery, a smokehouse, a large fruit dryer, a sunpit greenhouse, 3 kinds of spinning wheels, a carding machine, a table loom, and more.

Of particular interest are: a hand-operated, hand-powered drill press (reprinted from Popular Science magazine—see review on page 67); a pedal-powered saw (reprinted from Popular Mechanics magazine—see review on page 67); and a homemade honey extractor (reprinted from Countryside journal—see review on page 267).

Cloudburst 2 has much the same quality about it as **Cloudburst 1**. Simple text, lots of dimensional drawings. Just about everything included can be built from these plans, as long as the usual amount of imagination and skill is involved.

First Steps in Village Mechanization, book, 232 pages, George MacPherson, Tanzania Publishing House, 1975, £4.05 or US$9.30 surface mail from ITDG.

This is a handbook designed to assist village development workers in Tanzanian villages. The emphasis is on self-reliance.

"Millions of people have missed the chance to become self-reliant in mechanization matters, because mechanization was brought to them ready made. For example, many communities never made their own wheel, or even used a wheel before a visiting section of a different culture suddenly appeared with a wheelbarrow, or a wagon, or a bicycle. Therefore those people were introduced to the wheel as something which must be bought, rather than made for oneself. There are many such examples...(of) traditional technology, in many cases more suitable than the new technology, stagnating instead of developing to meet the needs of the community."

The emphasis here is more on the first steps and less on mechanization. It is a kind of village technology handbook, with a focus on getting village development to be self-perpetuating. It assumes that a village is chosen that has no craftsmen and few tools. The text describes training through the use of work projects such as making one's own workbench and vise. Concerned also with training the new craftsman to become an entrepreneur.

Construction details are given for simple furniture, foot-operated vise, simple hand tools, hollow-block mold, simple wheelbarrow, small carts, and a peg-tooth harrow. The training of donkeys and oxen, and the managing of cooperative workshops are also briefly covered.

Especially interesting is a design for a simple hand planter and fertilizer applicator; and for a hand cranked corn (maize) sheller made of wood. No pedal-power equipment is included, however.

"When village people have gained the confidence and experience of making and using their own tools and equipment, they will be eager and ready to move quickly forward to the profitable use of better and more complex equipment... the confidence is more important than the technology."

More relevant to circumstances in Africa than Asia or Latin America.

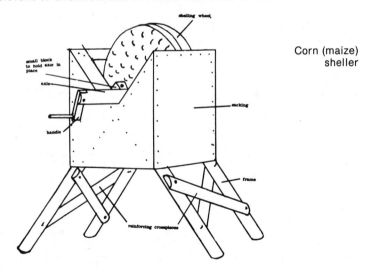

Corn (maize) sheller

Simple Working Models of Historic Machines (Easily Built by the Reader), book, 79 pages, A. Burstall, 1968, $5.95 from The MIT Press, Massachusetts Institute of Technology, Cambridge, Massachusetts 02142, USA.

35 different machines are presented in the form of drawings of simple working models. The emphasis is on the essential operating features of the machines. Most of the devices can be built with wood working tools in a small

workshop; some of them, however, require machined metal gearing. A description of the origin and use of each is provided.

The drawings include: great wheel lathe, treadle lathe, screw cutters for wooden screws (male and female threads), a variety of pulleys and other lifting devices, Chinese spoon-tilt hammer, escapement mechanisms in clocks, two kinds of bellows, and machines for pumping and raising water (Archimedes' screw, chain pump, suction pump, diaphragm pump, hydraulic ram).

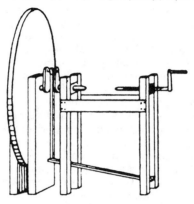

Leonardo's treadle lathe

The intent of the author is to "encourage a talent for experimenting and improvising." The drawings illustrate important principles in mechanical engineering. They can either serve as the basis for practical applications of these principles, or as teaching models. "Much appeared to be learned by feeling and touching a working model that otherwise eluded the students when only diagrams, slides, or cinema films were used."

Recommended.

Making Do, book, 148 pages, Arthur Hill, 1972, $3.95 from Ballantine Books, Inc., 101 Fifth Ave., New York, N.Y. 10003, USA.

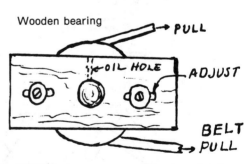

This book was written by a 69-year-old American in an effort to pass on some ideas learned during a lifetime of makings things for himself cheaply. The book gives an idea of the kind of inventive/handyman skills that were common in America from the time of the Revolution until after WWII, when they began to die out.

The book is divided into sections on the home, tool shop, garden, and yard. Full of rough drawings. While much of the contents can be found elsewhere (usually in more detail), the following are of particular note:

1) hand-powered rotating wooden drum **washing machine**—claimed to be "more efficient than the agitator type, using less water and therefore less soap or detergent."
2) simple design for a potter's kick wheel.
3) simple design for a band saw, table saw, and belt sander.

4) how to make drills from common nails.
5) homemade hinges.
6) oil-soaked wooden bearings for moderate speeds and loads.
Apart from these designs, there are also a number of practical ideas that you are unlikely to find in print elsewhere.

Technical Information Handbook, book, 90 pages, by the Dept. of Public Works in Papua New Guinea, free to serious groups, from DTWS.

This is Papua New Guinea's own "appropriate technology sourcebook." Each page contains a different entry, with a description and drawing, and an address to write for further, specific details. Some of the publications listed in this handbook are also listed here separately in our **Appropriate Technology Sourcebook** (see HOUSING). Information is provided on buildings (homes and community centers), a hydraulic ram, bridges, tools, water tanks, stoves, a latrine, a village garbage disposal, and more.

A soak pit for dish
and wash water

All of the sources listed are within Papua New Guinea, and the methods use resources and materials specific to that country. However, this is an excellent example of one country's attempt to catalog some of the information resources available. M.T. Somare, Prime Minister of Papua New Guinea, writes: "I hope that this handbook of rural technology will bring about an increased awareness of the development possibilities open to our rural communities." We do too.

Pictorial Handbook of Technical Devices, book, 600 pages, O. Schwarz and P. Grafstein, 1971, $12.50 from WETS.

This is an idea book for appropriate technology practitioners. Contains 5000 illustrations; an astounding variety of devices used for mechanical movements. Illustrations are grouped for their suggestive value. Major sections are: machine technology, magnetics and electronics, light and optics, industrial processes, power generation, structural engineering, comfort heating and cooling, and measuring devices. For anyone there will be at least a few items of interest here. Short descriptions are provided for some of the more complex devices. Materials used and exact dimensions are not given.

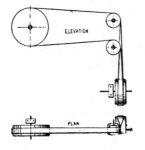

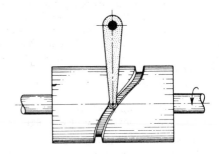

New Alchemy Institute's Journal No. 2, book, 132 pages, from the New Alchemy Institute, 1974, $6.00 from WETS.

This is a relaxed introduction to the work of the New Alchemy Institute, an organization working with appropriate technologies primarily for temperate (as opposed to tropical) climates. Important material is presented on a variety of subjects:

a) notes on New Alchemy Institute;
b) plans for a water-pumping windmill (see separate review on page 144);
c) windmill electronics (article);
d) a description of New alchemy Institute's ongoing project, the "Ark" — a "Proposed Solar-Heated and Windpowered Greenhouse and Aquaculture Complex Adapted to Northern Climates," 9 pages.
e) three articles on self-sustaining agriculture;
f) Research Report No. 1 on the cabbage worm butterfly;
g) Research Report No. 2 on "Irrigation of garden vegetables with fertile fish pond water";
h) aquaculture—42 pages on backyard, small-scale fish farming.
An excellent book.

New Alchemy Institute's Journal No. 3, book, 128 pages, 1976, $6.00 from WETS.

A continuing report on the activities of the New Alchemy Institute, this issue contains both practical and more theoretical articles on energy, land use and aquaculture. Some material is continued from **Jounal #2** (see listing above):
a) more notes on the Institute;
b) a newly designed windmill sail-wing;
c) a water-pumping Savonius rotor;
d) a solar collector for heating water;
e) "Further experiments in the irrigation of garden vegetables with fertile fish pond water";
f) more aquaculture—midge (larvae) culture, a low-cost method of sealing fish pond bottoms, and experimental cultivation of several fish species;
g) a philosophical piece on technology and agriculture, in both historical and modern perspective;
h) an article on women and ecology.

Indonesian Village Technology Booklets, by BUTSI (the Indonesian national volunteer organization), Indonesian language editions only, free if you send your publications in exchange, from Unit Teknologi Desa, Sekretariat BUTSI, Tromol Pos 3290, Jakarta, Indonesia.

This is a series of 16-page booklets on village technology and techniques. There are many illustrations, and a deliberately limited amount of text in the national language (Bahasa Indonesia—almost identical to Malay). The booklets serve two major purposes: 1) to publicize existing village technology now found only in one part of the vast archipelago so that the rest of the nation's villagers can benefit from it; and 2) to suggest new innovations that may have practical value at the village level. See drawings in the Appendix, page 302.

Village Development Notes and Booklets, from Tribhuvan University National Development Service, Kirtipur Campus, Kathmandu, Nepal.

The National Development Service of Tribhuvan University prints English translations of its village development notes and booklets. These cover a wide range of activities, from agriculture to teaching aids—all in a very clear, simple form. All university students in Nepal are required to serve for one year with the National Development Service after five years of university study, and much of this literature is apparently for the use of these student workers.

The booklets are a good example of how one country is proceeding with village and rural development using its own manpower and organizations. Some of the publications are:

a) The Why and How of Reforestation—describes the process of planting trees to replace those that have been cut down over time; well illustrated.

b) School Pupils Helping Village Development—suggests ways to involve school children in practical village development work.

c) Fish Farming in Ponds and Paddyfields.

d) Increasing Agricultural Production.

e) First Aid.

f) Notes on Road Construction and Maintenance.

Appropriate Technology and Research Projects, book, 66 pages, M.M. Hoda (Director of the Appropriate Technology Development Association), $1.00 from Appropriate Technology Development Association, Gandhi Bhawan, Lucknow, U.P. India.

This is a notable little book because it suggests possible student projects on practical applications of appropriate technology, and lists a large number of such projects currently being undertaken.

"It requires some imagination to conceive and formulate the problems and introduce them in the institutions. Real life problems should be given to the students rather than theoretical problems, if maximum benefit is sought to be derived from them. Before that can be done, the concept of appropriate technology has to be fully understood to apply its principles for the solutions of the problems. There are many constraints and impediments which seriously restrict the scope of working in a rural surrounding, like absence of electricity, lack of communication, unavailability of materials, servicing and repairs. The designer has to keep all these aspects in mind to design equipment suitable for village use."

The author also discusses: the early beginnings of the village technology movement in India, and the important roles played by Tagore, Gandhi, and the Sarvodaya movement; the current situation in India; the emergence of the Appropriate Technology Development Association; and the philosophy that underlies appropriate technology.

World Neighbors Newsletter, $2/year from World Neighbors, 5116 N. Portland, Oklahoma City, Oklahoma 73112 USA.

This newsletter sometimes has how-to-do-it information. In particular, the following issues may be of interest ($0.50 each):

Vol. 4, No. 1E: how-to section on visual aids.

Vol. 6, No. 1E: information on soil-testing.

Vol. 6, No. 2E: how-to section on contour ditches for soil conservation.

Vol. 7, No. 1E: information on growing, pruning, and grafting fruit trees.

Other printed materials from World Neighbors include:

a) **Visual Aids Tracing Manual**: Ideas and step-by-step instructions for making filmstrips by drawing on polyvinyl or acetate plastic. Pages of drawings included to aid an extension worker in making his or her own filmstrips. 20 pages. $2.00.

b) **The Use of Radio in Family Planning**: 60 pages of text and 100 pages of appendices including family planning radio scripts from 18 countries. (We haven't seen this one.) $2.00.

c) **Introducing Family Planning in Your Neighborhood**: Designed to help family planning workers organize their approach in the community, and to enable other community development workers to include family planning motivation in their current extension work. Includes 14 "experience stories" illustrating some of the problems faced and how they have been overcome. 44 pages. $2.50.

d) There are two catalogues listing filmstrips from all over the world. One is on health and family planning, and the other is on agriculture and community development. Descriptions of each filmstrip are in both English and Spanish. Ordering information is included. $0.50 for each catalogue.

World Neighbors has more than 40 **filmstrips** (described in the above catalogues and in a free price list of overseas development materials). Prices of the filmstrips range from $1.50 to $9.00. About half of these are on family planning. Other subjects include: rat control, fish farming, mushroom growing, grain storage, soil samples, agricultural irrigation, rabbit raising, and several on the care of young and sick children.

Liklik Buk—A Rural Development Handbook/Catalogue for Papua New Guinea, 270 pages, Melanesian Council of Churches, 1977 second edition, $5.00 from VITA; or K6.00 from Wantok Publications, P.O. Box 1982, Boroko, Papua New Guinea.

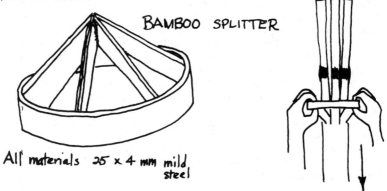

BAMBOO SPLITTER

All materials 25 x 4 mm mild steel

Liklik Buk contains a wealth of practical and access information for rural development in Papua New Guinea. Tells a great deal about who's doing what in PNG, and where to go for further information. Contributors from all over PNG, including government departments. This book would be of particular value throughout Southeast Asia and in other tropical countries. Such a book should be produced within every developing country.

There are 120 pages on crops and livestock, with attention to processing and utilization. Some coverage of village industries (good short description of silk-screen printing and soapmaking), food processing, and building and roads construction. 12 pages on health and nutrition.

The 65-page Design section includes many photos and drawings that are great sources of ideas; some of the equipment could be built from this information alone. Of particular interest are the pedal-powered thresher, winnowing machine, coconut scraper, oil press, and sugar cane crusher. Some information is presented on alternative sources of energy and water resource development.

The final 36 pages are filled with a list of further references.

An excellent model for what a national catalogue/handbook can be. The Papua New Guinea equivalent of the Whole Earth Catalog. A Papua New Guinea pidgin edition is projected for 1978, and a third English edition for sometime in 1979.

Highly recommended.

The Last Whole Earth Catalog, large paperback, 447 pages, Portola Institute, 1971, $6.00 in United States, $6.50 overseas, from WETS.

This is the proto-type of the low-cost catalog for information dissemination. It actually descends from the American Sears and Roebuck merchandise catalogs of 70 years ago, and the L.L. Bean catalog of outdoor equipment.

The Whole Earth Catalog was started in an attempt to provide information about where to buy good quality tools (including books as "tools"). The Catalog expanded from that vision to include books, products, and information on literally everything — from environmental law through french cookware to mysticism. It is now the ultimate source book for Americans.

The Whole Earth Catalog represents one of the best models for low-cost information exchange anywhere; but little from the original Catalog is appropriate to the needs of developing countries. In Papua New Guinea, the Melanesian Council of Churches has produced a kind of Whole Earth Catalog for development workers there. The contents are almost entirely information and resources from within PNG. It is a remarkable example of what can be done with this approach (see review of **Liklik Buk,** page 50).

The Last Whole Earth Catalog was, well, the **last**...except that the need still existed for coverage of new information and products. So along came the **Whole Earth Epilog** (the **last** Last Whole Earth Catalog). The third generation produced the quarterly journal **CoEvolution Quarterly,** which features a section on "soft technology." CQ might be called "the serialized further adventures of the Whole Earth Catalog" except that more attention is given to articles on a wide variety of subjects.

Another offspring of the Catalog is the Whole Earth Truck Store, which sells all the books reviewed in the Catalog, Epilog, and CQ, along with additional books that haven't yet been reviewed. Everything listed in the Appropriate Technology Sourcebook that is marked WETS is available from them, and probably covered by a review at one time or another.

Yet another descendant of the Catalog is the **Energy Primer** (see review, page 130), a cooperative effort of the best alternative energy groups in the United States (published by Portola Institute, which also parented the Catalog). The Energy Primer has what is basically the Catalog format: enormous newsprint pages jammed full of information, photos, and drawings.

Now that you have the family history straight, we can tell you that we've carefully looked through the Catalog, the Epilog, the Energy Primer, CQ, and the entire stock of books at the Whole Earth Truck Store. We've chosen what we think are the best practical books for use both here and in developing countries. You'll find them marked "from WETS." About 15% of the titles listed in the Appropriate Technology Sourcebook come from this source alone (we've included our own reviews). They're nice folks.

The Last Whole Earth Catalog, 447 pages, $6.00 in U.S., $6.50 overseas.

The Whole Earth Epilog, 318 pages, $4.00 in U.S., $4.50 overseas.

The Energy Primer, 200 pages, $5.50 in U.S., $6.50 overseas (see page 130). **CoEvolution Quarterly**, journal, 144 or more pages, 4 issues for $8 anywhere. **Whole Earth Truck Store Book List**, gives the latest prices. They plan to update this list every 6 months. $1.00. All from WETS.

The Cumberland General Store Catalog—A comprehensive selection of down-to-earth tools, catalog, 254 pages, 2000 entries, 1975, $3.00 from Cumberland General Store, Route 3, Box 479, Crossville, Tennessee 38555, USA.

The catalog includes a drawing of each entry—this is what is particularly useful about the catalog: it is an idea book, not a how-to book. All of the items listed can be purchased through the Cumberland General Store—but the drawings alone in many cases are sufficient to provide an idea for local production. Alternatively, in some cases it might be useful for a regional adaptive technology center to purchase some of the items and then determine how to produce them locally.

The items listed are mostly simple, hand-operated low energy-using pieces of agricultural and farm home equipment. Some books are listed also. Items listed include all kinds of simple food processing and preparation equipment, tools for animal-raising, plows, containers, pumps, blacksmith's tools, grinders, and a great deal more. Certainly a lot of this equipment could be produced with nothing more than a small blacksmith's shop.

The New UNESCO Source Book for Science Teaching, book, 254 pages, 1973, price unknown, from UNESCO (United Nations Educational, Scientific, and Cultural Organization, 7 Place de Fontenoy, 75700 Paris, France; or UNESCO book distributors; or UNIPUB Inc., P.O. Box 433, Murray Hill Station, New York, N.Y. 10016, USA; or low-cost Asian edition available at $3.25 plus postage (only to countries in Asia) from Charles E. Tuttle Co., 2-6, Suido 1-Chome, Bunkyo-ku, Tokyo, Japan.

This thorough book is intended for science teachers, for whom we recommend it highly. It will also be of considerable interest to others, because it describes how to make a whole range of simple equipment. There are hundreds of illustrations.

The principles of soldering are explained: you are told how to make solder and then how to use it in soldering. The composition by weight of the metals mixed to form bronze and casting brass is given, along with that of several low melting alloys.

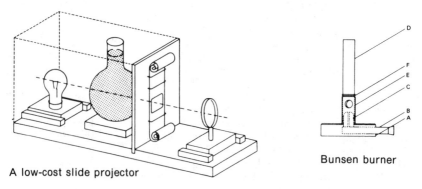

A low-cost slide projector

Bunsen burner

Complete information is given on how to make the following things: simple weighing devices, a slide projector, a bunsen burner (which can illustrate the same principles to be considered when making a simple burner for methane gas from your digester), several kinds of glues (including water-proof aquarium cement), soap, a dry cell battery, a simple thermometer, a model hydraulic ram, a model water wheel, and simple weather instruments such as a wind speed indicator.

Descriptions are given for the following processes: a method for depositing a bright silver mirror surface on glass; simple demonstrations of the comparative strengths of mud, clay, and sand bricks; the principles of heat transfer (important in the design of solar water heaters and insulated fireless cookers); and how to cut glass.

Another attractive feature of this book is that it suggests ways of avoiding the mold and rust on instruments associated with tropical conditions, particularly during the rainy season.

The authors' approach is to provide simple experiments or demonstrations to illustrate each scientific principle. As a science reference it is both thorough and broad in scope—covering chemistry, heat, magnetism and electricity (including circuits and fuses), wave motion, mechanics, fluids, biological sciences, rocks and minerals, astronomy and space science, and weather.

The book is intended as a guide for science teachers "for making simple equipment and for carrying out experiments using locally available materials." While it is successsful in this for the most part, one possible limitation is that it does make greater use of gadgets normally found only in science labs: stands, beakers (you can make your own graduated cylinders if you have one already), two-holed rubber plugs, test tubes, and lenses.

The language is not as simple as in **Build It Yourself Science Lab**, but the book has been translated into 30 languages (contact UNESCO at address given above for further information about this).

Build It Yourself Science Laboratory, book, 334 pages, Raymond Barrett, 1963, $6.95 from WETS.

This book shows how to make your own simple laboratory and experimental apparatus out of inexpensive materials. The contents are intended to be used in teaching science rather than as equipment to be actually used in the field. 200 ideas—single drawings are followed by suggested experiments.

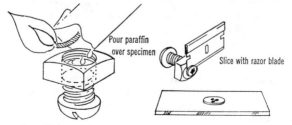

Pour paraffin over specimen

Slice with razor blade

Microtome: for slicing thin sections to be mounted on microscope slides

Several pieces of equipment included in this collection seem likely to supplement field work in agriculture, rural health care, alternative energy sources, and water supply. The thermometers and rain gauges included could make an agricultural extension agent's work easier, if his training course included practical applications of such data. Crude but effective microscopes, test tubes, culture plates, and slide apparatus could enhance a rural health clinic. Anemometers or similar gadgets could be very valuable for testing wind conditions for windmill applications, and various devices such as miniature solar stills, safety gas generators, or umbrella solar furnaces could increase people's awareness of alternative sources of energy.

Perhaps the most immediately practical tool would be homemade litmus paper, useful in checking the effluent from your methane digester, the condition of well water, or the suitability of soil.

"Purpose: Litmus paper is used to tell if a liquid is an acid, base, or salt.

Materials: Flower petals, purple cabbage leaves, water, and a pan.

What to do: In order to make a red litmus liquid, boil flower petals in water until most of the water evaporates and the color is very strong. Dip pieces of paper towel into the liquid and dry. These colored strips of paper towel serve as red litmus paper. Blue litmus paper is made in the same way except you use purple cabbage leaves instead of flower petals. The dry colored paper is called an indicator."

Construction and Use of Simple Physics Apparatus, book, 36 pages, R.F. Simpson, 1972, HK$5/U.K.50p./US$1.50 from Swindon Book Company, 13-15 Lock Road, Kowloon, Hong Kong.

This delightful book includes dozens of ideas for simple equipment and illustrative experiments. Everything from the behavior of ping pong balls to the use of a polished half biscuit tin as a reflector for light experiments, to the construction of hand-held stroboscopes. Written by a former school teacher who has since been training science teachers at the University of Hong Kong.

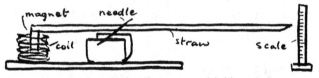

A measuring device that uses a drinking straw

"The use of simple apparatus constructed locally provides a magnificent opportunity for educators in developing countries to extract the essence of a good science education without the expensive frills that have become associated with Western models."

In addition to the obvious advantages of very simple, inexpensive physics equipment made of commonly available objects, "pupils may become aware that scientific principles apply to everyday things and are not just associated with special apparatus, usually imported from abroad, and only found in laboratories."

Dick's Encyclopedia of Practical Receipts and Processes, book, 607 pages, originally published in 1870, reprinted 1974, $7.95 from Mail Order Department, Whole Earth Access Company, 2466 Shattuck Ave., Berkeley, California 94704, USA.

This book is from an era when American families were largely self-sufficient. It contains 6400 formulas and recipes for a wide range of household and small workshop processes. It is **not** a cookbook, but instead covers subjects such as making soap entirely from natural raw materials, waterproofing, making glues and cements for many different applications, and making paints, inks and lacquers. The majority of these recipes will probably not be relevant to appropriate technology practitioners, but there is such an enormous volume of information here that the useful material may still make the book a good purchase.

Some of the terms used are no longer common in English, and a large number of the basic chemicals and substances will be unfamiliar. However, it may be easier to obtain these basic substances in some developing countries that have chemist's shops remaining from colonial times. We suggest this book for use only by people who understand English well.

2,000 Down Home Skills and Secret Formulas for Practically Everything, book, 368 pages, first printed probably 70 or more years ago, reprinted 1971, $3.50 from Gala Books, 2147 Laguna Canyon Road, Laguna Beach, California 92652, USA.

This is the same kind of book as **Dick's Encyclopedia** reviewed above, but with fewer formulas and recipes (2000 instead of 6400).

Both of these books we include with some hesitation. What is needed is a thorough review and testing of the recipes and formulas of most obvious value, with the aim of producing a modern English, easier to use book of perhaps 200 recipes.

Village Technology Handbook, looseleaf book, 270 pages, 1976, $3.00 plus postage, from Rural Communications, 64 West St., South Petherton, Somerset, England.

This is a looseleaf guide to international organizations and local groups around the world actively involved in appropriate technology for rural development. Addresses for 170 international groups listed by country. Local groups are also listed by country, and for these a contact person and a short description of interests, activities, and publications are included. 110 local groups in developing countries, and 80 in developed countries (mostly U.K. and USA.).

The third section of this guide provides a list of 55 books, periodicals and journals, with short descriptions and source addresses. Rural Communications will supply some of these to local groups in developing countries.

The loose-leaf format of the guide is to facilitate additions and updating. This book should not be confused with the VITA **Village Technology Handbook**, which is a manual of practical information.

A commendable effort to promote horizontal communications among appropriate technology groups by making them aware of each other.

Towards Village Industry, book, 70 pages, by Berg, Nimpuno, and Van Zwanenberg, contact Liv Berg, Industrial Designer SID, Chalmers University of Technology, Section A, Fack, S-402 20, Gothenburg, Sweden.

This book supplies the contemporary appropriate technology enthusiast with a whole new perspective—one which can be a good deal more valuable than other contemporary approaches. By analysis of what existed in the past (pre-colonial Tanzania is the example) the whole picture of a well-integrated naturally flowing economic order emerges—an order which is precisely what so many developing nations have intended to retain, but have lost due to colonization or media and physical exposure to Western societies. The authors state that one must have a genuine reverence for the technological and cultural history of the population—and give it at least as much emphasis as is placed on current economic and technical analyses. Completely local production in a labor intensive process is stressed.

This book cites Tanzania's pre-colonial industrial/agrarian specialized technologies and local trading patterns, to develop a historical basis for appropriate technology. Western appropriate technology development specialists often seem to introduce, the authors claim, a technically and even economically suitable technology, but a technology out of context with the culture and history of the people—which is often a reason for its failure to spread. The implication is that economic interdependence existed among the Tanzanian people before the colonial period, and that by reinvestigating that period important considerations for AT will be found.

Examining the products of East African village craftspeople today, the authors note the effect of the introduction of city-trained craftspeople into the villages. These people are commonly producing copies of devices they were trained to make in Western-oriented technical schools. Where mass-produced items are copied by craftspeople, the product is usually inferior in quality to the original. Superior products can be made through the craft processes, but only when following the methods that correspond to these processes and materials. The authors assert that the craftsperson should once again become a creator or innovator of technology responding to the needs of the rural people—which implies a major overhaul of the selection and training process. Ways in which this overhaul could be accomplished are suggested. Strong emphasis is placed on the development of useful village workshops. Equipment, workshop requirements, and types of training are identified.

Here is one of the best analyses of AT introduction. This perspective could be valuable to many people working in the field today. Highly recommended.

Economically Appropriate Technologies for Developing Countries: An Annotated Bibliography, book, 94 pages, compiled by Marilyn Carr, 1976, £2.30 or US$5.30 surface mail from ITDG.

This is an annotated list of 291 "reference materials on the economic aspects of intermediate technology and its appropriateness." Studies are of the following technologies: food, shelter, household goods, power sources, water supplies, health services, and transport. There are 36 entries on technical publications (these are the only practical references given) and 23 bibliographies. Most of the studies "have been aimed at assessing how 'intermediate' techniques compare in terms of capital and labour productivity, employment generation, cost of production, and generation of surplus with more conventional techniques."

Many of the conclusions of the reports are given. This is a very valuable reference book for scholars. Unfortunately, it will be difficult for most people to get a chance to look at the papers and books listed because no addresses or prices are given.

RAINBOOK:Resources for Appropriate Technology, book, 243 pages with index, by the editors of RAIN Journal of Appropriate Technology, 1977, $7.95 from RAIN Magazine, 2270 N.W. Irving, Portland, Oregon 97210, USA.

A compilation of information that has appeared in RAIN magazine (see review on page 283) plus a lot of new material. Describes reference materials, activities of U.S. groups, and includes articles on: appropriate technology, place, economics, creating community, communications, transportation, shelter, agriculture, health, waste recycling, and energy. The emphasis is on changing the U.S. towards decentralized, environmentally appropriate technology, and having fun doing it.

Like the journal, RAINBOOK is the best single reference for Americans looking for excellent resources for changing lifestyles so that we consume less of the world's resources, while becoming fuller human beings ourselves.

TOOLS TO MAKE TOOLS

Tools To Make Tools

This section is concerned with how to make tools, and how to use them. Of the books listed, some describe one specific tool (such as **Oil Drum Forge**); *others contain compilations of many tools and how to make them (such as* **The Making of Tools**); *and still others cover the skills and operations of a single craft (such as* **Welding Craft Practice**).

The use of tools, and the ability to make them using local resources and equipment, is obviously critically important in the development of appropriate technologies. In some areas where small foundries, blacksmith shops, wood-working or machine-tool workshops exist, many of the tools and processes listed may have already been in use for many years. In other areas, most of these crafts are unknown. Therefore, the tools listed in this section are of many different types, from simple hand tools to wood-turning lathes to metal-working equipment. Some may be made at the village level, others may require existing small metal-working shop facilities (machining, welding and casting). Once made, all of these tools allow a person, village, or region to become more self-reliant, less dependent on outside materials and resources, and thus better able to adapt existing technologies and develop indigenous ones.

We are very pleased to have found plans for about a dozen lightweight 'shop tools'—machine tools for use primarily in small wood-working shops. In many places, this kind of tool is usually imported at considerable expense; the items listed should be able to replace much of the lighter range of this equipment. These machines are typically powered by small electric or gas motors. In most cases they could easily be converted to be powered directly by waterwheels, animal power gears, pedal-power units, windmills or engines that use methane gas as the fuel. (Windmills will have to be large, heavy-weight units, and pedal-power may require two people pedaling for some applications—see PEDAL POWER section for important considerations. Methane gas cannot be used without special adaptations, because it is particularly corrosive when burned.)

The **LeJay Manual** *has some interesting suggestions for making electric welding machines from old generators. And a wide range of metal parts can be made by casting in sand molds—these include the large gears needed for the animal power gear (see page 134) and the wheels used in band saws.*

Also included are four books that are inventories of all the tools used in particular places; the simple drawings and explanations are sufficient for reproduction of the tools shown. All four books include some fascinating and still relevant tools that evolved under circumstances where craft skills were highly developed. The eye and the hand of the crafts person were of more importance than the technical capabilities of the equipment. Americans will be amazed at the range and sophistication of things still being made without the use of expensive machinery. A skilled blacksmith can produce twist bits for wood drills and tin snips for cutting sheet metal; and the heavy-duty scissors and carbon steel knives produced by these people are distinctly superior to those produced using industrialized processes.

Extending and improving already existing crafts is undoubtedly easier than introducing crafts previously unknown to the area. Unfamiliar tools and processes must be introduced with care, to ensure that they are truly needed, properly understood, and used to full advantage.

The Sensuous Gadgeteer, book, 114 pages, B. Abler, 1973, $3.95 from WETS.

 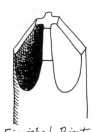

Cut corner   *Finished Point*

"The Sensuous Gadgeteer is a guide to tools, materials, and procedures that are within the reach of a small basement shop. The beginner and amateur (and low-budget) tinkerer, artist or scientist will find here plenty of information to see him through almost any project he can undertake, whether simple or complex. Because The Sensuous Gadgeteer begins with simple tools and materials (hammer, nails, wood, file, drill, saw, and wrench) the beginner can use it as an introduction to manual techniques. He will find step-by-step instruction leading him through the motions for using these and other basic tools and materials."

"After familiarizing you with basics, this book describes the use of abrasives, adhesives (solder, glues), plastics (plexiglas, epoxy), and finally molds and casting. The last chapter concerns efficiency and effectiveness in the use of manual techniques. An appendix of basic devices, a bibliography and an index are included.

"The description for each tool and material is presented with concrete examples (the section on sheet metal describes how to make a ring) so that when you work through the example to learn the procedures you will have a completed piece of work. But this is not a how-to book presenting instructions for the completion of a few projects; instead it gives you skill and insight into tools and materials so that you can plan and complete your own projects. The home tinkerer who wants to build a mold, or the scientist who wants to build a specialized gas burner will all find here not specific instructions, but plenty of information to guide the project to completion."

This book, is "directed at your imagination in the hope that, when you know what is already known, you will be able to think of new things (that you would never have been able to think of otherwise) by recombining processes and extending materials to satisfy each new demand you make of them."

Illustrations (literally hundreds of them) are included to accompany each step in the text, and ensure that the text will be understood by any reader. Each presentation is very clear and easily understandable. In particular, there is a valuable discussion of a variety of casting methods. The "Devices" section gives illustrations and simple explanations of 12 very useful simple devices (solar still, bicycle sprocket drive, set screw). Most of these would be quite valuable for a village technology handbook.

This is a valuable book, both because of the clarity of presentation, and the constant use of illustrations. Perhaps most of all, if adapted to local circumstances, its value lies in that it seeks to develop basic skills and an approach that is fundamental to future village-initiated development of appropriate technology.

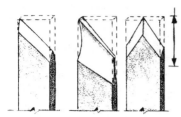

wood lathe-turning tools
made from old files

The Making of Tools, book, 93 pages, A. Weygers, 1973, $4.95 from WETS.

MATERIALS: high-carbon steel scrap, hardwood for handles

PRODUCTION: uses the following machines: grinder, drill press, side grinder, buffer, vise, anvil and forge

"This book teaches the artist and craftsman how to make his own handtools: how to design, sharpen, and temper them, using only basic shop equipment and scrap steel." There are many illustrative drawings on each page that show the "step-by-step progression from the raw material to the finished product—the handmade tool."

Raw material is usually high-carbon steel—from steel scrapyards and auto junkyards (US). Hardwood is used for the handles. The workshop tools that are required are obviously more than for **The Sensuous Gadgeteer**.

Contents include: tempering steel; sharpening tools; making a screwdriver, cold chisel and other simple tools; stonecarving tools; cutting tools; eyebolts and hooks, tool handles, hammers, gouges, seating cutter and hinge joints, tinsnips, wire and nail cutters, large shears, and pliers; applying color patina to steel surfaces. There is also a glossary of tool-making terms (useful to non-native English speakers).

The author was born in Java, educated in Holland as an engineer, and has worked in Java and the US before concentrating on art. This book, based on his teaching experience, is designed for the artist and craftsman who is interested (or forced) to make his own tools.

This seems to be a very useful guide if the required workshop tools are available.

The Modern Blacksmith, book, 96 pages, Alexander Weygers, 1974, $4.95 from WETS.

MATERIALS: high carbon steel scrap.

PRODUCTION: anvil, forge, tongs, hammer, water dipper, vise.

This book is very similar to Weyger's other book **The Making of Tools**, but the focus is on things that can be made with hammer, anvil and forge. The basic skills of blacksmithing are covered in detail.

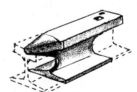

anvil made from scrap railroad rail

There is an initial chapter on elementary blacksmithing exercises: squaring and straightening a round bar, and shaping the end of a square rod. Further chapters include: tempering and hardening high carbon steel, making a right angle bend, forging simple tools, hinges, wrenches, drill bits, pliers, making a small anvil from a railroad rail (see drawing), and upsetting steel (making a bolt head). There is a glossary of blacksmithing terms.

This is a very good introduction to the skills of blacksmithing, with many drawings and examples.

Hardening and Tempering Engineers' Tools, book, 89 pages, G. Gentry, 1950, revised by E. Westbury and reprinted 1975, $3.00 from META.

"The efficiency of cutting tools employed in engineering and other crafts depends very largely on their correct heat treatment. In the past, the methods employed in these processes have often been governed mainly by rule of thumb, and experienced tool makers have often evolved individual methods which have been in some cases closely guarded as trade secrets. There is, however, no reason why even the novice should not be able to harden and temper tools quite successfully by adopting simple methods which can be applied without the need for elaborate equipment."

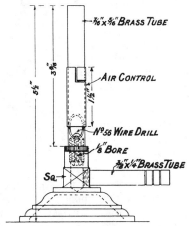

An easily made Bunsen burner for hardening and tempering small tools

This book contains all the relevant information on simplified processes available to craftsmen with small workshops to maintain their tools in proper working strength for a long lifetime. Detailed descriptions of case hardening and the latest processes, materials and equipment are included, plus valuable information on gas hardening, nitriding, and flame hardening. Although emphasizing modern appliances and conveniences such as welding torches and gas and electric furnaces, a very helpful chapter on forging reminds toolmakers of the importance of shaping steel by hot working under the hammer. This is precisely the state of the art for most traditional blacksmiths in developing countries, for whom the tempering suggestions should prove valuable.

Good illustrations with clear text.

Blacksmithing, book, 109 pages, James Drew, 1943, $4.00 from META.

This book covers most simple blacksmithing skills for forging metal parts— especially useful in making and repairing agricultural implements. The chapters include: forging iron and steel, simple exercises in blacksmithing, forging and tempering steel tools, plow work, soldering and brazing. The chapter on forging steel tools covers chisels, drills, and knives. The explanations are clear, although there are only a few drawings.

This book would be a useful introductory

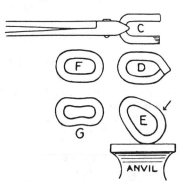

Steps in making a chain link

book in an area where blacksmith facilities are desired. Experienced blacksmiths, however, will probably find the information too elementary.

Oil Drum Forges, dimensional drawings, 40 pages, Ł1.30 or US$3.00 surface mail from ITDG.

MATERIALS: oil drum, fittings, bike parts, scrap steel, car or bike inner tube.
PRODUCTION: cutting the oil drum.

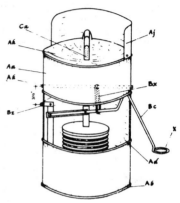

Making these forges requires no welding or brazing. One forge is bellows-operated, the other is fan-operated. Both are made from old oil drums. The plans are very simple—numbered drawings (with separate text, to simplify translation) with English and metric measurements.

These can be used by one person for any kind of blacksmith work. The author notes that these devices are also ''suitable as engineering exercises, as rural craftsmen must be able to make their own tools.''

A typical mold, with its pattern

Foundrywork for the Amateur, book, 108 pages, B. Aspin, 1954 (revised 1975), $3.50 from META.

MATERIALS: sand, wooden molds, crucible (ceramic container for holding melted metal).
PRODUCTION: fireplace or furnace hot enough to melt metal.

A basic skills book for making metal castings, describing the tools and techniques needed. The requirements are simple, although some of the tools described may not be locally available (such as a ceramic crucible). A foundry can be very useful for producing metal tools and replacement parts. Scrap metal can often be used, and the tools can often be made.

The book covers subjects such as furnaces, sand, molding boxes, how to make and ram a mold, and melting iron and aluminum. Illustrations of the tools used and the steps in the casting process are included. Useful examples are given, such as the casting design for an engine crankcase. Some of the English is a little complex.

Although this book was written for use in Britain, it should be valuable in rural areas where foundry skills are needed to produce things locally.

Metals for Engineering Craftsmen, book, 69 pages, CoSIRA, 1964, Ł1.80 or US$3.60 from CoSIRA.

This book is designed to be a simple guide to the properties of a wide range of metals, and be a useful alternative to very large technical books on metallurgy. The characteristics of most useful metals are all included, along with information such as the welding and casting properties of each. This is not a how-to book, but it is very informative.

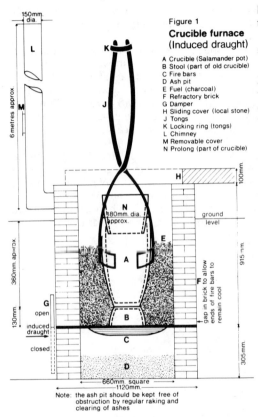

Figure 1

Crucible furnace
(Induced draught)

A Crucible (Salamander pot)
B Stool (part of old crucible)
C Fire bars
D Ash pit
E Fuel (charcoal)
F Refractory brick
G Damper
H Sliding cover (local stone)
J Tongs
K Locking ring (tongs)
L Chimney
M Removable cover
N Prolong (part of crucible)

Note: the ash pit should be kept free of obstruction by regular raking and clearing of ashes

The smallest scale of iron foundry
for producing small tools from castings

Industrial Profile: Iron Foundry, booklet, 19 pages, by the Industrial Liaison Unit of ITDG, 1975, Ł1.30 or US$3.00 surface mail from ITDG.

This booklet represents an attempt by ITDG to provide information about the technological choices available in the iron founding industry. It "includes information on the different levels of production equipment that can be employed; on the capital costs of equipment required for the different levels of technology; on the fuels that can be used; and on the labor requirements. The bibliography will be useful to anyone starting small scale foundrywork, or wishing to improve upon an existing simple foundry."

Two main levels of intermediate technology are examined: simple low cost operations using the crucible furnace, and more elaborate operations using the small cupolette type of furnace. Drawings of the furnaces are given, along with a description of the procedures. Capital costs for the two are less than $100 and about $3500, respectively. The booklet also covers molding, sands, core making, and pattern making.

Farm Shop and Equipment, booklet, 16 pages, 1953 (reprinted 1975), $1.50 from the Cumberland General Store, Rt. 3, Box 479, Crossville, Tennessee 38555 USA.

"Farm machinery is important to self-sufficiency. Effective care and repair of farm machinery requires an organized farm shop, as well-equipped as possible."

This booklet was originally written for small American farmers. It discusses the kind of work that can be done, desirable building features, and a simple equipment list for making repairs, in a farm shop. It shows how to sharpen and grind drill bits, and how to make a chisel. One of the unique features of this booklet is a full-page table in which the following are listed: major kinds of metals used in farm machinery, how to identify them, why the manufacturer used the particular metal, common causes of failures, and recommended method of repair. There are numerous diagrams and photos, including a farm-made substitute for a drill press that uses a hand electric drill and simple plumbing parts, and dimensional drawings for a medium-sized brick forge.

Welding Craft Practices, Volumes 1 and 2, book, 159 pages (volume 1), 182 pages (volume 2), N. Parkin and C.R. Flood, 1969, $3.00 for each volume from WETS.

"The two volumes of this book cover the ground necessary for the acquisition of the essential basic skills and safe working methods in welding, sufficient technology and related studies being included to provide a suitable background to the practical work and form a basis for further, more advanced studies. It is intended for all who wish to learn to weld and the ground covered will enable the beginner to obtain a sound knowledge of the equipment, an appreciation of safety and, by means of a graduated series of practical exercises, a good standard of skill.

"Volume 1 deals with Oxygen-Acetylene Processes and Weld Defects, Testing of Welds, and Welding Science; Volume 2 with Electric Arc Processes and Elementary Electricity, Classification of Electrodes, Welding Symbols, Engineering Drawing, Metal Plate Surface Development and Workshop calculations." These latter sections on drawing and welding symbols could be useful references for those who work with dimensional/mechanical drawings.

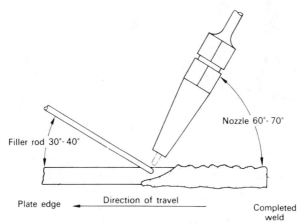

Nozzle 60°- 70°

Filler rod 30°- 40°

Plate edge ◄──── Direction of travel ────

Completed weld

The two volumes can be bought separately; both have drawings and a few photographs. While welding is a skill that must be learned by practice, usually with the help of an experienced welder, these two books are well suited to library or textbook use.

Fabricating Simple Structures in Agricultural Engineering, book, 68 pages, 1955 (reprinted recently), Ł0.90 or US$1.80 from Council for Small Industries in Rural Areas (CoSIRA), Information Section, P.O. Box 717, 35 Camp Road, Wimbledon Common, London SW19 4UP, England.

"This volume has been prepared by the Rural Industries Bureau as a guide to blacksmiths and agricultural engineers. It deals with the application of oxygen cutting and arc welding fabrications and therefore assumes knowledge of these two processes."

Castor wheel mountings

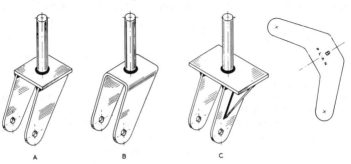

A   B   C

The structures described are all metal, and are generally used in farm applications: linkage mechanisms, wheels, rollers and brackets, bearing mountings, trusses, gates and a trailer chassis design. All pieces are made out of angle, channel and plate iron.

''The fabricated parts used to illustrate this book are intended to teach principles; they are not primarily intended to represent actual parts of machines. The object is not to show the precise way in which an exact number of fabrications can best be made, but rather to help the reader to become 'fabrication minded.' '' The emphasis is on helping the reader fabricate parts of his own design.

Machine shop facilities are necessary to made the structures indicated, as well as the welding equipment already mentioned. Drawings and photographs are included.

LeJay Manual, booklet, 44 pages, 1945 (reprinted many times since), $1.70 from LeJay Manufacturing Co., Belle Plaine, Minnesota 56011, USA.

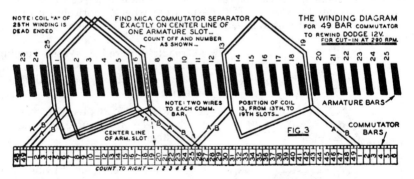

The winding diagram for rewinding an old Dodge 12-volt generator

This is an illustrated manual on how to rewind automobile generators for all kinds of uses: from direct drive windgenerators and waterwheels to arc welders and soldering irons. For windgenerators, rewinding is done so that the generator will begin charging at a lower rpm, thus avoiding the need for gearing. This allows the propeller to directly drive the generator shaft. The specific generators referred to have mostly disappeared; however, the principles remain the same.

3 **Welding Jigs—ITDG Complete Technical Drawings #19**, dimensional drawings, no text, 3 large sheets, R. Mann, ₤1.80 or US$4.15 from ITDG.

MATERIALS: mild steel parts, angle bar, bolts.

PRODUCTION: some welding.

Full-sized dimensional assembly drawings for 3 types of welding jigs are presented, in English measurements. Included are: a 'plow share' welding jig for repair or fabrication of irregular sections, a shift and stock jig, and a universal jig. Exploded perspective views are also included, along with materials lists. Although measurements are given, it is noted that "all dimensions and views are approximate", and can be varied to suit local availability of materials and particular jig requirements.

Practical only where welding facilities already exist.

Metal Bending Machine, dimensional drawings and photos, 24 pages, ₤0.80 or US$1.85 surface mail from ITDG.

MATERIALS: bolts, steel strips and channel iron.

PRODUCTION: welding, hole punching or drilling.

This remarkably simple machine can be used to bend thin strips of metal (the width can be varied), from right angle bends to circular rims for cart wheels. It is hand operated by two people, and has very few parts.

The booklet has very detailed drawings with English and metric measurements. It also includes instructions and photos on how to make cart wheels with an axle jig assembly. Several ITDG designs use wheels fabricated with this machine (see the agricultural leaflet entitled **Carts**). An ingenious piece of intermediate technology.

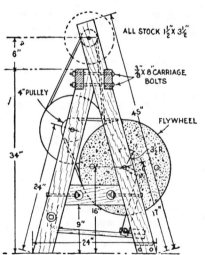

Treadle-Powered Wood-Turning Lathe, dimensional drawings with text, 3 pages, W.C. Lecky, in **Cloudburst 1** (see page 43).

MATERIALS: wood, plywood, concrete for flywheel, a few simple pipe pieces, bolts, steel rod

PRODUCTION: simple handtools

These are dimensional drawings with complete text and assembly information. English units used.

This unit is built almost entirely out of wood, and with only simple handtools. It has quite a variety of potential uses, though of course it cannot be used to work on metal. Potentially a valuable piece of equipment.

"With the exception of turned wooden pulleys (which can be made on this machine after it is built) and the form to cast a flywheel, you can build this efficient treadle lathe with a few hand tools.'' The flywheel construction is detailed carefully. It ''provides the necessary momentum to keep the spindle turning at a uniform speed.'' A 6'' or 8'' grinding wheel fitted to the outer edge of the rotating shaft both contributes to the momentum and provides a means for sharpening lathe tools and other tools. Some familiarity with treadle mechanisms would be useful, though not essential, for construction of the lathe.

The flywheel in this design is a good example of one that might be used with any kind of pedal-power unit for generating electricity or operating machinery.

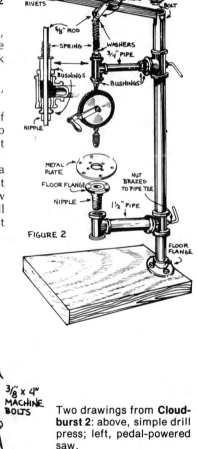

FIGURE 2

Hand-Operated Drill Press, plans, 1 page, A. Howe in Popular Science magazine, 1948, reprinted 1976 in **Cloudburst 2** (see review on page 44).

MATERIALS: 1½'' and ¾'' pipe, flat iron, bolts, bushings, spring, 5/8'' rod, (4) pipe T's, (2) floor flanges, a small hand-crank drill.

PRODUCTION: pipe cutting and threading, some hole-drilling and brazing.

A drill press can be a very useful piece of shop equipment, because it enables you to place your holes accurately and you don't have to lean hard on the drill while using it. This particular one is about as simple a design as any. There is room for a great deal of modification. It's also one of the few designs we've seen that uses a hand drill instead of a power drill. A lightweight wood-working tool.

Two drawings from **Cloudburst 2**: above, simple drill press; left, pedal-powered saw.

A **Foot-Powered Saw**, plans with text, 5 pages, a 1929 Popular Mechanics article that is reprinted in **Cloudburst 2** (see review on page 44).

MATERIALS: plywood or wooden planks, short lengths of pipe, rod, assorted small metal pieces (some of these will have to be machined).

PRODUCTION: some metal cutting, drilling and machining; some brazing.

This is a fascinating design because a number of rather sophisticated components are produced using remarkably simple materials. The result is a rather complex tool, but made entirely of easily available materials.

The saw is similar to a jig saw, in that a small sawblade is moved up and down for the cutting motion. The operator pedals while cutting with the saw.

Popular Mechanics Plans for Power Tools, listed below, (include reference number when ordering), from Popular Mechanics, Dept. CO, Box 1014, Radio City, New York 10019 USA.

These are photocopies of articles that originally appeared in Popular Mechanics magazine. Thus the photos do not reproduce very well. The drawings are generally quite clear, however. Other limitations are that the plans are at times rather brief—it is assumed that the reader has some background with shop power tools. Also, all of the designs include small electric motors (two of them can be adapted to pedal-power, however).

The designs do use commonly available materials of standard sizes. Skills required for production are not great. The machines are sturdy and versatile. In general, these designs (when combined with some imagination in adaptation) provide a good place to start.

The next three entries are Popular Mechanics shop tool plans:

a) **10-inch Table Saw**, plans with text, 10 pages, $1.45, (Reference No. X585) from Popular Mechanics (address above).

MATERIALS: wood, plywood, sealed ball bearings, angle iron, channel iron, flat iron, rod.

PRODUCTION: welding, metal cutting and drilling, perhaps some metal casting.

This unit would involve quite a bit of machine shop metal work, but the plans are quite clear, and the final product would be a solid, versatile table saw. The 10-inch circular blade can be raised, lowered, or tilted. The electric motor would be difficult to replace with another power source.

b) **4-Wheel Band Saw**, plans with text, 4 pages, $0.85 (Reference No. X36) from Popular Mechanics (address above).

MATERIALS: plywood, hardwood for framing, small metal parts, bearings, saw blade.

PRODUCTION: some metal cutting and filing, one small weld, wood-turning for the wheels on which the blade rotates.

"Except for ball bearings and retainers, metal yokes, sheet-metal cover, and such shafts and bolts as are necessary in the assembly, the machine is entirely made out of wood. Most of the parts are cut from a single piece of 5/8" plywood." The four wheels are made of plywood, and covered with pieces of inner tube to provide a surface against which the blade rubs as it rotates. A pulley can be changed to allow a second speed. Uses blades 10 feet long and up to ½-inch wide. The small electric motor could be replaced by a 1-2 person pedal-power unit with a flywheel. Will cut wood and light metals (this requires changing to a metal-cutting blade and operating at a lower speed). Clear drawings, sufficient for construction.

c) **Heavy Duty Drill Press**, plans with text, 4 pages, $0.85 (Reference No. X245) from Popular Mechanics (address above).

MATERIALS: standard pipe and fittings; steel angle, channel, rod and flat bar;

small pulleys; small bearings.

PRODUCTION: metal cutting and drilling, minor welding and metal reaming.

This appears to be a very sturdy, powerful drill press for heavy drilling in wood and metals. An imaginative design, yet reasonably simple to make. A small amount of machine shop work would be needed on a few minor parts. A small electric motor is used, but a geared-up pedal-power unit would work also. The drawings are quite clear and sufficiently detailed. This is a serious possible substitute for expensive heavy duty imported drill presses for many circumstances.

Gilliom Build-It-Yourself Power Tool Plans, several large sheets with drawings and photos, $2 for a set of plans for one power tool, from Gilliom Manufacturing Co., 1109 North Second St., St. Charles, Missouri 63301 USA.

These plans are all designed to accompany low-cost build-it-yourself kits that Gilliom sells; they are sold separately, however. Gilliom's kits include a number of useful castings that will have to be made if plans only are purchased. This should not be too difficult. Photos and drawings are included, along with full-scale patterns for cutting plywood parts. All of these plans use electric motors, but pedal-power or waterpower could be used (except to operate the two tilt saws). The plans are a good value; excellent for ideas.

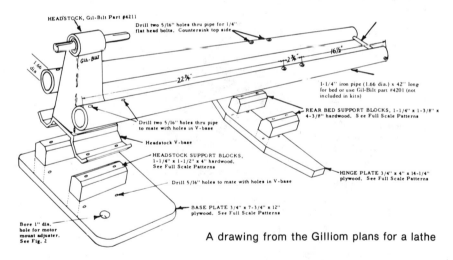

A drawing from the Gilliom plans for a lathe

Such kits (consisting of well-illustrated plans along with a small number of critical castings so that the buyer need only do woodwork and assembly) could represent an innovative distribution approach if imitated in developing countries using local designs.

Gilliom plans include:

No. 481 10 inch tilt/arbor floor saw (10'' diameter blade)
No. 461 9 inch tilt/table bench saw
No. 431 6 inch belt sander
No. 771 12 inch band saw (12'' refers to distance from back to blade)
No. 451 18 inch band saw (these plans even show wood wheel fabrication
           in place of the cast iron wheels supplied with the kit)
No. 421 drill press/lathe (a multiple use tool)

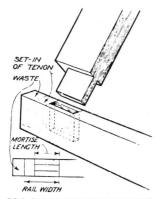

SET-IN
OF TENON
WASTE

MORTISE
LENGTH

RAIL WIDTH

FIG. 7. SIMPLE MORTISE-AND-TENON JOINT.
The waste piece at the end should always be allowed
as it helps to prevent splitting when mortising.
A haunch is desirable for good work.

Woodwork Joints, book, 176 pages, Charles Hayward, 1974, $4.95 from WETS.

"The craft of woodwork consists largely of joining pieces of wood together. In this book we have taken the basic joints, given their chief variations, and shown how to cut them. It is not suggested that the methods of cutting described are the only ones possible...but it can be taken that the way described is useful and has been proven by experience to be reliable."

This book is suitable for anyone experienced in working with wood who wants to learn different methods of making joints.

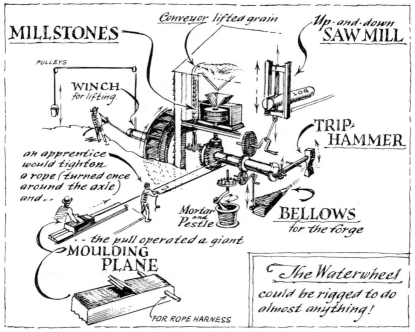

Some of the many ways in which a water wheel can be used to drive equipment (see review below).

Diary of an Early American Boy, book, 108 pages, Eric Sloane, 1965, $2.95 from WETS.

The AT value of this book is in about 10 drawings: a simple bridge building technique, a water hammer, a pole saw, bow saw and crank saw, a diagram which illustrates the multiple uses of a waterwheel (above), and a beam drill (in which a weighted bar replaces the lever of a hand-operated drill press). These are virtually all simple but useful do-it-yourself devices made of wood that do not depend on fossil fuel power sources.

A Museum of Early American Tools, book, 108 pages, E. Sloane, 1964 (fourth edition 1974), $2.95 from Ballantine Cash Sales, Box 505, Westminster, Maryland 21157 USA; or WETS.

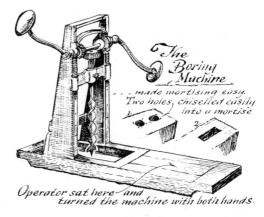

"Covers building tools and methods, farm and kitchen implements, and the tools of curriers, farriers, wheelwrights, coopers, blacksmiths, coachmakers, sawyers, loggers, tanners," and others. The tools were generally made from wood and iron.

This book was written by a collector of early tools, with the philosophy that tools represent extensions of the human hand. The book includes drawings of the tools, descriptions of their uses, and some production sketches. These are tools that were produced by blacksmiths and farmers—from an era when most rural Americans made many of their own tools out of local materials.

Interesting items include: making barrel staves, reaming, nail-making; and complete drawings of a boring machine (a simple drill-press—intermediate technology at its best—see above drawing), wooden jacks and lifts, and smithy tools.

This is an idea book, not a how-to book. But with the drawings provided and imagination it should be possible to reproduce most of the tools shown.

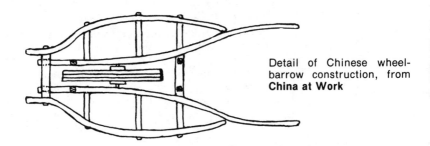

Detail of Chinese wheelbarrow construction, from **China at Work**

China at Work, book, 357 pages, R. Hommel, 1937 (reprinted 1969), $6.45 from MIT Press, Cambridge, Mass. 02142 USA.

The author lived in China between 1921 and 1930. In this remarkable book, he examines "primary tools, those which met people's basic needs: the handcrafting of tools, the providing of food, clothing, shelter, and transportation. The photographs and sketches are thoroughly documented and the various processes explained." There are more than 500 photos and sketches, and a very useful index with several hundred individual items of village technology listed.

Although much of the material in this book is quite dated and primitive, the book is so comprehensive that it undoubtedly includes a few useful items for any village technologist.

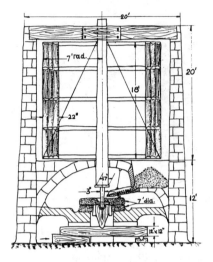 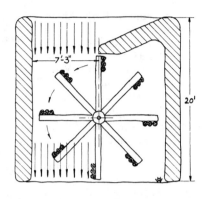

Two views of a Persian vertical-axis windmill that has traditionally been used to grind grain (see grindstones at bottom left).

Traditional Crafts of Persia, book, 304 pages, Hans Wulff, 1966, $7.95 from WETS.

An inventory with photos of the traditional crafts and tools used. Major topics are metal-working, wood-working, building, ceramics, textiles, leather, agriculture. Descriptive text. Among the most interesting items covered are: flour mills and rice hulling mills driven by wooden water wheels or vertical-axis windmills; the Qanat water supply system; and oil-seed milling.

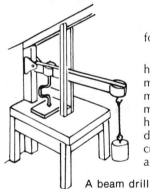

Country Craft Tools, book, 232 pages, P. Blandford, 1974, $5.95 (paperback) from WETS.

This is an inventory of traditional craftsmen's handtools in the U.S. and Britain. Chapters on: axes, mallets & hammers, knives, chisels, saws, planes, making holes, holding & handling, measuring & marking out, turning & roundwork, agricultural hand tools, and cloth-making tools. 40 pages of line drawings and 30 photographs. Short narrative descriptions of each tool's use. Few of these tools have any moving parts.

A beam drill

FURTHER REFERENCES ON TOOLS TO MAKE TOOLS

Simple Working Models of Historic Machines includes drawings of 2 different lathes, screw cutters for wooden screws, a variety of pulleys and other lifting devices, the Chinese spoon tilt hammer which can be used by a blacksmith, and two kinds of bellows; see drawing with review on page 45.

Oil-Soaked Wooden Bearings: How to Make Them and How They Perform (ITDG Agricultural Green Leaflet #40), see drawing and review on page 111.

Making Do has information on oil-soaked wooden bearings; see drawing with review on page 46.

AGRICULTURE

Agriculture

"Some of the best examples of ecological mis-application are to be found in the vast domain of agriculture. It is true that application of modern production factors such as mechanization, irrigation, fertilizers, pest controls and herbicides, as well as high yield crop varieties, can free the subsistence farmer from many of his limitations. However, they can also radically alter the functioning of the ecosystems and create ecological instability. In addition, these factors tend to shift the farmer's dependence from the food production capability of his land to the marketing of food and energy distribution systems."

—from the **Handbook on Appropriate Technology**

Agriculture is a basic economic activity in all societies, from those where the most common tool is the pointed planting stick to those where 50-horsepower tractors are becoming outdated. The need to produce food and cash crops for local and international markets is still a prime concern for most nations. In this section of the Sourcebook we have tried to sketch the dimensions of appropriate technology options for agricultural development, selectively presenting what we consider the most reliable and practical information available at the moment.

We have chosen to concentrate on the two most vital components of agriculture—the human and the environmental—to tie together the small peasant cultivator (a huge majority of the labor force in most developing countries) with a broad perspective on world food systems. While not all aspects will receive thorough coverage, it is hoped that an organized framework for action can be developed from the entries in this section.

The most important question in assessing agricultural systems is whether the yields are sustainable over long periods of time and do not overtax the land's capacity to continue producing for succeeding generations. Traditional manual and organic horticultural methods in the Orient have for over 40 centuries shown dramatic results, managing to feed 1.5 to 2 times more people per hectare than industrialized farming now does using mechanized chemical techniques. These intensive methods are still practiced in China and Japan, and increasingly by so-called 'organic agriculturalists' in Western countries.

The initial optimism of the 'Green Revolution' has been shaken by unanticipated negative economic, environmental, and social consequences. One good illustration of the drawbacks of a technical, one-dimensional approach is the case of the Indonesian small plot rice paddy cultivators. The paddy contains all of a family's life support needs—rice as a staple (and cash crop, if there is a surplus); a rich variety of protein sources within the irrigated paddy field itself in the form of shrimps, frogs, eels, and fish; and nutritionally significant vegetables, legumes, and tree crops grown among the rice plants, between seasons, or on the paddy embankments. The introduction of a hybrid monocul-

ture strain of rice, dependent on significant amounts of expensive and often unavailable synthetic fertilizer and pesticide, disrupts the balanced ecosystem. The fish, edible water greens, and other small organisms are reduced in number or eliminated entirely—a loss that does not appear in the statistics for crop yields. The farmer loses a measure of control over his land and food production, as decision-making moves increasingly into the hands of 'experts' and government planners.

Cultural practices too are affected by the 'Green Revolution', and other side effects include increasing vulnerability of crops to disease and insect attack, the potential eventual dangers to the soil due to accumulation of salts, leaching and erosion. The 'Green Revolution' does not appear to have improved the conditions of poor and landless peasants. In many cases, the equipment claimed to be necessary to handle increased yields has also eliminated the jobs of the poorest people. Appropriate tools and techniques must be combined with equitable land and resource organization and distribution if increased food production is to benefit the people who need it.

In all fairness, the 'Green Revolution' does seem to have had moderate success in raising yields, especially in China, but this appears to be a questionable achievement when longer term and other effects are considered. The controversy of organic versus chemical techniques is certain to continue vigorously in the near future.

Most of the world's farmers use no artificial fertilizers or pesticides because they cannot obtain them. The methods and techniques covered in this section are generally labor-intensive and capital-saving, making use of local resources. Diversification of crops, decentralization, and soil-conservation are stressed as the means to community and national self-reliance.

Erik Eckholm's Losing Ground is the most eloquent explanation of the current crisis in world food systems, and his ideas are complemented by the techniques suggested in The Ecological Methods. Fine as these theoretical works are, there is no substitute, in volume of information and practical approach, for The Samaka Guide, a Philippine manual for small plot farming (recently reprinted). It should be widely distributed, translated into other languages (as was done in Indonesia), and adapted for different conditions. This is the only publication available that directly addresses the agricultural problems of poor people in developing countries. The approach is community centered, and the well-illustrated book is simple yet complete.

Information on crops, soils, irrigation, composting, planting & cultivation techniques, plant protection, and garden & farm planning is covered in varying degrees by the other sources in this section. Such promising and innovative methods as greenhouse food production, hydroponics, and aquaculture are surveyed in systematic fashion.

The need for agricultural extension agents comparable to the 'barefoot doctors' is becoming increasingly evident. Their training will expose them to more information such as that provided in The Samaka Guide, give them a knowledge of intensive methods (such as those described in How to Grow More Vegetables), and ensure an understanding of the importance of perennial tree crops (as detailed in Forest Farming), as well as exposure to the innovative methods noted above. The training period should be thorough and realistic, and of sufficient length (perhaps 6 months or 1 year, with regular additional periods of short-term training). The organizers of the training effort will need to cover more than simply farming techniques, but should effectively consider credit, cultural practices, construction and use of farm tools, soil and plant analysis, seed propagation, crop storage, and related matters.

Losing Ground, book, 223 pages, Erik Eckholm, 1976, $3.95 from World-watch Institute, 1776 Massachusetts Ave. N.W., Washington DC 20036, USA.

Losing Ground is at once a disturbing and exciting book. It brings into sharp focus the struggle for survival of a large portion of the world's people—their immediate need for fuel and food has led to actions with potentially disastrous human and ecological consequences. The author thoughtfully analyzes the global extent of man-made environmental stress, and shifts attention from the pollution and inflation of industrial countries to the concerns of the world's poor, whose 'energy crisis' has largely gone unnoticed.

Eckholm sees the shortage of firewood as a central feature of this crisis. The uncontrolled clearing of remaining or replanted trees has its severe ramifications: precious topsoil erodes not in centuries as in the past, but practically overnight; a disastrous increase in flooding occurs on lowland plains; and new deserts and grass wildernesses are created in drier zones by inhabitants removing the remaining ground cover.

Both food production and economic development prospects in Africa, Asia, and Latin America are now dimmed by accelerating destruction of the land's productivity. Slash and burn shifting cultivation has in many places increased beyond the ability of the sensitive forest to recover. Massive forest-clearing operations by governments and corporations in places such as the Amazon river basin and Borneo are often followed by heavy grazing, which completes the land's destruction. The book surveys man-made environmental crises from the mountain highlands to the seas, where overfishing now endangers vital food sources.

The author (a member of Worldwatch Institute, which co-sponsored this book with the U.N. Environmental Program) calls for massive tree-planting campaigns, agricultural reforms to benefit peasant farmers, and a slowdown in world population growth.

"People hungry for land are not apt to leave forest or pasture lands unplowed, regardless of what ecological soundness dictates. Farmers hungry for bread are not likely to defer production this year to enhance soil quality for the next generation. Those with no other means than wood to cook their dinner cannot be expected to leave nearby trees unmolested even if they are labeled 'reserved' by the government. And people brutalized by exploitive economic and social systems will probably not treat the land any more gently and respectfully than they are treated themselves."

"Measures will never succeed until the populace has the technical and financial means to cooperate, and this means reaching the masses with ecologically-sound agricultural advice and with credit facilities; maximizing rural employment on farms and in small-scale industries; and breaking down the social, legal, and economic structures that deny the poor basic opportunities for advancement. It means creating participatory institutions, whether through local government, cooperatives, or communes, that give the poor a sense of responsibility for and control over their own destiny. That these prerequisites of ecological recovery are identical to the tactics of a more general war against poverty and hunger should come as no surprise."

Highly recommended.

The Ecological Methods, leaflets, 1976, $1 donation, from The Agricultural Consulting Bureau for the Tropics, Ranonkelstraat 119, The Hague, The Netherlands.

This group of experts in tropical agriculture has formed a non-profit foundation in The Netherlands, which proposes permanent, ecologically-sound cultivation methods to regenerate tropical soils and make them productive. Their principles take into consideration the delicate nature of tropical ecosystems, which are endangered by natural and human activity. The leaching and erosion of soils by torrential rains are being furthered by slash and burn or clear-cutting operations. The protective canopy provided by trees and other vegetation is eliminated, converting huge areas into steppes, savannahs, or 'green deserts.'

The Agricultural Consulting Bureau for the Tropics proposes simple and time-tested methods for reversing these trends: Planting a perennial leguminous cover crop, deep-rooted to retain moisture and bring up nutrients to the surface. This carpet of vegetation acts as a 'living mulch'—to protect the variety of fruit, vegetable, and tree crops planted in the topsoil. The methods are labor-intensive, require virtually no capital, and have the potential of making the last unpopulated areas of the world suitable for food cultivation without ecological disaster.

A contribution of $1 brings the correspondent various pamphlets and other literature explaining the 'ecological methods.' The Bureau is also prepared to respond to questions by mail and is genuinely interested in global applications for these life-giving and restoring techniques.

Forest Farming, book, 197 pages, J. Sholto Douglas and Robert de J. Hart, 1976, Ł4.25 or US$8.50 surface mail from Conservation Tools and Technology, 143 Maple Road, Surbiton, Surrey KT6 4BH, England.

Although we haven't been able to obtain a copy for review, all indications from reliable sources suggest that this book is a vital contribution to agricultural development. **Forest Farming**, co-authored by J. Sholto Douglas (who wrote **Hydroponics: The Bengal Method**), updates and expands J. Russell Smith's classic **Tree Crops: A Permanent Agriculture**, showing that ''in food productivity alone tree crops can produce 10 to 15 times as much food per acre as field crops.''

The authors discuss the role of forests and tree crops in farming and offer detailed advice and information on various economic species, the use of their products for food and raw materials, planting techniques and suggestions, and guidance for the layout and operation of schemes of forest farming.

Douglas and Hart state: ''The 'tool' with the greatest potential for feeding people and animals, for regenerating the soil, for restoring water-systems, for controlling floods and droughts, for creating more benevolent micro-climates and more comfortable and stimulating living conditions for humanity, is the tree.''

More Water For Arid Lands (Promising Technologies and Research Opportunities), book, 137 pages, report of a National Academy of Sciences panel, 1974, free from the Commission on International Relations (JH215), National Academy of Sciences, 2101 Constitution Ave., Washington DC 20418 USA.

''Little-known but promising technologies for the use and conservation of scarce water supplies in arid areas are the subject of this report. Not a technical handbook, it aims to draw the attention of agricultural and community officials and researchers to opportunities for development projects with probable high social value.

''The technologies discussed should, at present, be seen as supplements to, not substitutes for, standard large-scale water supply and management methods. But many have immediate local value for small-scale water development and conservation, especially in remote areas with intermittent rainfall.

With further research and adaptation, some of the technologies may prove to be economically competitive with standard methods of increasing the water supply or reducing the demand."

This report attempts to address the need for "fresh innovative approaches to water technologies, particularly those designed to meet the needs of arid regions in the less developed world, where there has often been improper application of practices developed in regions with higher rainfall or more abundant water supplies. Also, we need to reconsider practices developed in arid regions by ancient agriculturalists."

The report is divided into two parts: water supply and water conservation. It includes the following subjects: rainwater harvesting, runoff agriculture, irrigation with saline water, wells, reducing evaporation from water sources, trickle irrigation, use of greenhouses, and other innovative irrigation and water collection methods. For each subject, methods, advantages, limitations, stage of development, and needed research and development are briefly covered.

Although some of the techniques mentioned are high-technology, most of them are simple, low-cost methods gathered from all over the world. Photos and diagrams abound. This booklet has more immediately useful techniques and technology than the other NAS reports. An excellent overview of the subject—includes quite a list of selected readings. Resume in French and Spanish.

The Samaka Guide to Homesite Farming, book, 173 pages, Colin Hoskins, 1973, $3.00 surface, $4.00 airmail from Samaka Service Center, P.O Box 2310, Manila, Philippines.

The Samaka Guide is an excellent introduction to homesite farming, encompassing the vital skills of homesteading from seed-sprouting to goat-skinning. The Guide is closest to the needs and socio-economic level of the bulk

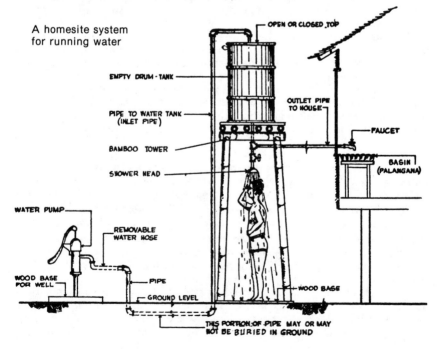

A homesite system for running water

of the people in developing countries; the emphasis on village self-reliance, cooperation and respect for traditional methods make it widely applicable outside its Philippine setting.

A summary of the Samaka Guide's contents: well drilling, composting, special directions for growing various indigenous vegetables and fruits, building plans for livestock pens, operation of a family fishpond, and care of assorted animals such as rabbits, chickens and water buffaloes. Also briefly covered are home industries, sanitation, tenant rights and barrio fiestas (neighborhood parties). This wealth of information is presented systematically, for an integrated model homestead of 600 to 1000 square meters (1/5 acre). The book is well illustrated and detailed for widespread use.

More than any other book on agriculture and related subjects, the Samaka Guide is immediately applicable at the village level (the English used is simple and non-technical). An Indonesian/Malay edition is available from Percetakan Arnoldus, Penerbitan Nusah-Indah, Ende-Flores, Nusah Tenggara Timur, Indonesia for Rp. 250. Hopefully, translations in other languages will appear soon, as this is a tremendously useful guide.

Five Acres and Independence, book, 397 pages, M.G. Kains, 1973 (reprinted from 1935), $2.95 plus postage from Dover Publications, 180 Varick Street, New York, N.Y. 10014, USA.

Five Acres and Independence is a text on farming for self-sufficiency, emphasizing intensive cultivation techniques on small, diversified farms which depend on legumes, crop rotations and organic manures to supply nutrient needs and maintain fertility. These were the ideas typical of American agriculture before large mechanized farms.

This book should be read as a sourcebook of key knowledge on which to build a self-contained agricultural unit. It is an excellent companion to **The Samaka Guide** (see listing in this section), although of less use to tropical countries. The sections on water supply and sanitation, organic crop production and orcharding are highly recommended.

The Basic Book of Organic Gardening, book, 377 pages, edited by Robert Rodale, 1971, $1.50 from WETS.

A basic introductory text, this book compresses the essentials of organic gardening into a readable, practical format. For its low price, compact size, and detailed information, it deserves widespread circulation. Although without any illustrations, the book redeems itself with a common-sense approach to plant protection and other standard techniques in the organic arsenal. Organic fertilizer equivalents of the figures cited in the AID **Handbook of Tropical and Subtropical Horticulture** (see review in this section) can be easily calculated —simply substitute ground fish heads or seaweed for urea and super-phosphate, for example. Although some of the information applies to temperate climates only, the philosophy and methods are easily adaptable to all conditions.

This book "tells you what soil is, how to create good soil, the fundamental rules about mulching and composting, why you need birds and insects, how to grow marvelous tasting and nutritious fruits and vegetables: it is packed with information about organic materials and foods—and where to get them."

Rodale Press is the foremost publishing and research organization dealing with organic gardening in the world today. Their information, however, is most immediately applicable to temperate climates, and that of the eastern region of the United States in particular. Outstanding and comprehensive Rodale books which deserve mention here are: **How to Grow Vegetables and Fruits by the Organic Method,** (1961, 926 pages, $11.95 from WETS). This book thoroughly covers soils, compost, mulch, and plant varieties (again, mainly from North America) and is well illustrated. A more advanced treatment intended for experienced gardeners is Rodale's **Encyclopedia of Organic Gardening** (1968, 1145 pages, $12.95 from WETS). **The Organic Way to Plant Protection** (1966, 355 pages, $8.95 from WETS) is the best treatment on biological plant pest controls available with specific information on which beneficial bird, insect, companion herb or plant, barrier, decoy, trap or organic pesticide to use with the particular disease or pest invading a particular plant. Those people wanting further information can write Rodale Press for a list of their publications. A series of reprints from their monthly magazine **Organic Gardening and Farming** is also available. Lately, **OG&F** has given good coverage to appropriate technology tools for agriculture and home use, such as bicycle-powered grinders. Write to Rodale Press, 33 East Minor St., Emmaus, Pennsylvania 18049, USA.

How to Grow More Vegetables, book, 82 pages, John Jeavons of Ecology Action, 1974, $4.00 from Ecology Action, 2225 El Camino Real, Palo Alto, California, 94306, USA; or WETS.

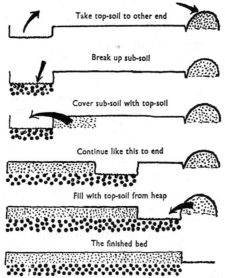

Take top-soil to other end

Break up sub-soil

Cover sub-soil with top-soil

Continue like this to end

Fill with top-soil from heap

The finished bed

An illustration of double-digging (from a different source)

"A primer on the life-giving bio-dynamic/French intensive method of organic horticulture." Initial research at Ecology Action's garden "seems to indicate that the method produces an average of 4 times more vegetables per acre than the amount grown by farmers using mechanized and chemical agricultural techniques. The method also appears to use ½ the water and 1% of the energy consumed by U.S. agriculture per pound of vegetable grown." It is significant that this small-scale intensive approach is very compatible with conditions in developing countries, where small-plot farming predominates.

The text is very readable, standard English with few technical terms. Illustrations and comprehensive tables complement the text. Chapter headings are: history and philosophy, raised bed preparation, composting, seed propagation, companion planting, and insect life.

The bio-dynamic/French intensive method draws from historical sources—using organic materials which guaranteed soil health and fertility over many centuries. Practical techniques are adapted from the intensive system of cultivation perfected by French gardeners in the 19th century. This consists of a series of raised planting beds, with heavy additions of organic fertilizers such as manure and compost, prepared by a technique known as 'double-digging' (see drawing). "The crops are grown so close to each other that when the plants are mature their leaves barely touch. The close spacing provides a mini-climate and a living mulch which reduces weed growth and helps hold moisture in the soil."

The theoretical element comes from the ideas of Austrian Rudolf Steiner, developed in the early 1920's. "He initiated a movement to scientifically explore the relationship which plants have with each other. From centuries of farmer experience and from tests, it has been determined that flowers, herbs, and weeds can minimize insect attacks on plants. Many plants like each other. Strawberries and green beans produce better when grown together. In contrast, onions stunt the growth of green beans."

Much of the material presented here could be directly used in other parts of the world. The bio-dynamic/French intensive method is labor intensive—the only farming implement required is a simple hand spade. However, it is also 'skill-intensive,' implying a sustained period of training to master the techniques (6 months to 1 year is a minimum). This points out a severe limitation of this or any other book promoting complex and intensive farming schemes. A wide gap still exists between being moved by the ideas and convinced of their value, and actually implementing them on a mass scale in developing countries where the need is so acute. Also, differing climatic zones and cultural practices require the employment of relevant tools, seeds, and forms of 'companion planting' which must be developed before this method can be successful elsewhere.

Ecology Action, of which John Jeavons is a key member, is involved in ongoing research on fertilizers, spacing, temperature, crop varieties, human nutritional needs, marketing, and other variables. They are very interested in promoting the bio-dynamic/French intensive method worldwide. Planned is the development of a system for demonstrating their method on a small-scale, such as with one 100-square foot garden bed. Ecology Action will send a list of their publications plus provide free advice to whoever requests it.

The Postage Stamp Garden Book, book, 150 pages, Duane Newcomb, 1975, $4.95 from WETS.

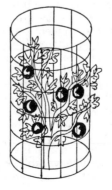

Subtitled "how to grow all the food you can eat in very little space by intensive gardening techniques," this book covers the same material as **How to Grow More Vegetables** (see listing) in more pages and at a slightly higher price. The emphasis is also on the Biodynamic French Intensive method, although more attention is given to individual vegetable varieties.

If the funds are available, buying and comparing both this book and **How to Grow More Vegetables** would be useful. If not, we recommend Jeavons' book.

Farming — Sources for a Social and Ecologically Accountable Agriculture, book, 68 pages, Henry Esbenshade, 1976, $2.00 from Dept. of Applied Behavioral Sciences, University of California, Davis, CA. 95616, USA.

This is the first of 8 planned volumes of an annotated bibliography and guide to organizations involved with "ecological and socially accountable agriculture." A continuing project of the Alternative Agricultural Resources Project of the University of California at Davis, this sourcebook stresses "decentralized, cooperative, accountable, and self determined" methods for dealing with the basic resources and operations in agriculture. This first section focuses on farming, with reviews of publications on soils, animal husbandry, machinery, urban gardening and other subjects. Addresses and descriptions are given for an international list of alternative and organic agriculture groups.

Although the emphasis is on indigenous North American responses to overgrown corporate industrial food systems, care is taken to make vital links with people in developing areas. Some of the books mentioned are annotated, while some are simply listed; price and address information is often not included.

Future volumes will focus on land, nutrition, cooperatives, energy and networking, using methods that are labor intensive rather than capital intensive.

Handbook of Tropical and Subtropical Horticulture, book, 186 pages, E. Mortensen and E. Bullard, 1964 (reprinted 1970), $3.90 (Stock No. 044-001-00022-5, Cat. No. S18.8:H78/970), from Superintendent of Documents, U.S. Government Printing Office, Washington D.C. 20402, USA.

"Based upon an extensive survey of available literature...(this manual) is written in layman's terms so that it may be understood by the non-specialist who is called upon to work with farm families in solving their agricultural problems. It also serves as a reference and guide for teaching courses."

"Major tropical fruit, nut, and tree crops are discussed in the second chapter with emphasis on such important points as spacing, pruning, fertilizing, budding, and disease and insect control. A few temperate zone fruits are included to stress that they can be grown only a higher elevations in the tropics, due to chilling requirements. Crops are listed alphabetically and scientific names are given for reference purposes."

"The Handbook continues with a description of all major vegetable crops. Information is presented on seed storage, vegetable varieties, fertilizer recommendations, plant spacing, temperature requirements, soil and cultivation. Major diseases with their controls are presented in a table for easy reference."

This handbook is heavily slanted toward row-cropping, the use of synthetic fertilizers and toxic chemicals, and a highly technical approach to agricultural development. The information it provides, however, on plant varieties, nutrient needs, and nutritional content is very helpful to anyone working in the field. To people seeking locally-available organic resources and techniques, a great deal of this book must be disregarded. Recommended as a secondary reference resource.

Rural Africa Development Project: An Example of a Farm Level Survey Technique Using Local Resources, handbook, 26 pages of text and 19 pages of sample charts, R. Mann, 1974, Ł3.55 or US$8.15 surface mail from ITDG.

Report by an ITDG joint project in Zambia. Presents a technique that uses local people without special agricultural training to determine the details of the farming calendar, including the cropping sequence and labor bottlenecks.

"Development plans are missing a link with the dominant type of production unit in agriculture, the smallholder." The author attempts to develop a methodology for determining the needs and circumstances facing the small farmer. He notes that the small farmer "himself is the key to essential information about his activities and his whole environment. His short term and long term memory are excellent, and the data gathered will be meaningless if put through a computer."

The report includes a method for the production of charts which enable the survey team to combine the variables of climatic patterns, crop planting and harvesting, livestock enterprises, off-farm equipment, and more on a single calendar chart. This makes the labor bottlenecks quite evident. Sample questionnaires and charts are included.

A farm-machinery-needs survey system is then described, which is used in combination with the labor chart, to provide "guidelines on which action is taken in engineering development, farm-level testing and modification of equipment, and training procedures for initiating rural craftsmanship and small-scale local manufacture in rural areas." (see following entry)

Expensive, but an interesting model of a low-cost survey technique.

Report on the Farm Equipment Development Project, Daudawa, Nigeria, report with some dimensional drawings for some of the equipment developed, 111 pages, John Boyd, 1974, Ł4.55 or US$10.45 surface mail from ITDG.

The project objectives were to "study the pattern of local agriculture, assess which labor bottlenecks limit production and introduce appropriate machinery to alleviate these bottlenecks." The project itself was in an area with an average farm of 9 acres. The goal was to systematically develop equipment that could be produced locally to meet local requirements. Weeding was identified as a labor bottleneck, and improvements in methods of weed control became a primary objective.

The report includes a description of the farm equipment development project, objectives, obstacles, and results. There are sample questionnaires presented, used to determine the results and local reactions to the project. Dimensional drawings with production and assembly information are included for the following: granule applicator, high-clearance rotary hoe, groundnut lifter, rotary rice weeder, expandable cultivator, and a number of drawings for various attachments. There are photos of much of the equipment built. All of these dimensional drawings are available separately (see pages 104-12).

This report would be useful to regional adaptive technology centers. Expensive for what you get.

How to Perform an Agricultural Experiment, booklet, 23 pages, G. Pettygrove of VITA, 1971, (also available in Spanish), $1.50 from VITA.

"Improved varieties, new fertilizer practices, irrigation, pesticides, new feed mixtures, and improved harvest procedures are just a few of the more important innovations which must be thoroughly tested at the local level before they are passed on to the farmer by extension methods...The purpose of this paper is to provide local agriculturalists with an understanding of the basic considerations in the design, execution, and measurement procedure of an agricultural experiment.''

Backyard Composting, booklet, 17 pages, Helga Olkowski, 1975, $0.50 plus postage, from Berkeley Ecology Center, 2179 Allston, Berkeley, California 94704, USA.

This is a brief summary of the Berkeley Fast Composting Method, where organic wastes can yield a nitrogen-rich humus in just 14-21 days. The technique covered in this booklet takes attention and human energy, but its high quality and quick results warrant the effort.

Composting bin

sawdust   ⟶

grass clippings   ⟶

sawdust   ⟶

manure   ⟶

dry leaves   ⟶

wet garbage   ⟶

sawdust   ⟶

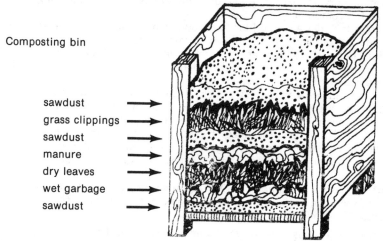

Build your compost pile with alternating layers of fresh materials, dry matter and manure.

''This compost will provide a plant fertilizer as well as act as a soil amendment and mulch; fly and rodent problems will be kept to minimums; high temperatures will be reached that will kill most plant pathogens, and even take apart pesticides.''

The drawings depict the tools needed for this method: a system of bins (at least 3), simply-constructed of wood, bamboo, or other available materials, to facilitate storing and turning the organic matter; a pitchfork; and a tool to chop, shred, or otherwise reduce the size of organic wastes for easier decomposition. The raw materials are leafy vegetable material, animal manure, kitchen scraps (or market refuse), and a high carbon substance such as sawdust, rice straw, corn husks, etc. Often animals kept in cages prove to be the most effective 'compost shredders,' and a chopping tool made of a long-handled blade hinged to a block of wood can be very useful. Pitchforks can be manufactured by local blacksmiths.

We recommend this method and booklet to anyone interested in efficient village or city-based compost production. Berkeley Ecology Center also offers another interesting publication, a 44-page companion pamphlet entitled ''How to Raise Rabbits & Chickens in an Urban Area,'' by Tom Javits, also $0.50. Although somewhat oriented to conditions and laws in Berkeley, California, good plans and drawings on rabbitries and slaughter and pelting techniques are included.

Composting — Sanitary Disposal and Reclamation of Organic Wastes (Who Monograph #31), book, 200 pages, 1956 (reprinted 1971), H. Gotaas, available from World Health Organization's regional offices; or 32 Swiss Francs (about US$13.00) from WHO, Distribution and Sales Service, 1211 Geneva 27, Switzerland; or $12.80 from WETS.

This is a solid, important reference book for anyone seriously interested in composting as part of fertilizer policy. Most of the book deals with fundamentals of composting: decomposition, raw materials, sanitary importance, etc. There are 26 pages on composting methods for villages and small towns. The book also includes a chapter on methods and planning for cities. The facts, figures, and illustrations are comprehensive. Coverage of continuous operation low-impact techniques suitable for developing countries such as the Bangalore/Indore method (see illustration) for handling assorted wastes is outstanding.

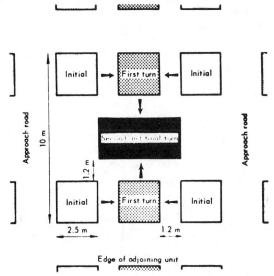

Layout of a composting station in the fields

One feature of this recommended manual is a 23-page chapter on methane gas recovery in farms and villages. It contains important information on gas pressure and the biological composition of waste input into digesters, as well as a good general introduction. However, the design itself is an unproven one, and from our experience not very workable in practice.

A Global Review of Greenhouse Food Production, book, 150 pages, Dana Dalrymple, 1973, $1.50 domestic postpaid (Stock No. 0119-00285), from Superintendent of Documents, U.S. Government Printing Office, Washington D.C. 20402, USA.

This is an excellent overview of past and recent developments in the field of greenhouse agricultural technology. Although a bit lengthy on statistics, good coverage is give to the important aspects of environmental control: ventilation, carbon dioxide enrichment, the use of evaporative coolers, heating techniques, artificial soil, and the possibility of using distilled sea water in arid nations.
The book is divided into categories of crops, designs, economics and country

by country analyses, with distinctions made between the needs in developed and developing nations. With the new potential brought by alternative energy sources, greenhouse agriculture may provide benefits over conventional cultivation under special circumstances. Although capital costs are higher, yields are also greatly increased.

"The Philippines is the only tropical country in the world where greenhouse food production is known to be carried out commercially. The main reason is for protection from heavy summer rains, but the warming effect can also be important at higher altitudes. In addition to physically protecting the plant from the force of the rain, the structure provides other benefits of water control such as reduced leaching of fertilizer, less washing of insecticides, and reduction of disease incidence. Weed control is also made easier. And the harvesting period may be prolonged.

"In 1967, a variation of the high tunnel type, consisting of plastic over bamboo, was tested and found to be suitable for the heavy rains and high winds of the region...The Philippine experience in using simple greenhouses for rainy season fruit production could well be instructive for other tropical nations."

Small Plastic Greenhouses, leaflet, 12 pages, Robert Parsons, 1974, free to serious groups (Publication No. 2387), from Publications, University of California, Division of Agricultural Sciences, 1422 South 10th Street, Richmond, California 94804, USA.

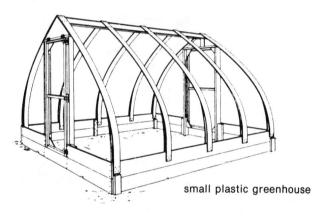

small plastic greenhouse

This set of 5 plans for plastic-covered light frame greenhouses can serve as a practical counterpart to **A Global Review of Greenhouse Food Production** (see review). Unlike glass-covered greenhouses, which require expensive glass and heavy wood beams for support, these structures are simply built, low-cost, and lightweight. The plastic film covering, where obtainable, is easily installed and unbreakable. There would be a need to periodically change the worn-out plastic. It is unclear whether the plastic film could withstand heavy tropical monsoon winds and rains.

The Survival Greenhouse, book, 165 pages, James DeKorne, 1975, $7.50 from The Walden Foundation, P.O. Box 5, El Rito, New Mexico, 87530, USA.

This is an informative account of the author's successful greenhouse system on one acre of land in the semi-arid highlands of New Mexico. It is a very functional integrated life-support system, producing vegetable and animal food, using only renewable resources and complete recycling of wastes for nutrient self-renewal.

Solar and wind energy are used to solve such problems as summer over-heating and rapid heat loss during colder periods. Windgenerators provide electricity for small pumps which move water through solar collectors and into the thermally-balanced building. Such pumps are also used for circulating the fluids in the hydroponic system, and to circulate water through the biological filters of the fish tanks. Ventilation is natural, and the need for adequate carbon dioxide in the greenhouse is met by raising animals such as earthworms and rabbits who release the carbon dioxide when they breathe.

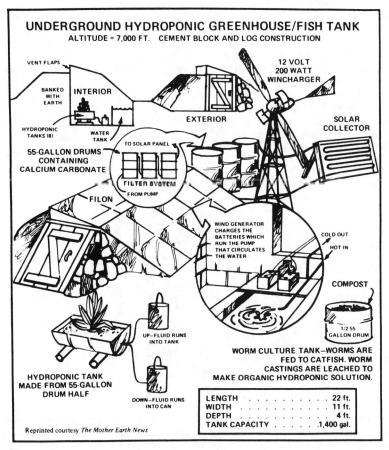

UNDERGROUND HYDROPONIC GREENHOUSE/FISH TANK
ALTITUDE = 7,000 FT. CEMENT BLOCK AND LOG CONSTRUCTION

VENT FLAPS

BANKED WITH EARTH

INTERIOR

12 VOLT 200 WATT WINCHARGER

HYDROPONIC TANKS (8)

WATER TANK

EXTERIOR

SOLAR COLLECTOR

55-GALLON DRUMS CONTAINING CALCIUM CARBONATE

TO SOLAR PANEL

FILTER SYSTEM

FROM PUMP

FILON

WIND GENERATOR CHARGES THE BATTERIES WHICH RUN THE PUMP THAT CIRCULATES THE WATER.

COLD OUT

HOT IN

COMPOST

1/2 55 GALLON DRUM

UP—FLUID RUNS INTO TANK

WORM CULTURE TANK—WORMS ARE FED TO CATFISH. WORM CASTINGS ARE LEACHED TO MAKE ORGANIC HYDROPONIC SOLUTION.

HYDROPONIC TANK MADE FROM 55-GALLON DRUM HALF

DOWN—FLUID RUNS INTO CAN

LENGTH	22 ft.
WIDTH	11 ft.
DEPTH	4 ft.
TANK CAPACITY	1,400 gal.

Reprinted courtesy *The Mother Earth News*

The drawings are simple and clear, and the detailed discussion of green-house basics (light, plant growth, and vital nutrients) is excellent. The practical information on the interaction of wind energy systems, solar energy, hydro-ponics and human needs make this book highly useful.

''In theory, at least, we have created a self-sustaining eco-system: a basic food-producing unit capable of supplementing the diet of a small family. With skill and proper management, greenhouses between 150 and 250 square feet are capable of providing a large part (but not all) of a family's diet.''

An Attached Solar Greenhouse, booklet, 18 pages, Bill and Susan Yanda, 1976, $1.75 domestic and $2.00 foreign, from The Lightning Tree, P.O. Box 1837, Santa Fe, New Mexico 87501, USA.

''An attached solar greenhouse is unique in that it serves the dual function of growing food and producing usable heat. It also is unique in that it is extremely inexpensive, by any measure, and lends itself to custom design, owner construction, and retrofitting (use with already existing structures)...The unit provides a bright warm recreation and living area for the entire family all winter...Throughout the coldest period, the highs in the greenhouse average 26 degrees C., and the family can harvest a fresh green salad every other day. Several plantings and transplanting of leafy vegetables, tubers, root crops, herbs, and flowers keep a good harvest going almost all year. At current market prices for fresh vegetables and seedlings, the unit has a one-year payout.''

''Solar greenhouses designed and built in northern New Mexico by the Solar Sustenance Project have proven that solar energy can be put to work **now** by low-income families,'' state the authors of this short but stimulating booklet. Included are detailed sketches, photos, and a bilingual text in English and Spanish. The only faults we can find are the brevity of the text, and the seeming lack of an effective Spanish translation of the working drawings. Overall, the information is excellent, with commendable stress on native materials, locally-available resources, and culturally-sensitive building practices.

Attached
Solar
Greenhouse

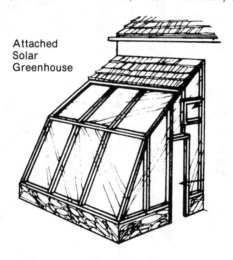

Although these designs come from a North American environment, it seems very likely that they are also useful for the highlands of tropical countries or any colder areas of the globe where space heating is a priority. Attached greenhouses employ a 'passive' solar heating concept. The structure acts both as a collector and a storage unit for solar energy, through the heat-absorbing combination of glass or plastic, concrete, adobe, and water-filled containers. During daylight hours, the last three of these substances store heat, and at night they radiate it to the living spaces. No expensive, complicated, or breakdown-prone devices such as pumps, heat exchangers, bulky collectors, or massive storage tanks are required. All that is needed is a good design and an active and alert person to regulate the vents, openings, and natural energy flows in the dwelling. This approach clearly has great potential for wider use in the future.

Bill Yanda has informed us that he has completed a definitive book called **The Food and Heat Producing Solar Greenhouse: Design, Construction, Operation**, containing up-to-date information from greenhouse innovators all over the USA. 161 pages, many illustrations. $6.00 plus $0.50 postage from John Muir Publications, P.O. Box 613, Santa Fe, New Mexico 87501, USA.

Hydroponics: The Bengal System, book, 185 pages, Sholto Douglas, 1975, $4.25 from WETS.

This highly regarded book, in its 5th printing since its original issue in 1951, is the most complete and comprehensive to be found, incorporating innovations, designs and methods in the field of hydroponics, the science of soilless cultivation of plants. The author is the originator of the Bengal System of hydroponics, which is suited to developing countries and can be used successfully in areas where normal soil cultivation is impossible, such as in Sahel savannahs, crowded urban areas or village settings.

The author is careful to give the reader a solid foundation in the theory of hydroponics. The system uses watertight containers filled with materials such as sand and gravel. This is continuously recharged with a nutrient solution with proper aeration and drainage. Douglas provides many ideas for low-cost systems, including detailed data and types of organic non-chemical fertilizers (the Sharder process) and such construction materials as erosion-resistant mud plaster and alkali-puddled clay.

The systems described are low in capital costs and are labor intensive, employing existing resources and materials. They are characterized by a high immediate rate of return. Well illustrated, supported with vital statistics, construction details and maintenance information, **The Bengal System** is a definitive, essential book.

Rainwater Catchment Tanks and Micro-Irrigation in Botswana, booklet, 74 pages, 1969, L1.30 or US$3.00 surface mail from ITDG.

This is suited to low rainfall areas where water is difficult to obtain. When it does rain, however, a large runoff must be generated, and only due to this runoff are the catchment tanks successfully filled.

The catchment tanks are essentially lined pits that catch runoff water. The pits are covered to reduce evaporation, and reinforced to resist the forces of the flooding waters. Lining and reinforcement are through the use of cement-sand

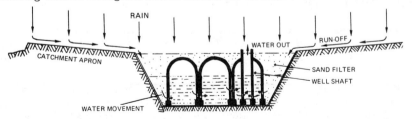

"sausages," that have polythene sheeting as "skins." The cement-sand sausage construction involves a 1 to 14 ratio of cement to sand. Moisture is retained for 3 weeks inside the polythene tubes, so that the full strength of the cement mixture can be achieved.

The booklet includes a full description of the building method, materials used, test results, and information from micro-irrigation experiments using a variety of vegetables.

Underexploited Tropical Plants with Promising Value, book, 188 pages, National Academy of Sciences, 1975, free from Commission on International Relations (JH 215), National Academy of Sciences, 2101 Constitution Avenue, Washington D.C. 20418, USA.

This is a remarkable survey of rarely utilized or underexploited tropical plants which offer promise as sources of food, forage, or industrial raw materials for developing countries. Compiled by a panel of international agricultural experts. 37 species of cereals, tubers, vegetables, fruits, oilseeds, forage, and miscellaneous crops are presented.

What makes this book especially valuable is the inclusion of selected readings on each crop **and** personal contacts for research and seed sources. The reader can immediately put the information to use. A sampling of the entries:

Grain Amaranths (**Amaranthus** species): The seeds of these almost totally neglected Central American grain crops have extremely high levels of protein and of the nutritionally essential amino acid lysine, which is usually deficient in plant protein.

Wax Gourd (**Benicasa hispida**): This large, melon-like vegetable is easy to grow and can yield three crops per year. Its outstanding feature is that the fruit can be kept without refrigeration for as long as 12 months.

Durian (**Durio**): The common durian is a large, spiny fruit that is enjoyed by many for its taste and dislike by others for its odor. Newly discovered odorless species might be more esthetically acceptable and could open a world market for this crop.

Jojoba (**Simmondsia chinensis**): This subtropical, North American desert plant is unique in the vegetable kingdom; it secretes liquid wax in its seeds instead of the glyceride oils secreted by other plants. Liquid waxes are important in industry. They are difficult to synthesize, and the only other source is the sperm whale. The development of jojoba as a crop promises to provide important economic benefits to arid tropical and subtropical regions.

Tamarugo (**Prosopis tamarugo**): A hardy, leguminous tree, native to the forbidding Atacama Desert in Chile, tamarugo grows through a layer of salt sometimes 1 meter thick. The nutritional quality of its pods and leaves allows sheep to be stocked at rates approaching those of the best forage areas of the world.

Spirulina (**Spirulina platensis and Spirulina maxima**): These high-protein algae grow in brackish and alkaline waters. Unlike some other algae, spirulina's large clumps make it easy to harvest by net or other simple means. It is palatable and is already eaten in Chad and Mexico.

The Winged Bean: A High-Protein Crop for the Tropics, booklet, 27 pages, 1975, free from Commission on International Relations (JH 215), National Academy of Sciences, 2101 Constitution Ave. N.W., Washington DC 20418, USA.

Edible legumes are excellent sources of dietary protein and oils. This report focuses on the exceptional promise offered by a minor tropical legume that has received little scientific attention. The panel that produced this booklet consisted of people who are familiar with this bean. They are convinced that "with research the winged bean can become a significant food crop in the humid tropics," and that this bean may be as important as the soybean in the future. Currently the winged bean is eaten throughout Southeast Asia, although it is not nearly as important a food source there as it could be.

This booklet represents an overview of what is known about the winged bean, its potential and research needs. The booklet is intended for development assistance agencies and institutions concerned with agriculture in tropical countries. Lists researchers who might supply seeds or advice. The winged bean has these characteristics: 1) it grows in humid zones but can also grown in drier or higher altitude zones (up to 7000 feet); 2) the entire plant is rich in protein and the tuberous roots have 10 times the protein concentration of cassava, potatoes, sweet potatoes, or yams; 3) its nitrogen-fixing capability enables it to grow in poor soils; 4) the whole plant can be eaten and it does not have the bitter beany flavor of the soybean, but is quite tasty; 5) it is suited to the small farm, requiring staking and harvesting over many months.

Fields and Pastures in Deserts: A Low Cost Method for Agriculture in Semi-Arid Lands, large book, 37 pages, 1976, $4.00 from Information and Consultation, Wadi Mashash, Erzbergerstrasse 16, 6111 Heubach, Germany BRD.

This is a report from an experimental farm, Wadi Mashash, in the Negev desert. The average annual rainfall is about 110 mm, most of which falls within a few hours during the occasional heavy rains. The farm uses simple techniques developed thousands of years ago to trap rainwater. The loess soil of the area (often found in other arid regions as well) leads to a high percentage of runoff when there is rain. Trees were planted in basins, each the lowest point in a 250-square-meter micro-catchment area. When there is rain, all the runoff from this larger area goes to the trees—providing all the water the tree needs, even during long periods without rain. Forage crops for sheep are also grown. This technique has been successfully tried in other places. 45 drawings and photos. A fascinating, low-cost method for making productive use of arid land, requiring no outside resources.

Aquaculture Bibliography, 7 pages, W. McLarney, 1976, $1.00 from New Alchemy Institute, P.O. Box 432, Woods Hole, Massachusetts 02543, USA.

The author has put together an excellent bibliography, including all the essential works on the current and traditional aquaculture practices worldwide. However, as with many other bibliographies, the annotation omits prices and ordering information. There are some excellent books included, such as the FAO's **Handbook on Fish Culture in the Indo-Pacific Region.**

Aquaculture—The Farming and Husbandry of Freshwater and Marine Organisms, book, 868 pages, Bardach, Ryther and McLarney, 1972, $15.75 from Wiley Interscience, 605 Third Ave., N.Y., N.Y. 10016, USA; or WETS.

''Aquaculture, that is, the growing of aquatic organisms under controlled conditions can make a unique contribution to nutrition in many parts of the world by virtue of both its extremely high productivity in many situations and the fact that aquatic crops are primarily protein foods rather than sources of starchy staple foods...Certain aquatic organisms may be better converters of primary foods than cows, fowl, or even pigs.'' Emphasizing the potential of producing large quantities of low-cost, protein-rich food (e.g., shrimp, eels, frogs, and algae), the authors have listed information on aquaculture from all over the world. There is a discussion of general principles, including biological and economic considerations. The next part of the book is organized by groups of organisms: true freshwater fish, fish which adapt to varying levels of salt content in water, true marine fish, invertebrates and aquatic plants. An appendix treats some principles of construction and management of ponds.

Aquaculture is a very comprehensive and complete text. It is thoroughly referenced and illustrated. Included are surveys of intermediate and simple

Fig. 1 Chinese Carp Culture

Habitat and feeding niches of the principal species in classical Chinese carp culture. (1) Grass carp (*Ctenopharyngodon idellus*) feeding on vegetable tops. (2) Big head (*Aristichtys nobilis*) feeding on zooplankton in midwater. (3) Silver carp (*Hypophthalmichtys molitrix*) feeding on phytoplankton in midwater. (4) Mud carp (*Cirrhinus molitorella*) feeding on benthic animals and detritus, including grass carp feces. (5) Common carp (*Cyprinus carpio*) feeding on benthic animals and detritus, including grass carp feces. (6) Black carp (*Mylopharyngodon piceus*) feeding on mollusks.

technology in aquaculture in Japan, Israel, Taiwan and other countries, and a discussion of Chinese carp polyculture. However, the price and technical language of this book will limit its use to universities and regional research centers.

Fish in Ponded Areas, leaflet, 9 pages, 1976, free to serious groups, from Action for Food Production (AFPRO), Technical Information Service, Community Centre, C-17, Safdarjung Development Area, New Delhi-11 00 16, India.

An excellent, compact introduction to fishpond construction and maintenance, presented by AFPRO, a grass-roots technical information service for village development. Very practical schemes with simple drawings are described, with consideration given to problem areas in pond aquaculture (including lining, stocking rates, fertilization, and induced breeding).

The authors point out that ponds can be hurt by an overabundance of algae which uses up the oxygen in the water that the fish need to survive. ''In such cases, continuous circulation of water through the pond is very helpful (because it provides the needed oxygen and discourages algae growth). Poisoning due to collection of noxious gases is immediately diluted by addition of aerated water...Raking the pond bottom also prevents collection of poisonous gases...To kill parasites and control excessive bacterial growth, ordinary washing soda, wood ash and potassium carbonate are also useful though the required strength has not been worked out. Banana leaf juice or leaves floated on the pond surface help stabilize pond pH...Preventing the spread of a disease by removal and destruction of infected fish is by far the most effective method of control.''

FURTHER REFERENCES ON AGRICULTURE

Liklik Buk has information on a large number of tropical plants; see review on page 50.

AGRICULTURAL TOOLS

Agricultural Tools

There are a number of appropriate technology principles that specifically concern agricultural tools. Such tools should be produced within the country, in part simply because of the large numbers involved. They should be sufficiently simple in design that they can be produced at the local level; and if this is not possible, a minimum requirement is that they be repairable at the local level. Because much of agriculture is characterized by short intense periods of activity, farmers cannot afford delays caused by equipment failures.

Local availability of land has a critical effect on the kind of agricultural tools needed. In areas where the land is intensively cultivated, most mechanized equipment will not increase the amount of food produced, but will only decrease the amount of labor required. Productivity per hectare or per acre may in fact decline, if these large tools require extra space to manuever and wide lanes to drive or roll over. Obviously, the tools required under such circumstances, even if supported by unlimited resources, would be very different than those used in most parts of the United States, for example, where if all the cultivated land were evenly divided among the population the plots would still be relatively large.

The tools that are needed in circumstances of intense cultivation in poor countries are obviously not those that displace labor—these people have no place to go (an organized community can of course use such equipment to free labor for other purposes; typically, however, the result in unorganized communities is that the poorest, landless peasants are the ones whose labor is 'saved'—leaving them with no productive work opportunities at all). What is needed are tools that can be used during periods when everyone is working and there is still not enough labor available; pumps which can extend irrigation to areas that would otherwise have less productive dry land cultivation (see ENERGY: WIND for water-pumping windmills); techniques which can be used to extend farming or gardening into areas that would otherwise be unfit for food production (see AGRICULTURE) through ecologically sound agriculture in tropical rain forests (see **The Ecological Methods**, reviewed on page 76), composting to reclaim barren land, and perhaps even rooftop gardening in some places; greenhouses that can extend the growing season (see AGRICULTURE); water-conserving irrigation methods for arid lands (see AGRICULTURE); tools that help to conserve expensive fertilizers and pesticides if these are to be used (to reduce cash costs and the environmental side-effects of these chemicals); intermediate level processing equipment for threshing, winnowing, and milling that enable a greater recovery of the crop at each of these stages; and crop driers and small-scale storage silos to reduce crop losses after harvesting (see FOOD AND CROP PRESERVATION AND STORAGE).

In areas with low population density and a large amount of cultivable land, the tool requirements will be considerably different. There will be more need for tools which allow the people to farm a larger area; still, the advantages of *small-scale intensive agriculture should not be overlooked.*

The FAO book **Farm Implements for Arid and Tropical Regions** *includes a list of important general principles for appropriate agricultural tools, some of which go beyond the general criteria for appropriate technology included in the INTRODUCTION:*

"Research and extension workers undertaking programs for the introduction and improvement of hand and animal-powered farm implements should stress the following points when attempting to improve tools and implements. Such tools should be:

a) adapted to allow efficient and speedy work with the minimum of fatigue;
b) not injurious to man or animal;
c) of simple design, so that they can be made locally;
d) light in weight, for easy transportation (there are also considerable advantages when threshers, winnowers, and machines like coffee hullers can be easily moved to where they are needed);
e) ready for immediate use without loss of time for preparatory adjustments;
f) made of easily available materials."

There are many different kinds of tools for different conditions listed in this section. There are two catalogues of commercially available small-scale equipment; these should be seen as sources of ideas, either directly from the catalogues or from a few pieces imported with the intent to adapt and produce them locally. We have also included two entries on small-scale logging and lumber-milling equipment which could help some countries to shift away from the destructive clear-cutting with expensive equipment often practiced by large, multi-national lumbering companies, and replace this with locally-controlled selective cutting and milling that is not environmentally damaging.

Farm Implements for Arid and Tropical Regions, book, 159 pages, H. Hopfen, U.N. Food and Agriculture Organization Development Paper No. 91, 1960 (reprinted 1976), $5.50 from META.
new edition price unknown, from META; or FAO booksellers.

This is a significant resource book. The more important hand tools and animal-drawn machinery suitable for arid and tropical regions in developing

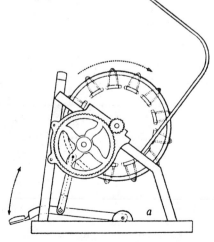

Japanese pedal-operated rice thresher: foot action at the pedal drives a rotating wooden drum which knocks the grain loose from the straw held by the farmer; behind the thresher is a cloth screen which prevents the rice and straw from scattering over a wide area.

countries are presented in clear descriptions and illustrations. Excellent coverage of the historical development of specific tools, such as the evolution of the moldboard plow from ancient to modern times. Included are tillage implements (from simple hand spades to water buffalo-powered cultivators), seeders, sprayers, harvesters, threshers, winnowers, handling and transport equipment, and workshop/maintenance tools.

The author stresses: "A great variety of implements has been developed indigenously all over the world, reflecting the experience handed down for many generations. The introduction of new techniques has the best chance for success when there is a full appreciation of local conditions and traditions before and during the process of introducing new ideas and improvements on the old ones."

"While this publication doesn't claim to be exhaustive, it aims to show how improvement in output can be obtained in areas where it is most needed. It is in fact oriented toward dry-farming tools, rice-growing implements and those used for row crop planting in tropical areas. The implements discussed are not necessarily representative of those found in all areas, but have been chosen because they are common in certain countries; some show how simple modifications can be made to improve performance; others provide examples of the more effective types which have been developed and which could profitably be introduced into areas where they are unknown."

Highly recommended.

Farm Tools, book, 235 pages, Michael Partridge, 1973, $7.95 from New York Graphic Society Ltd., 200 West Street, Waltham, Massachusetts 02154, USA.

This is a verbal and pictorial description of the evolution, use and construction of the tools and machines used by farmers in Europe and America during the 18th, 19th, and early 20th centuries. The book doesn't quite reach modern times.

An overhead
animal power gear

Interesting drawings include a hand-cranked thresher, straw-cutting machine, animal power gear, broadcast sower, metered corn sower attached to a plow, seed drills, harrows, plows and cultivators, mole plow (for drainage) and all kinds of specialized hand tools; over 200 illustrations.

There is an interesting but too brief section on power: animal power gears, windmills, water wheels, steam engines. The animal power gear ''provided a cheap portable source of power, well within the range of the ordinary farmer's pocket...By about 1860, (this unit) had reached the peak of mechanical efficiency, and most farmers owned one...'' Straw-burning steam engines involved the use of ''an enlarged firebox with belt-driven rollers at the door for conveying straw into the flames. The compression of the rollers caused the material to 'fan-out' as it entered the firebox, so that each straw caught fire instantly...3½ to 4 lbs. of dry straw would produce the same amount of steam as 1lb. of the best coal in a well constructed boiler.''

Finally there are some insightful comments about The Tractor: ''the designer's answer to the farmer's requirements, especially those farmers with vast acreages in the west of America, whose measure of work was beyond the capabilities of larger horse teams...It was World War I and the accompanying shortage of food, man and horse power that did most to hasten the production and general introduction of tractors on both sides of the Atlantic.''

Thresher for Rice and Other Small Grains, plans, $1.50 surface mail from SPATF, Office of Village Devel., P.O. Box 6937, Boroko, Papua New Guinea.

Made of wood, bicycle parts, wire and ordinary hardware. Foot-powered, using a treadle system. Some electric welding and use of a drill press are required; simple hand tools for the rest. B.D. Williams writes ''A bit complex for manufacture at the village level, but easy enough for a simple machine shop.'' Five workers and a treadle thresher can handle 1000 kg. of dry paddy or 500 kg. of wet paddy daily. Easy to understand plans.

Treadle Operated Peanut Thresher — Complete Technical Drawing #20, (5) 24'' X 36'' sheets of technical drawings with 3 pages of instructions, Ł2.80 or US$6.45 surface mail from ITDG.

MATERIALS: plywood, wood frame, steel rod, long bolts, angle iron, flat bar, flat sheet metal, variety of bicycle sprockets and bearings, bicycle chain, bore pipe.
PRODUCTION: brazing, drilling holes in metal and wood, some welding.

This is a simple piece of equipment, but the tolerances are small enough to require relatively accurate craftsmanship. Probably best if built by a small workshop that would produce dozens of units. Standard sizes of lumber are used (English measurements only). The plans may need to be adapted for the use of materials locally available.

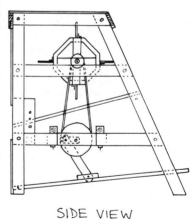

SIDE VIEW

Pedal-Powered Thresher and Winnower, dimensional drawings with production notes/technical details, 32 pages, Alex Weir, 1974, $1.00 from Alex Weir, Faculty of Agriculture, University of Dar es Salaam, Box 643, Morogoro, Tanzania.

MATERIALS: some bicycle parts (can be made of wood), wood, and steel pipe/bar/angle.
PRODUCTION: some welding and grinding.

The dimensional drawings have metric measurements with English pipe diameters. There are 22 sheets of drawings; some of them are very difficult to read due to poor reproduction. There seems to be sufficient information included to make the machines at a local level.

The thresher and winnower were designed for use on sorghum and millet—two crops that survive well under dry conditions. The thresher appears to represent the larger gain—it seems to substantially reduce the work formerly done by hand through bag threshing. The winnower's output is approximately 3 times that of a 3-person team using wind and a basket—however, separation of grain and chaff, while good, is not as good as the hand operation. Output for the thresher (max.) is given as 150 kg/hour with 4 persons (2 pedaling and 2 feeding grain). For the winnower it is 400 kg/hour for 3 persons. A rough estimate of the per-unit cost is given as US$80-115 for the thresher; $30-35 for the winnower.

Some of the design elements, particularly the wooden oil-soaked bearings, could be usefully incorporated into the design of other pedal-powered equipment or other different equipment.

The text includes some interesting suggestions of other promising applications of pedal-powered equipment. The work still needs to be done on these, however.

The Winnower, booklet with dimensional drawings and assembly information, 37 pages, technical report of the Dutch Microprojects working group at the Technische Hogeschool Eindhoven, 1973, $2.05 from TOOL; or ITDG.

MATERIALS: plywood, wood, wood screws, wire, fanbelt.

PRODUCTION: simple hand tools.

The authors claim the winnower is easily produced, operated, and maintained. It is operated with a hand crank, but could certainly be adapted to use a pedal-powered chain-drive system. Dimensions and materials are given for each part of the winnower. This unit was designed from an earlier prototype with consideration given to the conditions in developing countries. However, it has not yet been extensively tested.

Some prefabricated kits are available. However, the booklet is intended to provide sufficient information for local manufacture.

Groundnut Huller, simple drawings with assembly information, 5 pages, P. Krusch of VITA, $.50 from VITA.

MATERIALS: scrap motor vehicle parts, including 4 wheel rims of slightly different sizes; ½'' pipe, and cement.

PRODUCTION: some welding—most of the parts are bolted together.

These plans were supplied by a VITA volunteer who designed and operated the huller in Sierra Leone. ''Since automobile and truck rims come in a variety

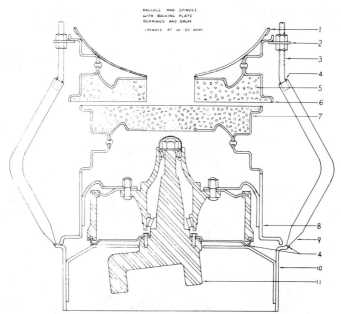

The VITA groundnut huller, using different sized wheel rims from motor vehicles. The groundnuts (peanuts) are poured in at the top, and the hulls are knocked off by the smooth cement surface.

of shapes and sizes, anyone desiring to construct this huller must by trial and error first find a combination of rims and a spindle that will fit together in a simple manner as depicted...Power to turn the lower rim may be transmitted from a waterwheel, small petrol engine, or wheel powered by animals...using a belt.'' Certainly, it is also adaptable to a bicycle or hand-powered system. The huller can be adjusted to work well with assorted sizes of groundnuts. ''With well sun-dried nuts and a well-adjusted huller, the amount of splits and cracks should not exceed 6%.''

An imaginative, yet simple piece of equipment. The assembly information is simple and straightforward.

Plans for Low-Cost Farming Implements: Groundnut Sheller, Platform Carts with Drying Pans, Hay Press, leaflet, 13 pages, 1974, on request from Agricultural Research Organization, Institute of Agricultural Engineering, The Volcani Centre, Bet Dagon 50-200, Israel.

The pamphlet includes dimensional drawings (metric units) for 3 different agricultural implements developed by a Laos-Israeli team in 1973.

The **groundnut (peanut) sheller** is made of wood and a metal barrel. It is hand-cranked. Capacity is 80-100 kg. per hour with 3 workers. The product has to be cleaned and sized using hand sieves.

Platform carts with drying pans are made almost entirely of wood. They are for crop drying in areas with frequent rains, so that the crops can be brought in under a protective roof easily.

The **hay press** is a simple device made of wood. It enables workers to easily produce baled hay, which maintains its quality longer than stacked hay.

Polyrow Peristaltic Pump Sprayer—ITDG Complete Technical Drawings #23, dimensional drawings, no text, 3 large sheets, 1972, L1.70 or US$3.90 from ITDG.

Dimensional drawings with English units. This hand-pushed unit is designed so that the single large wheel pumps the liquid by means of rollers that compress a plastic hose. This action takes place only while the unit is actually

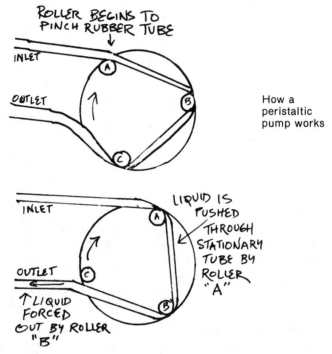

ROLLER BEGINS TO
PINCH RUBBER TUBE
↓
INLET
Ⓐ
OUTLET ↑ Ⓑ
Ⓒ

How a peristaltic pump works

INLET
Ⓐ
OUTLET Ⓒ
↑
LIQUID IS PUSHED THROUGH STATIONARY TUBE BY ROLLER "A"
↑LIQUID FORCED OUT BY ROLLER "B"
Ⓑ

moving. The drawings are clear enough, but the lack of any explanatory text is a limitation. Great if you already understand the principle of the peristaltic pump. Some substitution of materials would be possible.

Carts, dimensional drawings, 8 pages, 1973, L0.65 or US$1.50 surface mail from ITDG.

MATERIALS: hardwood, steel bar, bolts, angle iron.

PRODUCTION: some welding, metal bending using ITDG Metal Bending Machine.

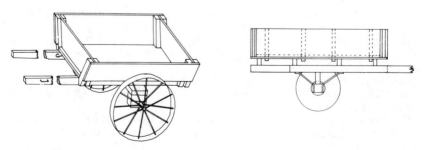

Dimensional drawings with English and metric measurements are given for 3 different cart designs (formerly offered as Agricultural Green Leaflets 1,2, and 3). The method of fabrication is clear from the drawings. The first two designs require the use of the ITDG Metal Bending Machine (see page 66) for fabrication of the wheels; the third design uses old car wheels. The first two designs use wood block bearings. The bodies of all 3 carts are made of wood. Carrying capacity is given as 700 and 1400 lbs. (318 and 636 kg.) for the first two carts; no capacity information is given for the cart that uses old car wheels.

Dahomey Ox-Cart, dimensional drawings, 15 pages, free (Reference No. CL/AT/3), from Commission on the Churches' Participation in Development, World Council of Churches, 150 Route de Ferney, 1211 Geneva 20, Switzerland.

MATERIALS: steel rod or pipe for axles, sheet iron, hoop iron, wood.

PRODUCTION: handtools, forge, 12mm die (if bolts are to be made), optional welding.

This is a very simple ox-cart with a 700 liter or 1000kg capacity. Frame and body are made of wood. Very detailed information is provided on an ingenious method of wheel manufacture. Hoop iron rims with 16mm rod spokes riveted in place form the outer part of the wheel; the axle is welded to hub plates. Wood block bearings are made using a piece of axle pipe filed to form a hole saw.

Produced in series of ten in Dahomey beginning in 1968. Design came to WCC from CIDR in Paris.

International Rice Research Institute Agricultural Equipment:

The agricultural engineering department of the International Rice Research Institute (IRRI) in the Philippines has been working on the research and development of agricultural machinery for the past 10 years. The equipment they have fully developed is suitable to the conditions prevailing in the rice-producing countries of Asia, although it has been designed specifically to fit the capabilities of small manufacturers in the Philippines. All of it can be manufactured in small shops. IRRI is primarily interested in small-scale equipment that is needed in support of the 'Green Revolution's' high-yielding varieties of rice. The agricultural engineering department is aware of the many problems that have been caused or intensified by the 'Green Revolution.' To the extent that such problems can be addressed by an engineering approach, the staff is doing an impressive job.

In the past, IRRI's emphasis has been on equipment that represents a significant leap beyond existing technologies, on the assumption that such things as pedal threshers can be innovated by local peasants without IRRI help and encouragement. Most of the designs that have been released fall into this category. It appears that the agricultural engineering department may be beginning to give more consideration to equipment that has one or more of the following characteristics: smaller in size that the equipment that has previously been released; non-motorized; use alternate sources of energy; conserve expensive fertilizers and pesticides. The following are some of this kind of equipment that IRRI is experimenting with: an improved Savonius Rotor (see drawing of blade modification) for low-lift water-pumping using wind power; a centrifugal pump made of pipe parts to be driven by the Savonius Rotor (see drawing on the next page—this pump design has since been dropped); a root-zone fertilizer/insecticide applicator which conserves the liquid used; rice mills, parboiling equipment, solar grain driers, and a variety of pumps.

Cross-section of Savonius rotor and an experimental low-lift centrifugal pump that it can be used to operate with minor modifications.

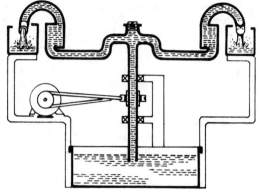

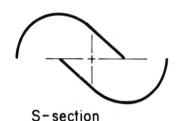

S-section

Pump operating above 48 rpm.

Two of the low-cost machines that IRRI is now experimenting with

IRRI has had a policy of working directly with interested manufacturers. Design drawings are given free of cost to these manufacturers in return for certain agreements with respect to quality and final selling price of the product (IRRI does not earn royalties), and IRRI assists them with initial production problems, testing of prototypes, and field service problems. IRRI welcomes inquiries from serious, involved people regarding particular designs which may have applications in the areas in which they are working. Most of IRRI's equipment is particularly suited to Asia; however, some of it is being produced in Ecuador, Guatemala, and Ghana.

The agricultural engineering department has decided to produce a short series of construction leaflets on some of the simpler equipment they are developing; such equipment can easily be produced without the need for close technical cooperation with the IRRI staff, by anyone who can read basic drawings. The most widely known example of this kind of simple equipment is the bellows pump for low-lift irrigation, operated by a person who stands on the pump and rocks back and forth. This has now been replaced by a very similar diaphragm pump (see description below and drawing on opposite page) which is easier to make and more durable. The first leaflet with full drawings covers the root-zone fertilizer and insecticide applicator (see previous page).

In general, all IRRI equipment has been designed for simplicity of construction, versatility of application, durability, ease of operation, and low-level of maintenance.

The following designs have been released to manufacturers for production:

Six-Row Rice Seeder: for direct seeding instead of transplanting; hand-pushed; fabricated of steel (see drawing of metering mechanism).

Diaphragm Pump: (mentioned above), for irrigation, drainage, and other low-lift applications; operated by one person standing on the pump and rocking back and forth; made using auto innertube as a diaphragm, with a wood and steel frame; long-lasting and easy to repair; capacity similar to the Bellows Pump which it replaces (195 liters/minute for a lift of 1 meter, 115 liters/minute for a lift of 2 meters).

Grain Drier: uses rice hull burner or kerosene burner to heat air, driven by a low horsepower fan into a steel bin which holds the grain.

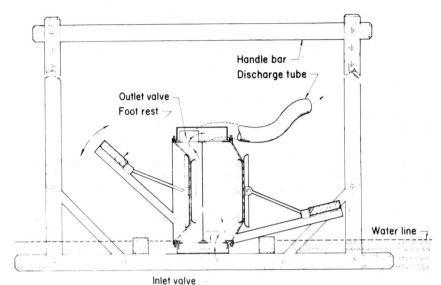

Handle bar
Discharge tube
Outlet valve
Foot rest
Water line
Inlet valve

SEED HOPPER
SEED POCKET
SEED ROLLER
SHAFT
SEED GUIDE
BRACKET

A
A'
FRONT VIEW
SECTION A–A'

Metering device for six-row multihopper seeder

Oscillating conveyor-screen
Threshing drum
Adjustable louvers
Straw thrower
Peg tooth

Feed tray
Blower

Top: diaphragm pump
Middle: a part of the 6-row rice seeder
Bottom: power thresher

Small gas engines (3-12 hp) are required for the following IRRI equipment:

Multi-Crop Axial Flow Thresher: (see drawing) 7 hp engine; a smaller thresher that requires only a 3 hp engine is being tested.

Power Weeder: widely used only in Japan, due to a relatively expensive engine.

Power Grain Cleaner: engine size unknown.

Propellor Pump: engine size unknown.

Single Axle Power Tiller: 5-7 hp engine.

Power Tiller: 8-12 hp engine.

IRRI's agricultural engineering department is experimenting with a considerably wider variety of equipment than they have released in the form of production drawings, and will undoubtedly continue to be a source of new developments in the future.

IRRI has two excellent papers available on request: "Mechanization Technology for Tropical Agriculture," by Amir Khan, head of the Agricultural Engineering Dept.; and "Development of Agricultural Mechanization Technologies at the International Rice Research Institute," by Amir Khan and Bart Duff (also of Agricultural Engineering Dept.).

Both papers and further information regarding IRRI agricultural equipment can be obtained by writing to **International Rice Research Institute, Agricultural Engineering Dept., P.O. Box 933, Manila, Philippines.**

The following plans, called "Agricultural Green Leaflets", are offered by ITDG (see address on page 27). The leaflets are available for L0.50 or US$1.15 each, surface mail. Most of these tools were designed for agricultural conditions in Africa.

These leaflets were originally intended for distribution to experienced agricultural engineers in the field, and the descriptive text is often brief. This is unimportant in most cases, but for some of the equipment the precise use is unclear to anyone unfamiliar with African agricultural practices. Construction details are quite easy for anyone to understand.

4—Kabanyolo Toolbar, dimensional drawings, 5 pages.

MATERIALS: mild steel flat/pipe/bar/channel/angle/box section.
PRODUCTION: some welding.

Dimensional drawings with English and metric units. Simple but sufficient for local construction. Basically, this is a locally-built (and locally-repairable) steel plow that also functions as a cultivator/weeder. A simple skid is used instead of a depth wheel.

5—Chitedze Ridgemaster Toolbar, dimensional drawings, 6 pages, origin: Malawi.

MATERIALS: mild steel tube/bar/box/angle/rod, 7'' diameter cast-iron wheel.

Dimensional drawings with English and metric units. Simple but sufficient for local construction. This is a locally-built and repairable combination steel plow, ridger, and cultivator. "The unique design of this toolbar is that it combines lightness with adequate structural strength, the main parts being fabricated from rectangular hollow section mild steel."

6 — Prototype Multi-Purpose Ox-Drawn Tool, dimensional drawings, 3 pages, origin: Nigeria.

MATERIALS: thick mild steel, nominal bore pipe.

PRODUCTION: some welding, metal hole drilling, cutting flat steel along curves.

Dimensional drawings with English and metric units. Simple but sufficient for local construction. This is a prototype of a tool to be used for ridging, splitting ridges, cross-tying, weeding, and breaking capped soil in the furrows. The tool frame was designed with an offset beam to avoid blockage when lifting groundnuts. The share is adjustable to allow these different operations to be carried out.

10 — Clod Crushers, Two Designs, dimensional drawings, 3 pages, origin: Malawi.

MATERIALS: eucalyptus or similar wood poles, steel draught chain, steel round bar (first design only).

PRODUCTION: simple hand tools.

Dimensional drawings with English and metric units are given. Fabrication is very simple and obvious. "These two simple and cheaply-constructed implements are used for reducing the size of dirt clods in cultivated land prior to ridging up the soil." They are both animal-drawn, and use wooden pegs on rollers to break up the clods as the implement rolls over them.

11 — Ox-Drawn Tie-Ridger/Weeder Implement, dimensional drawings, 3 pages, origin:Malawi.

MATERIALS: steel pipe, flat steel, steel bar, angle iron, and an old plow disc.

PRODUCTION: some welding and metal-bending.

Dimensional drawings with English and metric units. Fabrication is straight-forward, and uncomplicated, requiring some welding. The instructions for field use are vague.

"This implement is an attachment only, designed for use with the 'EMCOT' ox-drawn ridging plow." It can be used for cross-tying during ridging, and for both cross-tying and weeding after ridging. Precisely what 'cross-tying' means is not made clear for anyone unfamiliar with the technique. Ridging and cross-tying, it is claimed, have resulted in substantial crop yield gains on certain free-draining soils in Africa. This attachment (with the EMCOT plow) cut the labor requirement for use of this technique in land preparation and weeding by an estimated "60% when compared with cultivation by hand."

12 — IDC Weeding Attachment for EMCOT Plow, dimensional drawings, 3 pages, origin: Nigeria.

MATERIALS: flat steel, sheet metal, thick high-grade steel, steel square bar.

PRODUCTION: some welding, cutting, and bending metal.

Dimensional drawings with both English and metric units. "This attachment enables weeding in ridged row crops to be carried out by animal power instead of by hand." However, this is only an attachment, to be used with the EMCOT plow. "The tool...can be adjusted for height, and also for width according to the row spacing. The sides of the ridges are remade by the ridger body following behind." Essentially, the attachment consists of two steel blades that are pulled along through the earth on the sides of the ridges.

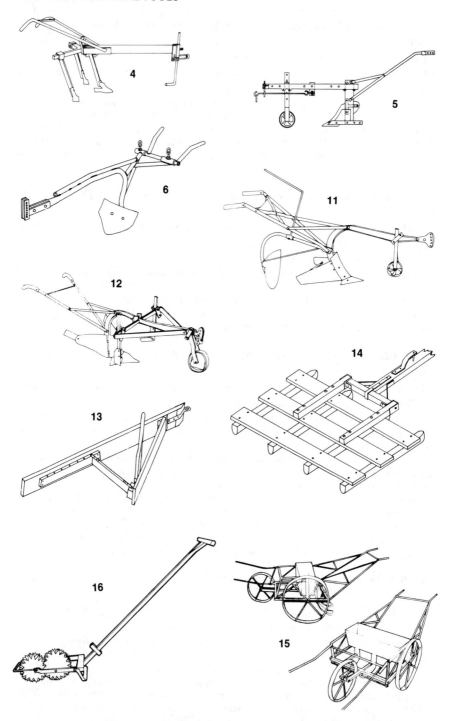

13 — Adjustable Width V-Drag Ditcher/Bund Former, dimensional drawings, 3 pages, origin: US Dept. of Agriculture.

MATERIALS: sheet metal, strap iron, hitch ring, hinges, hardwood, wood, bolts, and screws.

PRODUCTION: metal-drilling.

Dimensional drawings with both English and metric units. Simple, straight-forward construction.

"This implement is used for making irrigation ditches, and can also be used to construct low-height contour embankments for border irrigation. When making earth ditches for conveying water to crops or drainage channels, a furrow is first opened with a plow (running down and back the required number of times according to the depth required) along the line of the ditch. The V-Drag is then used with the runner board riding in the furrow bottom, the crowder board deflecting the soil sideways. Weight can be added by the operator standing on the runner board. The depth of cut can be increased by placing additional weight towards the front of the implement and/or lengthening the hitch." Animal-drawn.

14 — Sled-Type Corrugator Irrigation-Furrow Former, dimensional drawings, 3 pages, origin: US Dept. of Agriculture.

MATERIALS: wood, strap iron.

PRODUCTION: simple hand tools.

Dimensional drawings with both English and metric units. Very simple, straight-forward plans.

"The function of this implement is to make small furrows, or corrugations, for distributing water over a field. The corrugations are run down the slope of the land. This implement can be used after the field has been broadcast seeded or before row-crop planting. The implement design shown can be modified in size to suit animal-draught or tractor-hitching as required." This tool is essentially a sled with four runners that is dragged (loaded) over a field.

15 — Single-Row and Three-Row Rice Seeders, photoprints, 3 pages, origin: Zambia.

MATERIALS: several sizes of pipe and rod; 2"X3/16" flat steel for wheels.

PRODUCTION: metal-bending and some welding.

Photoprints only. Two pages on the single-row seeder and one page on the triple-row seeder. English units only (important with pipe and rod diameter). This set of plans asks for more local imagination and ingenuity than most ITDG plans do — somewhat hard to understand.

These implements seem to be designed for dry rice fields. They have probably little or no application to Southeast Asia, for example, because they were designed to allow a man to cultivate a larger area (such as in sparsely populated areas of Africa). Where available land is already under intensive cultivation, such equipment would probably lower the total production per hectare.

16 — Rotary Weeder for Row-Planted Rice, photoprints, 1 page.

MATERIALS: metal angle/flat bar/rod; 1/8" and 3/32" flat plate; wood for handle.

PRODUCTION: some welding and hole-cutting.

A single page with four photos. The rotary weeder is a very simple piece of equipment, only about 1½ feet long at the base, with a long handle. Measurements are English units only. Two rotary, star-blade clusters are pushed along between two rows. A blade follows the two clusters.

17 — Multi-Action Paddy Field Puddling Tool, photoprints, 1 page, origin: Japan.

MATERIALS: wood frame, steel sheet, steel bars, 2″ and 3″ diameter pipe.
PRODUCTION: some welding, steel-cutting, riveting.

Photoprints with English units only. Some imagination would have to be used by whomever would build from such plans. However, the basic principles are quite clear from the photoprints. Ox-drawn. Apparently, the farmer simply follows along behind, controlling the animal only. Some weights may need to be attached for effective use.

27 — Cassava Grinder, dimensional drawings, 10 pages, origin: Nigeria.

MATERIALS: plywood, galvanized iron tube for frame, conduit tube, bicycle pedal-drive unit, steel angle, 20 gauge mild steel sheet, 26″ bicycle wheel, (12) 9″ hacksaw blades, other bicycle parts.
PRODUCTION: some welding, riveting and brazing.

Dimensional drawings with English units only. The exact application of the cassava grinder is not made explicit. No text is included, only assembly instructions. This is a bicycle-pedal, chain-driven grinder. Production is straight-forward; certainly possible on a local level.

28 — Rotary Corn (Sorghum) Thresher, dimensional drawings, 10 pages, origin: Nigeria.

MATERIALS: angle iron, steel plate/rod/square section, bicycle pedal and bearings, ½″ plywood, "free wheel" bicycle sprocket, bicycle chain, galvanized iron tube.
PRODUCTION: some welding, bending, cutting, and drilling metal.

All dimensions are in English units. This set of plans has no real text, only a few words with each drawing. Harder to understand than most ITDG plans. This unit, operated with a hand-crank, is actually for guineacorn (sorghum). Probably operated by two men.

29 — IDC-Bornu Groundnut Lifter and IT Groundnut Lifter, dimensional drawings, 8 pages, origin: Zambia and Nigeria.

MATERIALS: steel rod/leaf/plate/flat, angle iron, metal wheel, bore pipe.
PRODUCTION: some welding or smithy work.

This set of dimensional drawings has two items. The IDC-Bornu groundnut lifter is only an attachment for an EMCOT plow. It is pulled by a draft animal, with two depth wheels and a plow-like bar for lifting up the groundnuts. Units are both English and metric.

The IT groundnut lifter is a complete piece of equipment in itself. "A lightweight lifter suitable for groundnuts grown on 75cm spaced ridges in sandy soils. Suitable for manufacture by village blacksmiths." The minimum equipment required would be a forge, anvil, hammer, tongs, chisel, and punch. This groundnut lifter has no wheels. A flat bar is dragged across the ground, with a man steering it from behind. Animal-drawn.

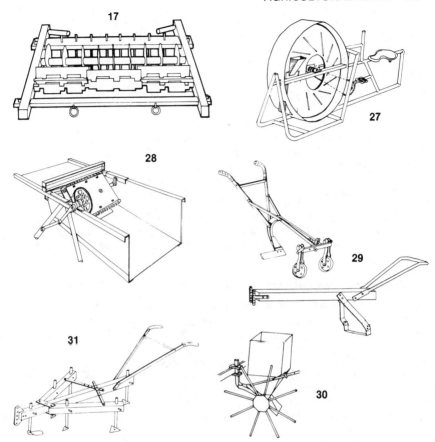

30—IT Granule Applicator, dimensional drawings, 14 pages, origin: Nigeria.

MATERIALS: mild steel sheet, water pipe, reinforcing rod.

PRODUCTION: welding.

Dimensional drawings with both English and metric units. Some of the drawings are not very clear, but the unit should be reproducible. The materials and dimensions can be altered to fit local conditions.

There is a metering mechanism in place of a mechanical weeder. These plans include a calibration chart for the applicator at various flows and row spacings.

31—IT Expandable Cultivator, dimensional drawings, 7 pages, origin: Nigeria.

MATERIALS: hardwood beams, mild steel plate/pipe/spring leaf.

PRODUCTION: a village blacksmith can make this with a forge, anvil, hammer, tongs, punch, and chisel.

Dimensional drawings with metric units only. Simple but sufficient for local construction. This design requires a lot of hole drilling or punching, and thus accuracy in measurement.

''A lightweight cultivator designed for weeding of crops planted in 70-90cm spaced rows in sandy soils, to be pulled by one or two oxen or donkeys. Tines are individually adjustable for depth, making the implement suitable for flat or ridge cultivation." The width is also adjustable for the unit as a whole.

32—Seed Dressing Drum (Hand-Operated), dimensional drawings, 5 pages, origin: Malawi.

MATERIALS: oil or water drum, wood or bamboo for supports, sheet metal, steel wire, rubber inner tube.
PRODUCTION: possibly soldering or riveting.
   Dimensional drawings with English and metric units. The fairly simple design can certainly be made by local craftsmen with very few tools.
   Fertilizer and seed are poured into the top of the drum; it is rotated 20-40 times; and the mixture is poured out from the bottom. "It was found that this drum had a capacity of 30 lbs. (13.6 kg.) of Chalimba groundnuts, 35 lbs. (15.9 kg.) of soya beans or maize, and 38 lbs. (17.2 kg.) of fertilizer when filled correctly. In a durability test, a total of 1½ tons of fertilizer was mixed without signs of damage. The drum was also used for seed-dressing of groundnuts and maize with satisfactory coverage performance and no apparent adverse effect on germination."

33—IT High-Clearance Rotary Hoe, dimensional drawings, 7 pages.

MATERIALS:steel bars, metal water pipe, hardwood, some bolts.
PRODUCTION:some welding, metal-bending, metal hole drilling.
   Dimensional drawings with metric measurements only; brief but sufficient.
   "This animal-drawn implement is designed for seeding of crops grown or ridges at 75-90cm spacing. It cultivates both sides of one ridge at a time and therefore, unlike cultivators drawn between the ridges, does not require straight and parallel ridges for efficient weeding…This implement is not suitable for use in very hard soil conditions. It can be used in wet soil and has been used successfully for weeding cotton while water was standing in the furrows."

36-The Weeder-Mulcher, dimensional drawings, 8 pages, origin: India.

MATERIALS: wood beam, mild steel (flat, plate, rod and pipe), (2) 125mm diameter metal wheels.
PRODUCTION: metal bending, cutting, drilling; welding optional.
   Dimensional drawings with metric measurements. "This animal-drawn self-cleaning weeder was originally developed for use in sugarcane plantations (by the Indian Institute of Sugarcane Research). It is designed to destroy weeds, leave a mulch on the soil surface to conserve moisture and give a high work output per day (up to 5 or 6 acres of row crop work per 8 hour day). It can be used on most row crops with a spacing of 30 inches (75cm) or more…The blades can easily be replaced by a village blacksmith."

37—Foot Powered Thresher (same plans from Papua New Guinea on page 97.)

38—The 'Rasulia' Bladed Roller Thresher, dimensional drawings, 4 pages, origin: India and Iran.

MATERIALS: wood, 2" flat strips of iron or steel for blades.
PRODUCTION: simple hand tools, plus some blacksmith work on the blades.
   Dimensional drawings with English units and metric conversion table. Text

provides instructions for construction. Uses wooden bearings which are not described.

This implement was seen in use in Iran, and subsequently built in India by Ed Abbot at the Friends' Rural Development Centre in Rasulia. It is pulled by a draft animal, with the driver seated on the unit. It is estimated to be 60% more efficient than the traditional Indian method of using bullocks to trample the harvested crops.

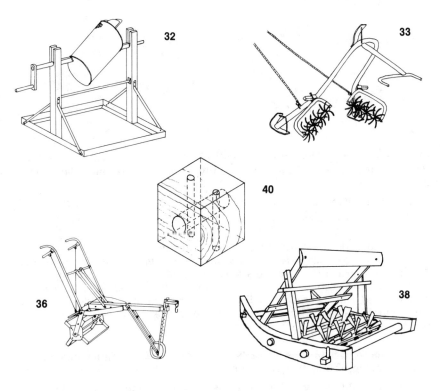

40 — Oil Soaked Wood Bearings: How to Make Them and How They Perform, leaflet with drawings and text, 10 pages, information from tests done in Zambia.

Unlike the other ITDG agricultural green leaflets, this has a considerable amount of text. The authors consider the characteristics of wood to be used, how to determine the size of the bearing required, and oil-soaking in the case of high-moisture content of the wood to be used. The oil used was groundnut (peanut) oil or discarded engine oil. Three types of wood bearings are presented and evaluated: solid block, split block, and bush bearings. "The drilling of radial holes for lubrication purposes is only recommended by Pearson for the bush type of bearing. He found that if lubrication holes were drilled in block bearings not only were the bearings weakened but also the holes acted as dirt traps."

Hardwood is required. The bearings are well-suited to low-speed applications such as in carts and water wheels.

Highly recommended.

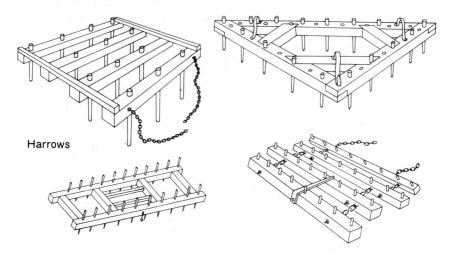

Harrows

41—Harrows: High-Clearance Peg Tooth (East Africa), Triangular Spike Tooth (India), Flexible Peg Tooth (Iran), and Japanese Harrow, dimensional drawings, 8 pages.

MATERIALS: hardwood, steel pieces for teeth, steel chain, eyebolts.

PRODUCTION: metal bending, cutting and drilling for two of the designs; only use of simple hand tools for the other two designs.

Dimensional drawings with English and metric measurements. This leaflet is a combination of what were formerly offered as Agricultural Green Leaflets 7,8, and 9. Construction is quite simple and evident from the drawings.

These harrows can all be pulled by animals. The function of a harrow is to prepare seed beds by breaking soil clods, cover seeds after broadcast seeding, and control weeds. Several of these harrows are designed to leave weed residue on the soil surface to conserve moisture.

Tools for Agriculture: A Buyer's Guide to Low-Cost Agricultural Implements, catalog, ITDG, 1976, price unknown, from ITDG.

Originally entitled **Tools For Progress,** and then **Guide to Hand-Operated and Animal-Drawn Equipment,** this third revised version of the guide identifies more than 300 manufacturers of various types of simple, low-cost agricultural implements from all over the world.

The simple drawing or photograph that accompanies each listing could be useful in generating ideas for local production of some of the equipment. Or, a regional adaptive technology center might purchase a selection of appropriate equipment, and use it to produce modified designs for local production using local skills, labor, and materials. As a buying guide, we feel this isn't really appropriate technology, because all the machines would have to be imported unless the manufacturer happens to be located within the user's country.

Categories include equipment for cultivating, sowing, planting, distributing manure, crop protection, irrigation and water supply, harvesting, threshing and cleaning, crop processing, and other miscellaneous agricultural equipment.

''The information contained in it is based on that supplied by manufacturers. ITDG has no facility for carrying out tests or trials of machinery in commercial production. The group aims merely to identify sources of supply.''

Guide Book for Rural Cottage and Small & Medium Industries: Paddy Rice Cultivation, illustrated catalog, 158 pages, by CeCoCo (Central Commercial Company), 1965 (revised 1975), $10.00 airmail from CeCoCo, Chuo Boeki Goshi Kaisha, P.O. Box 8, Ibaraki City, Osaka, Japan.

CeCoCo is a very unique business enterprise. The main interest of this Japanese firm is promoting food production and employment opportunities in developing countries. This 'Guide Book' is a catalogue of the hand and machine implements marketed by CeCoCo for the cottage and small industry sector.

A sample of the contents: rice plant cutter, hand seeder and planter, bird and animal scarer & bang (!), noodle making machine, tapioca & fish processing machinery, peanut digger, coconut husk processing machinery, rattan and bamboo weavers, and hydraulic ram pump.

The catalogue includes a wealth of ideas and implements. CeCoCo has drawn heavily from the Japanese historical experience, in which a feudal agricultural economy was gradually converted into a mixed modernizing one. The Japanese were able to control their own pace of development and filter Western technologies to suit their own needs. There is much of interest in these examples of ingenious labor-intensive, locally-manufactured agricultural equipment marketed by CeCoCo, many of which contributed significantly to Japan's economic development in the first half of this century.

"The CeCoCo policy concerning development, as outlined in this guidebook, indicates that the import of their implements and machinery should be viewed as the first step in the ultimate indigenous production of these tools," the **Handbook of Appropriate Technology** notes. Our personal contacts with this remarkable organization indicate that they are very receptive to questions from foreign sources.

Tree Trunk Rice Mill in Sumatra

This device is entirely made of wood. Rice is placed in the hollowed-out removable log which forms the top piece. As this piece is rotated back and forth by the user, the rice is hulled by the rubbing action of the two pieces of wood. The rice and hulls spill out onto the mat.

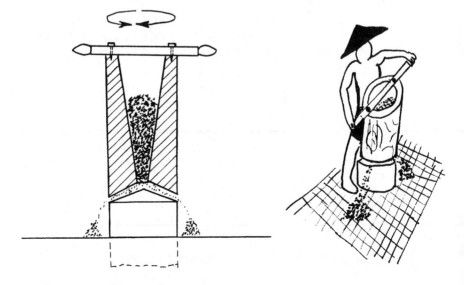

Selection and Maintenance of Logging Hand Tools, booklet, 65 pages, International Labor Organization, 1970, $3.00 from META.

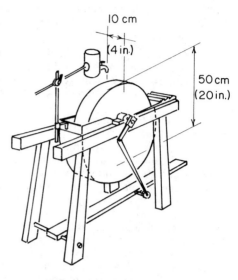

"An illustrated manual for foresters, loggers, and workers. This manual is intended to provide the necessary basic information on: the selection of suitable logging hand tools, the proper maintenance of these tools, and how to make certain tools locally. A special attempt has been made to adapt this manual to conditions in developing countries, to describe in simple terms only really essential tools and to avoid describing maintenance operations which only a specialist worker could use. It is hoped that the manual will be widely used as a basis for the training of foresters, loggers, foremen and workers."

Complete and well illustrated, this book should be of particular interest in areas where commercial logging is being rapidly expanded. The use of traditional hand logging methods can make it possible to harvest trees more efficiently and less destructively—making it unnecessary to remove entire forests. This manual helps to visualize a viable, employment-generating alternative to clear-cutting by foreign companies.

Alaskan Sawmill, promotional literature (leaflets and booklets), 1976, free from Granberg Industries, Inc., 200 S. Garrard Blvd., Richmond, California 94804, USA.

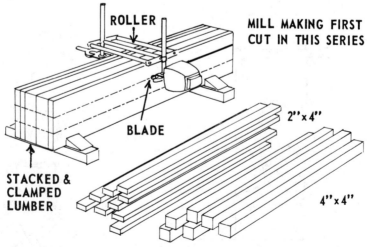

MAKING DIMENSION LUMBER FROM SAWN PLANKS

The Alaskan Mill is a marvelous tool for accelerating forestry operations in developing countries, allowing for intermediate level, small-scale wood processing and lumber production. This device consists of an attachment to a standard gasoline-powered chainsaw (6 horsepower minimum gear drive, with 2:1 gear ratio), which enables the users to cut lumber of any assortment of sizes from rough timber. 1-person to 3-person mills are available. According to reliable estimates, an average of 1000 board feet (approximately 2.25 cubic meters) of finished lumber can be achieved daily with the 1-person operation.

In all areas where an alternative to the extremes of the inexact, time-consuming 2-man handsaw or the high-technology sawmill is sought, the Alaskan Mill is a sound option. The Mill utilizes indigenous labor to a much greater extent than large lumber mills, and can encourage self-reliance, release materials for low-cost housing and other national building priorities, and encourage more prudent forestry practices.

Granville Industries manufactures various models of these clamp-on chain saw mills, plus accessories such as ripping chains and precision file guides to keep saws uniformly sharp and effective. They will send detailed information free; some people may wish to build their own mills from this. Granville Industries does not sell chain saws themselves. The commonly referred-to American sources (from the Whole Earth Catalog) are: 1) McCulloch Corporation, 6101 West Century Blvd., Los Angeles, California 90045, USA; and 2) Homelite, Port Chester, New York 10573, USA.

LATE ADDITIONS

Coffee Huller Designed by Villagers in Bali, Indonesia: This machine was designed and built in a coffee-growing village in northern Bali. The coffee is poured into a container at the top of the machine, and slowly drops down between two wooden wheels, where pieces of rubber and metal knock off the hulls without damaging the beans. The

machine is powered by a low horsepower engine that drives a belt. Capacity is 75 kg/hour. The machine is carried to small plots for use. The wooden wheels will last about 3 seasons.

Animal-Drawn Agricultural Implements, Hand-Operated Machines and Simple Power Equipment in the Least Developed and Other Developing Countries, report, 45 pages, March 1975, (Publication ID/148), free to serious groups, from United Nations Industrial Development Organization (UNIDO), P.O. Box 707, A-1011, Vienna, Austria.

This is a report of a Manufacturing Development Clinic (conference) held in New Delhi, India during October 1974. There were participants from 22 developing countries. One of the valuable parts of the report are 49 photos of agricultural tools.

Eight Simple Surveying Levels (Agricultural Green Leaflet #42), drawings with text, 17 pages, Ł1.00 or US$2.00 surface mail from ITDG.

These levels, made of wood and rubber or clear plastic tubing, were built and evaluated by an ITDG team. Details are given on the construction, accuracy, and usefulness of each device. All the levels are made using simple hand tools, and are cheap and easy to construct. These levels are quite sufficient for most rural drainage, irrigation, roadmaking, building and other earthmoving work, where extreme accuracy is not needed.

FURTHER REFERENCES ON AGRICULTURAL TOOLS

Manege: Animal-Driven Power Gear is well-suited to driving most post-harvest processing machinery; see drawing with review on page 134.

Cumberland General Store Catalog, see review on page 52.

Liklik Buk has numerous drawings and photos of agricultural tools; see review on page 50.

First Steps in Village Mechanization has a number of items of interest; see review on page 44.

FOOD AND CROP
PRESERVATION AND STORAGE

Food and Crop Preservation and Storage

Various estimates are that 1/4 to 1/3 or more of the grain crops grown in the developing countries are destroyed by pests or mold. This means that simple, low-cost, small-scale systems for storage and preservation are critically important, with the potential for more effect on the supply of food available to humans than dramatic gains in agricultural productivity might have.

Included in this section are designs for low-cost grain silos (which protect the crop from destruction by rodents, birds, insects, and rain), grain driers (which reduce losses from mold), methods and equipment for the preservation of meat and fish, and driers and sun-drying methods for vegetables and fruits. Fresh vegetables and fruits can also be stored in pit silos (in colder climates) and in iceless coolers (in hot, dry climates); both of these methods are described in the VITA **Village Technology Handbook.**

Enclosed solar cabinet dryers have some particularly attractive characteristics: they use solar energy but also avoid damage during the drying period caused by rodents, insects, birds, rain, and dirt.

Fresh Produce Handling and Distribution, booklet, 11 pages, R. Guillou of VITA, $0.50 from VITA.

This is a brief survey of important considerations when handling and storing fresh produce—ripening, cooling requirements, and packing for transport. Useful general principles and some specific suggestions for how to cool and protect produce with simple, low-cost methods. Principles, rather than techniques or equipment, are the primary content.

The author stresses that before introducing new techniques, "the reasons for traditional methods should be understood. Possible changes should be tested before they are put into practice."

Home Storage of Fruits and Vegetables, book, 148 pages, E. Loveday, 1972, $3.00 from WETS.

This book is primarily recommended for U.S. residents, though it does cover some material potentially valuable in developing countries. Much of the book is on canning (preserving in sealed containers—usually glass jars) and freezing. These methods require more investment in equipment than most people in developing countries can afford.

Of more universal interest are low-cost methods of outdoor storage in colder climates (mounds, pits, barrels, cartons, and ground storage); illustrations of each of these are provided. The chapter on drying includes plans for 4 home-built food driers, one of which uses no artificial heat source (a solar drier).

Dry It, You'll Like It, book, 74 pages, G. MacManiman, $3.95 from Mother Earth News; or WETS.

This book covers drying for food preservation. Dried food is nutritionally better than canned food. No preservatives, chemicals or electricity (freezer) are required. Dried food takes up 1/6 or less of the usual storage space required, and can usually be stored a couple of years.

This is a simple little book with general instructions for all food drying. Specific information is given for most American fruits, vegetables, and some herbs. Two pages on meat and fish are included, along with recipes.

Plans for a food dehydrator using simple tools and made largely of wood are complete and easy to follow. It does require some source of low heat that remains constant near 100 degrees Fahrenheit—the dehydrator could possibly be suspended over a wood-burning stove while other cooking is taking place.

How to Dry Fruits and Vegetables, leaflet, 12 pages, 1976, free to serious groups, from Action for Food Production (AFPRO), Technical Information Service, Community Centre, C-17, Safdarjung Develop. Area, New Delhi-11 00 16, India.

The purpose of this booklet is to give practical information to people in the rural areas of India "on how to dry fruits and vegetables, which can then be preserved from times of plenty to be used in the lean seasons of the year. It can also be used as a handbook to teach village level Community Development workers."

The information is comprehensive, with tables on preparation hints, treatment before dehydration, dehydrated product yields, description of dried condition, and specific fruit and vegetable refreshing data. Heavy emphasis is given to treatment of various fruits with sulphur, which prevents discoloration during the drying process and provides some protection against insects in storage. (We however do not feel that it is yet clear whether the widespread use of sulphur is justified, due to the added expense and potential health side-effects of this preservative—editors.)

Sun Dry Your Fruits and Vegetables, booklet, 26 pages, US Dept. of Agriculture, 1958, free from Office of International Extension, USDA, Washington DC 20250 USA.

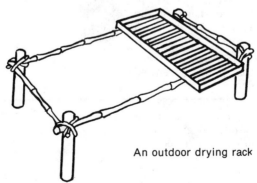

An outdoor drying rack

This illustrated step-by-step guide was written for extension workers in simple English. Other than simple household equipment, the only items required are wooden trays, and for some fruits, a large box to cover the trays while sulphur is burned inside. The booklet emphasizes the need for cleanliness and hot, dry air that circulates freely. A chart gives directions for many different fruits and vegetables. Steaming is recommended prior to drying for most vegetables. A step-by-step description of the use of sulphur when drying some fruits is provided, as are notes on the preparation of dried food for use.

How to Build Food Drying Equipment, leaflet, 17 pages, John Magee, 1975, $2.00 from California Wood Plans, P.O. Box 541, San Luis Obispo, California 93406, USA.

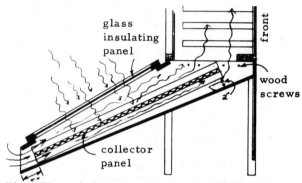

Flow-Through Cabinet with attached Collector

''With these plans, you can build most of the equipment alternatives that are practical and useful for home food drying. We start out by showing you how to build a simple drying tray. We include plans for building simple screened or glassed-in sun drying cabinets, and more complex flow-through and recirculating artificially heated cabinets.'' The latter designs include a solar collector attached to the drying tray (see drawing above).

The authors state in this well-illustrated pamphlet that it is important to standardize any equipment that is made so that it can be used with any system or with more sophisticated equipment. Detailed and practical.

How to Make a Solar Cabinet Dryer for Agricultural Produce, booklet (#L-6), 11 pages of text, diagrams and charts, 1965 (revised 1973), $1.25 from BRACE.

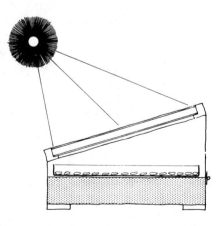

MATERIALS: wood, masonite, hose, aluminum foil, steel plate, galvanized wire, glass, sealant
PRODUCTION: simple handtools

The dryer is essentially a solar hot box, in which fruit, vegetables or other matter can be dehydrated.'' It dries produce cheaply for storage, without insect or dust contamination, and reduces moisture content to the lowest necessary level. The dryer is a rectangular container, insulated at the base and sides, with a transparent roof and circular air flow. The framework can be made of virtually any material — woven bamboo, metal, plywood, adobe, or brick. Insulation could consist of ''locally available materials such as wood shavings, sawdust, bagasse, coconut fiber, reject wool, or animal hair.''

The capacity of the dryer is 7.5 kg per square meter of drying area. Brace's protype units have dried 3 kgs of onions or okra in 2 days. A model in Syria cost $14.00; one in Barbados cost $23.00 to build. Brace estimates the annual operating cost at $6.89. The temperatures inside reach 70-80 degrees C., so the dryer can also be used for warming foods and other materials.

A production drawing for this dryer can also be obtained from Brace (see below).

Production Drawing for a Solar Cabinet Dryer, 1972, 1 large sheet, $2.00 from Brace.

This is drawing #T-85 from Brace, designed for use with the booklet listed above.

Construction of a Brick Hot Air Copra Drier (Technical Bulletin #9), booklet, 29 pages, S. Mason, 1972, Papua New Guinea, free to serious groups, from DTWS.

MATERIALS: bricks, wood planks and panels, mild steel plates.

PRODUCTION: possibly some cutting of steel plates.

''The purpose of this bulletin is to assist the indigenous copra owner who has had no experience in construction work, to construct his own drier, so that a better quality copra can be produced more economically.''

The drier consists of a brick building with a minimum of timber exposed in areas subject to the heated air flow from the firebox. Fuel such as wood or coconut shells is fed into the firebox at the front of the drier. The heat from the fire warms a mild steel radiating plate on the hot air chamber which in turn heats the air within the drier.''

This drier was designed to have an output of six 155-pound bags of copra per week. Construction details, materials list, glossary of technical terms, drawings of the drier, and drawings of a wooden mold for making individual bricks are all provided. This manual does not tell you how to make the bricks. ''**Selection of Materials for Stabilized Brick Manufacture (Technical Bulletin #5)** should be studied to assist in selecting materials suitable to make bricks'' (see review on page 230).

One limitation of this leaflet is that the assembly drawings are hard to read. However, this appears to be a sound design, one that the author claims prevents accidental fires.

Simple Grain Drier, 2 descriptive articles plus complete dimensional drawings and photos, 15 pages total, W. Chancellor, free to serious groups, from UNIDO (United Nations Industrial Development Organization), P.O. Box 707, A-1011 Vienna, Austria.

MATERIALS: sheet metal, metal pipe, steel bar for stirring tool, small piece of steel plate.

PRODUCTION: cutting and drilling sheet metal and metal pipe, small amount of welding.

This information includes clear production drawings and a report from field tests in Asia.

''Local availability of drying facilities not only can reduce spoilage losses in storage but also can promote increased production through strengthening the practicality of double cropping in irrigated areas where the offseason crop is harvested in humid weather.''

This drier has the following elements: ''a horizontal metal surface placed over a fire pit; use of animal power to stir the shallow layer of grain placed on the metal surface; grain temperature, and thus the rate of moisture evaporation, controlled by adjusting the rate of fuel use.''

An animal stirring the drier

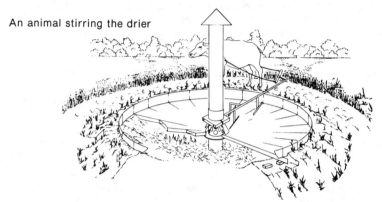

The drier is made mostly of sheet metal, and is of simple design. It is easy to build and requires no special skills to operate. It can be disassembled for easy transport and storage. The stirring blade is attached to the smoke stack base with a wooden bearing. A durable thermometer is needed, but the operator can estimate temperatures from the smell and feel of the grain. Cost of all materials was approximately $160.

This unit is for use in humid or rainy conditions when sun drying would not be effective. ''In tests using rice straw as the fuel, it was determined that the straw contained in the grain bundles brought to the threshing site would provide enough fuel to complete the drying operation.'' Grain dried by this process did not germinate, however, so this should not be used for seed.

More than one animal is needed, to allow the animals to rest alternately. Two persons are required. The 16-foot diameter design is capable of drying 1000 lbs. of rice at a time, reducing moisture from 24% to 14% in 4 hours. 160 lbs. of moderately dry straw was used as the fuel.

'Thailo' Ferrocement Rice Bin, booklet, 10 pages, by Vietmeyer, Kampempool, Nutalaya, Desathien, and Pataragetvit, 1976, write to Applied Scientific Research Corporation of Thailand, Bangkhen, Bangkok 9, Thailand.

''Ferrocement can be briefly defined as a form of reinforced concrete made of cement mortar plastered on wire mesh reinforcement. It possesses unique qualities of strength and serviceability and could be constructed with readily available materials and minimum skilled labor. Having long been proved to be suitable for boat building, it has many other tested and potential applications in agriculture, industry, and housing.''

In many developing countries a sizeable portion of harvested crops are lost due to insects, birds, fungi, poor storage, and spillage, sometimes up to 30 percent. The Applied Scientific Research Corporation of Thailand found that ''cheap, airtight bins made of ferrocement were considered to be a solution to the problem. Such bins could be made to hold 4-10 tons of grain or other foodstuffs (e.g., corn, peanuts, soybeans), salt, fertilizer, pesticide, cement, or 7,600 to 19,000 liters of drinking water. In a typical test an experimental bin was loaded with 3.5 tons of sun-dried rice paddy. For 10 months the bin gave

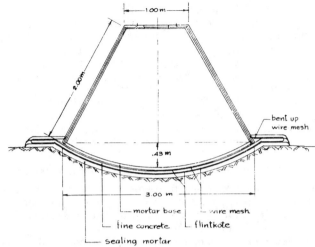

Cross-section of a 5-ton Thailo ferrocement rice bin

complete protection from birds and rodents; insect damage was only 0.7 percent (even though the bin was opened for inspection every 2 months); and the germination potential of the rice fell less than 1 percent. Rice paddy stored in a bin from March 1969 to the present (1976) still appears to be in sound condition."

This small booklet is very stimulating for several reasons. First, it demonstrates low-cost, simple techniques of building sizeable grain silos. The cost of the unit (a 5-ton silo costs $136) would certainly be recovered within 2 seasons by the grain losses avoided. Secondly, it gives solid clues on the art of ferrocement construction. Although this booklet is a bit brief on construction techniques, it would give a clever builder enough insight into the process. One suggestion we would make is to be certain to plaster the mesh from both the inside and outside of the silo.

Low Cost, Lightweight Metal Silos in Guatemala

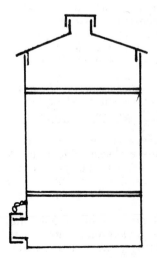

Some friends examined these silos during a recent trip through Guatemala. They are in the shape of a cylinder, and are so lightweight that they can be moved quite easily when empty. The drawing is ours; the following description of the same silos is from a news review by the Tropical Products Institute in England:

"Small metal silos have been a popular and successful method of storage in Eastern Guatemala for over 30 years. Most farmhouses in the area have 3 or 4 small metal silos under their eaves or in a room adapted as a grain store. Maize (corn), sorghum, and beans are the most common crops stored in the silos which are easy to construct from low cost materials. The blacksmiths of the district weld the silos from galvanized steel sheets to give capacities ranging from 225 to 1,100 kg. For approximately US$10.00 it is possible to buy one with a capacity of 450 kg.

"The largest of the silos are two meters in height by one and a half meters in diameter and they have a conical top, in the centre of which is the opening for filling (10 cm in diameter). On the side near the base is a similar opening for taking out the grain. Both openings are stoppered with caps made of metal sheet. To prevent the pressure exerted by the grain cracking the sides, the latter are supported by one or two metal bands and the users place the silo on a platform of firm ground, as the base is of sheet metal and easily deformed."

Some of the farmers use one of several fumigation techniques. Others do not fumigate and instead seal the openings with adhesive tape to form an hermetic storage unit (in which insects cannot survive due to the lack of oxygen).

Grain Silo, dimensional drawings with text, 6 pages, $1.00 from TOOL.

Simple drawings and text. English and metric units. This 1½ cubic yard silo has a concrete cover on the top, and a wooden chute on the bottom. Both are sealed with mud when grain is inside. The grain produces carbon dioxide (CO_2) gas which kills any insects in the silo.

Rocks are needed for the foundation, and the main body of the silo is made of 325 4x4x6-inch sun-dried clay blocks. The inside and outside of the silo are plastered with sand/soil/cement mortar. The inside bottom slopes toward the chute opening, so that the grain will easily slide out when desired.

Small Farm Grain Storage, book, 500 pages, by Carl Lindblad of Peace Corps and Laurel Druben of VITA, 1976, about $5.00 from VITA.

This enormous, well-illustrated new book is certainly the most comprehensive available in a simplified form. It is prepared for use by local development workers. "Using a format of plain language and informative illustrations, the handbook gives some background to the world's grain storage problem; presents construction plans for grain dryer and storage facilities; offers information on insect and rodent control (with and without the use of poisons); provides shortened, illustrated versions of text material to serve as guidelines for extension agents who wish to prepare their own materials.

"A main aim of the manual is to present its material in a form as close as possible to the way in which the extension agent needs the information in order to pass it on successfully. Ideally, the only adaptations an extension agent should have to make using the material are to translate it (not in all cases) and/or to add culturally specific illustrations or photos. Or the manual material can be used as a base for audio-visual presentations. The idea is for the manual to serve as an idea facilitator and communication link between the development worker and his audience."

The authors explain the storage problem; the characteristics of grain and how these affect grain storage considerations; grain, moisture and air and the interaction between these; and important notes on the preparation of grain for storage.

There is a major section on grain dryers (95 pages) which includes complete production and operating instructions for 3 different solar driers, pit & above-ground oil barrel dryers, and improved traditional units such as the maize (corn) drying and storage crib (made of bamboo). Instructions for sun-drying using plastic sheets, and descriptions of the University of the Philippines and IRRI rice dryers are provided.

Storage methods are covered in 150 pages, including use of the following: baskets, cloth or burlap sacks, airtight structures, underground pits, plastic sacks, metal drums and bins, earthen structures, cement and concrete structures, and ferrocement pits and bins.

The VITA leaflet **Waterproofing Soil Construction** (see review, page 226) and production information on the Thailo ferrocement silo (see review in this section) are reproduced here.

Highly recommended.

Home Techniques—Volume 1: Food Preservation, leaflets, total of 60 pages, FAO, 1976, on request from Dr. Ludmilla A. Marin, Chief, Home Economics and Social Programmes Service, Human Resources, Institutions and Agrarian Reform Division, Food and Agriculture Organization, Via delle Terme di Caracalla, 00100-Rome, Italy.

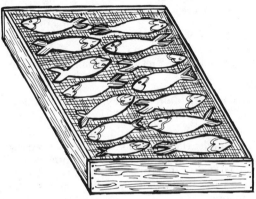

This is the first of a planned series of Food and Agriculture Organization (FAO) publications on equipment and techniques related to food preparation, handling, and storage. Drawings illustrating the steps in the preservation of fish and meat are presented, with text in English, Spanish, and French. Includes cleaning, filleting, splitting, dry salting, wet salting, smoke drying, sun drying, and storage of fish; and salting, salt-drying, rendering fat, and storage of meat. Drawings of all the tools needed include 10 different simple designs for smoking ovens made of commonly available materials.

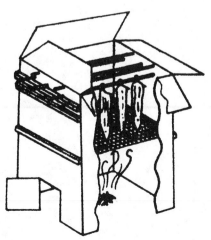

Smoking Fish in a Cardboard Smokehouse, pamphlet, 9 pages, also available in French, $0.50 from VITA; also reprinted in **Cloudburst 1** (see page 43).

MATERIALS: cardboard carton, steel wire, wire mesh

PRODUCTION: simple handtools

This leaflet explains how to make a cardboard smokehouse, and includes explanations of smoking methods. Local experimentation with local fish is necessary to determine some of the necessary time periods. Smoking requires 5-6 hours. The instructions are very simple, and all measurements are in both English and metric units. Good, complete instructions.

Smoked fish still must be specially stored to avoid spoilage—refrigeration, canning, freezing or salting is necessary. The cardboard smokehouse obviously cannot be exposed to rain.

How to Salt Fish, pamphlet, 9 pages, D. Casper of VITA, also available in Spanish, $0.50 from VITA; also reprinted in **Cloudburst 1** (see page   ).

''The process of salting fish is influenced by weather, size and species of fish and the quality of the salt used. Therefore, experience is needed to adapt the process outlined here to your situation...Salted fish, if properly packed to protect it from excessive moisture, will not spoil.''

The leaflet covers the complete process—preparing the fish, salting, washing and drying to remove excess salt, and air drying. It is a simple process requiring only knives, waterproof vats, and large amounts of salt. Curing in the brine takes 12-15 days in warm weather, up to 21 in cold weather. 6 days of warm weather are required for drying.

A simple, straightforward leaflet that is complete enough to do the job.

Late Addition

A Survey of Solar Agricultural Dryers (**Technical Report T99**), book, 144 pages, December 1975, $7.00 from BRACE.

This book focuses on experiments on the use of small-scale agricultural driers in rural areas of developing nations. Includes a representative sample of different types of driers; emphasizes local improvements and adaptation. There are 24 case studies of different driers in a variety of countries; each one has photos, full construction drawings, and the address of the people involved. Highly recommended.

FURTHER REFERENCES ON CROP PRESERVATION

Plans for Low-Cost Farming Implements includes drawings of platform carts with drying pans for crop drying in areas of frequent rains; crops can be brought in under a protective roof quickly; see review on page 99.

ENERGY: GENERAL

Energy: General

The use of alternative natural sources of energy is attractive because of the high price and limited availability of oil, the pollution that is associated with the burning of fossil fuels, the tremendous expense and dangers of nuclear power, and a variety of other reasons. In developing countries the first reason is of particular importance because their industrial development, coming at a time of low-cost plentiful oil supplies, has resulted in a greater reliance on this single source of energy than is true in the developed countries, despite the fact that the latter use tremendously larger quantities. For industrialized countries such as the United States, practical and economically-competitive alternative energy systems already exist that could replace the entire nuclear power contribution to U.S. energy supplies.

For village-level applications, there are many very promising existing technologies. The five sections which follow explore each of these in more depth: sun, wind, water, methane gas, and pedal power. These technologies are small-scale and necessarily decentralized. This, rather than any other technical inferiority, is the primary reason earlier forms of these technologies were eventually passed over in the industrialized countries; it remains one of the primary reasons why improved versions of these systems are not being used extensively in North America despite the fact that they could make a major contribution to energy supplies. While these units cannot very effectively be used for the power needs of large industry, they are admirably suited to the needs of decentralized villages and small communities. They are typically low in cost, relatively simple in construction and maintenance, made of materials available in villages and small towns, and involve little or no environmental pollution or destruction.

Energy from natural sources must be used carefully if the greatest benefit is to be obtained. Each of the above is best suited to particular applications. It is important to note that energy conservation is cheaper than extra energy production (thus the significance of insulation in homes in cold climates and in solar water heaters and solar ovens). Energy use should not be confused with energy needs—North Americans, for example, typically waste extraordinary amounts of energy. Equally important is the fact that energy is 'lost' each time it is changed from one form to another. For example, it would be more efficient to use a water wheel to directly drive small machinery than to generate electricity, run it through the batteries, and use it to operate electric motors on the equipment. For the same reason, solar energy is best used in the form of trapped heat.

The best application for wind power is for water pumping, because of the intermittent availability of wind. Water tanks can serve as the 'batteries'— filling up during periods when there is plenty of wind, and providing stored water when no wind is available. If wind power is to be used to irrigate a large garden, a slightly elevated tank would provide this needed storage capacity and a gravity system to distribute it. *Windgenerators can be a good choice for lighting and operating radios in a small group of homes, where the total power demand for a single wind-machine is about 500 watts.*

Solar energy is initially captured in the form of heat, and is therefore best used for a variety of heating purposes. Solar water heaters for hospitals and clinics, solar steam cookers, and solar ovens are good, practical applications right now in the tropics. The technology involved is simple, low-cost and effective. Solar water heaters are already a practical economically-competitive source of energy in the United States, despite the fact that they are relatively labor-intensive to produce. While it is possible to generate electricity directly from sunlight, the costs involved and the technology needed to produce the very pure silicon crystals required, do not at present make this a practical alternative.

Small water wheels can be used to directly grind grain and drive a variety of light machinery. Water wheels turn relatively slowly, driven by moving or falling water. Water turbines operate on a different principle and are designed to rotate at the much higher speeds required to generate electricity. The water turbine is considered to be the best natural source for the small-scale generation of electricity. The use of small-scale turbines has been very important in the development of decentralized rural industry and rural electrification in China.

The methane gas digester is in some ways the most difficult system to operate effectively. The principles are relatively simple: animal wastes are mixed with water and allowed to decompose through the action of bacteria. This takes place within a sealed container. As the manure decomposes, one of the products is methane gas, which can be collected and burned for cooking and lighting (at about 2/3 the BTU of natural gas). Yet this process is a delicate one, and the costs are difficult to justify on the basis of the gas production alone. Fortunately, rich fertilizer is another product, and there are several other benefits or using a digester as part of an 'integrated system' (see introductory remarks in the ENERGY: METHANE GAS section).

Pedal-power is significant because it is the most effective way to use the muscles in the human body, and because the bicycle itself is in many ways the most efficient machine ever created by man. Pedal-power is advantageous both for transportation (the bicycle, pedi-cab, or pedalled cart) and as an easily movable short-term power source (threshers, winnowers, grinders etc.). Stationary pedal-power is particularly appropriate when relatively small amounts of power are needed at irregular intervals—driving a small saw, for example. One person can also use a pedal-power unit to produce up to 75 watts of electricity continuously for one hour; a small amount, but clearly useful in some circumstances.

An additional source of power can come from harnessing an animal to some simple machinery. One of the units which does this most effectively is the 'animal power gear' (reviewed at the end of this section). A set of large gears are used to convert the power of a draft animal walking in a circular path into the rapidly spinning motion of a drive shaft. The drive shaft can be connected to a variety of threshing, winnowing and other equipment. The animal power gear can be built using sand form casting methods, and the tolerances are large; thus it can be easily produced by a small foundry.

One other item of interest is the fireless cooker. This is an insulated container, into which a pot of boiling food is placed and then covered. The insulated walls of the cooker prevent the heat from escaping, and the food will cook by itself in two to four hours. One design for a fireless cooker is reviewed *at the end of this section.*

The small-scale technology for harnessing alternate sources of energy represents more than a possible answer to the dilemma posed by the high price of oil. It also represents an opportunity for the village to regain its viability as a modern way of life. It symbolizes the beginnings of the kinds of opportunities and village-controlled development that may end the mass migration to the cities. For the first time in a century, the momentum of world events may be on the side of the village as a way of life, to be enriched but not destroyed through development.

Energy Primer, large paperback book, 200 pages, Portola Institute, 1975, $5.50 in United States, $6.50 overseas surface mail from WETS.

An extraordinary book. One of the most valuable books we've reviewed. Although much of the material included (particularly the books reviewed) deals with rather theoretical questions, there is also a huge volume of information directly useful at the intermediate technology or village level. The Energy Primer is successful in being scientifically accurate and realistic, while at the same time remaining understandable to readers who have no technical training.

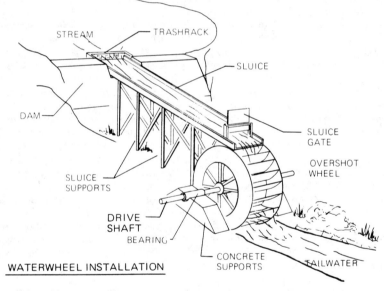

WATERWHEEL INSTALLATION

''The Energy Primer is a comprehensive, fairly technical book about renewable forms of energy—solar, water, wind and biofuels. The biofuels section covers biomass energy, agriculture, aquaculture, alcohol, methane gas, and wood. The focus is on small-scale systems which can be applied to the needs of the individual, small group, or community. More than ¼ of the book is devoted to reviews of books and hardware sources. Hundreds of illustrations and a dozen original articles outlining basic principles are used to describe the workings of solar water heaters, space heaters and dryers, waterwheels, windmills, windgenerators, wood-burning heaters, alcohol stills, and methane digesters. The final section of the book focuses on the need for energy conservation and some of the problems and potentials of integrated energy systems.''

The highlights of the Energy Primer include:

a) solar energy: drawings of solar stills, solar dryers, solar water and air heaters, with informative text.

b) water power: "This section...written by a mechanical engineer, covers engineering and cost considerations...measuring stream flow and head, constructing a dam, and using channels and pipes. Completely illustrated building and working chapters on more than seven different types of water wheels and water turbines are also included (this does not mean that you can build all of these from the information given—Ed.). The entire discussion is geared to systems that can be built by individuals and small communities." There is also a table of water wheel and water turbine specifications that allows some useful comparisons between designs, and a glossary of technical terms.

c) wind power: There are charts and general rules, 2 articles, plans for a 12-volt wind generator you can build (these plans require quite a range of hardware store materials, and depend on 'the use of other plans—e.g., for blade design).

d) biofuels: This has some good coverage of aquaculture and methane digestion.

In all sections of the Energy Primer, there are dozens of excellent book reviews. Simple how-to-do-it plans mentioned are also covered by the **Appropriate Technology Sourcebook**, usually in greater detail.

On the whole, this is simply an excellent book for a variety of levels of technology. It goes well with **Other Homes and Garbage** (see page 42). Highly recommended. A second, revised edition is in progress.

Producing Your Own Power, book, 283 pages, edited by Carol Stoner, 1975, $3.95 from WETS.

This is an anthology of articles on small-scale power production. Articles have been gathered from a variety of sources, and some of them are available separately elsewhere. There is also a glossary of technical terms.

The chapters are:

a) Electricity From the Wind, by Henry Clews. This has good wind power information in a very readable form. A reprint of Clews' pamphlet of the same name (see review on page 147).

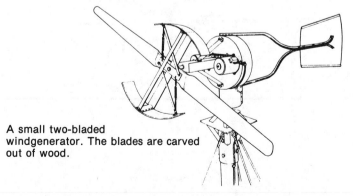

A small two-bladed windgenerator. The blades are carved out of wood.

b) Do-It-Yourself Windgenerators, by James DeKorne. He attempts to outline the limitations of homebuilt windmachines, along with possible ways to overcome these limitations. His suggestions presuppose easily available surplus equipment such as would be found only in industrialized countries. A good chapter for American alternative technology people; not as useful in developing countries.

c) Small Water Power Sites is a complete reprint of VITA's booklet entitled **Low Cost Development of Small Water Power Sites** (see review on page 155).

d) Hydraulic Rams is also a VITA reprint. Briefly describes how they work and how to build one with standard plumbing parts (see review on page 208).

e) Heating and Cooking with Wood explores house, fireplace, and stove designs for maximum efficiency. It includes a simple design for a heating stove made of two oil drums.

f) Methane Gas Digester for Fuel and Fertilizer is a reprint of the first 25 pages (out of 40) of the New Alchemy Institute publication of the same name (see review on page 186). The working models have not been included.

g) Our Four-Cow Bio-Gas Plant was written by people who have worked with Indian bio-gas plant authority Ram Bux Singh. They have had a methane digester operating for 2 years in Vermont, USA. A description with diagrams.

h) Space Heating with Solar Energy is "intended to provide ideas that might be adapted, on a smaller scale," for heating one's own home. Mainly for North Americans.

i) Homemade Solar Water Heaters provides the necessary information for the construction of several home-built units. Diagrams and text. "The easiest, most practical application of solar energy on an owner-built basis is the heating of water."

j) Combining Alternative Energy Systems, and Conservation of Energy in Existing Structures were written for American homes.

Handbook of Homemade Power, book, 367 pages, Mother Earth News Magazine, 1974, $2.20 from Mother Earth News.

This book is an anthology of articles—reprints from past issues of Mother

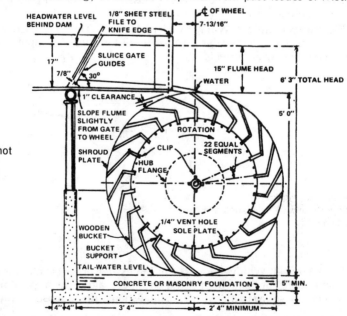

Earth News magazine and other publications, written for the American home-steading movement. Major sections are on wood, water, wind, solar, and methane power. While the emphasis is mainly on stories by people who've worked with these power sources, there are a few concrete plans presented. These include working plans for two kinds of water wheels, and the dams and hardware that go with them (a reprint of a 5-part 1947 Popular Science article that is quite comprehensive); a good 8-page set of instructions for building a solar focusing cooker, mostly out of cardboard and aluminum foil; an 8-page set of instructions for building and using a solar oven (uses mainly 28 gauge galvanized iron and window glass, and costs $10.00 or less). The last unit is similar in design to Rodger's **Solar Scotch Oven** (reviewed in solar energy section). Both the solar cooker and the solar oven are reprinted from Halacy's book **Solar Science Projects** (also reviewed in the solar energy section).

Other than the above-mentioned plans, there is little practical information here.

Energy Book #1: Natural Sources and Backyard Applications, large format book, 112 pages, edited by John Prenis, 1975, $4.25 from Running Press, 38 South Nineteenth Street, Philadelphia, Pennsylvania 19103, USA.

This book presents information on alternative sources of energy. It does not pretend to be comprehensive, but attempts to selectively give the reader a flavor of some of the designs. Clearly rated behind such thorough books as the **Energy Primer** and **Other Homes and Garbage**.

This book does have some good articles, such as "Solar Energy—A Better Understanding," "Utilization of Sun and Sky Radiation for Heating and Cooling of Buildings," and a brief look at various sail windmills that the American group Windworks has experimented with (Windworks no longer offers plans for all but one of these).

The following valuable articles are either reprints or very similar to articles by the same authors in other publications: "The Sailwing Windmill and its Adaptation for Use in Rural India" (**New Alchemy Journal No. 2**, see page 144), a part of "Electric Power From the Wind" (see page 147), and an intro-duction to the Savonius rotor (by the authors of **Wind and Windspinners**, see page 148). There are also a number of reprints from Alternative Sources of Energy magazine (see page 282).

A group with a thorough collection of alternative energy publications will probably find this book redundant. It does have value as an introductory book, as its articles and illustrations give the reader a beginning practical under-standing of alternative energy principles, in a compact, simplified form.

Survival Scrapbook #3—Energy, book, 110 pages, S. Szcelkun, 1974, $3.95 from WETS.

This is a book of information on basic ways to use alternative sources of energy. The contents were selected based on the following criteria: "Able to be used and controlled on all levels by individuals and small communities: small-scale; decentralized; able to be constructed, used, and maintained by ama-teurs; makes use of local or commonly available resources wherever possible."

Good drawings are included on flat plate collectors for solar water heating, solar stills, focusing collectors for water heating or cooking (parabolic cyclinder and parabolic dish type), a small wind machine for generating electricity (probably not very efficient), and windmill control devices for high wind conditions. Some of this information is incomplete; diagrams range from excellent step-by-step details to single simple sketches.

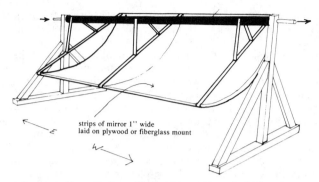

strips of mirror 1" wide
laid on plywood or fiberglass mount

A parabolic cylinder will provide extremely hot water.

To Asians this book will appear to have a very odd format. The text is sometimes off the subject. However, there are many valuable ideas in this book.

Manege: Animal-Driven Power Gear, booklet with separate instructions for associated machinery, 30-page booklet, 8-page leaflet, UN Division of Narcotic Drugs, 1975, free from the UN Division of Narcotic Drugs, Palais Des Nations, Geneva, Switzerland.

The manege is adapted to any task that can use mechanical power transmitted through a drive shaft—especially agricultural activities such as threshing grain. The booklet describes two sizes of the manege, along with five associated pieces of equipment that can be operated with it: thresher, chaff-cutting chopper, grinding mill, winnower, and root-cutter. All of the above pieces of equipment are on operating display at the Laboratoire de Techniques Agricoles et Horticoles de Chatelaine, near the UN office in Geneva.

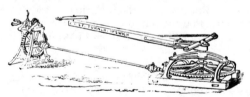

''The animal-driven power gear works on the same principle as a bicycle...an arrangement of levers and gears that transforms slow leg movement into the speedy rotation of a wheel...Two wooden bars or levers, each about 4 meters long, are bolted to the center of the large horizontal input gear. They extend like two spokes of a large wheel.'' Speed of rotation is increased by a factor of 50. Equipment to be operated is located 10 meters away from the center of the power gear.

No complex or precision parts are necessary. The production of all the components in developing countries should not present serious problems. Gears are rough iron casting which can be made from scrap metal. Melting and pouring facilities are needed, as are sand molds. The gears are used just as they come from the mold—no finishing. Other metal parts could be forged by a reasonably-skilled blacksmith. Only machining requirement: a drill to cut holes for bolts to join the components. Animal fat can be used for occasional lubrication. (from the booklet text.)

The instructions for use of the associated equipment give technical specifications and a description of the operation of each of these pieces of equipment.

Photos but no detailed plans are given for the manege and the associated equipment. With a great deal of imagination, only the manege could be constructed with this booklet alone. The UN Division of Narcotic Drugs may be willing to send technical drawings.

The Haybox, 1 large information sheet with drawings, $0.50 plus postage, from Low Energy Systems, 3 Larkfield Gardens, Dublin 6, Ireland.

This describes the principles of a fireless cooker. Ideas for design and materials are given. For use with foods which can be cooked slowly (2-4 hours): beans, sauces, stews. The food is brought to a boil in a heavy pot, then removed from the heat and placed inside the Haybox. It cooks in its own heat which is unable to escape.

Two fireless cookers: Above, the Haybox, for which an information sheet is available; below, a unit that can be purchased.

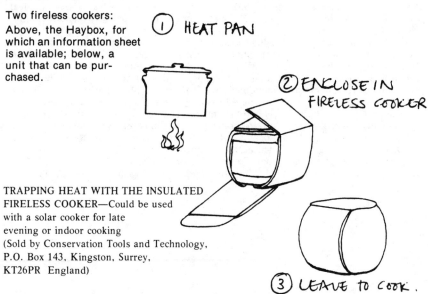

① HEAT PAN

② ENCLOSE IN FIRELESS COOKER

TRAPPING HEAT WITH THE INSULATED FIRELESS COOKER—Could be used with a solar cooker for late evening or indoor cooking (Sold by Conservation Tools and Technology, P.O. Box 143, Kingston, Surrey, KT26PR England)

③ LEAVE TO COOK.

Proceedings of the Meeting of the Expert Working Group on the Use of Solar and Wind Energy, Energy Resources Development Series No. 16, book, 147 pages, by the United Nations Economic and Social Commission for Asia and the Pacific, 1976, UN Publication Sales No. E.76.II.F.13, $9.00 from United Nations, Sales Section, Room LX 2300, New York, NY, 10017, USA.

This book contains reports and documents from a March 1976 conference in

Bangkok.

Wind power: basic information and characteristics of different rotor types; pump characteristics; recommendations for activities in support of further development of wind power in the region; discussion of characteristics of Greek cloth sail windmills, industrially-produced wind pumps, and wind-generators; many drawings of simple low-cost windmills and pumps; use and potential use of wind energy in India, Thailand, New Zealand, Australia, Korea and Indonesia.

Solar energy: sample drawings and discussion of solar water heaters, stills, cookers, driers, and pumps; conversion to electrical and mechanical power; use and potential use of solar energy in India, Japan, Australia, Southeast Asia, and Pakistan.

For both topics there is a list of references and organizations worldwide.

FURTHER REFERENCES ON ENERGY: GENERAL

Other Homes and Garbage is an excellent reference book on most small-scale alternative energy systems; see review on page 42.

Radical Technology has a good overview of the different small-scale alternative energy technologies being experimented with around the world; see review on page 35.

Alternative Sources of Energy magazine is essential reading for people in developed countries interested in following the activities of the blue-jeaned but serious experimenters in this field; see review on page 282.

Energy for Rural Development: Renewable Resources and Alternative Technologies for Developing Countries is the title of a 301-page report issued by the National Academy of Sciences in 1976. This is a summary of the state of the art of **currently manufactured** or already tested alternative technologies frequently suggested as solutions to rural or individual family energy needs in developing countries. Covers direct uses of solar energy, wind power, hydro-power, photosynthesis, microbiological conversion of plant materials to liquid fuels, geothermal energy, and energy storage. Employs a primarily technical and economic evaluation of the applicability of these systems based on production by current methods in industrialized countries. The authors do not include in their calculations the labor-generating effects and potentially very different forms such technologies might take in developing countries. The panel that produced the report recommends the formation of a decentralized international energy research network, noting that ''development and local adaptation of alternative energy technologies are not likely to be accomplished'' in a centralized energy institute. Copies of the report can be obtained free of charge from Commission on International Relations (JH215), National Academy of Sciences, 2101 Constitution Ave NW, Washington DC 20418, USA.

ENERGY: WIND

Energy: Wind

Wind machines can be used to pump water or to generate electricity. It is also possible to use them to drive machinery directly; the giant Dutch windmills reached up to 14 horsepower and were used to grind grain into flour in addition to pumping water (see **Windmills and Watermills**, reviewed on page 159 for more on these Dutch windmills and direct use of wind power to drive equipment).

The word "windmill" in a strictly technical sense refers only to a type of machine that drives a mill to grind flour. In fact, however, the word is often used as a general term for wind machines of all kinds. "Windgenerator" is only used to describe a machine that generates electricity.

There are many different designs for wind machines. Water pumping windmills usually have a slowly turning wheel with many blades. Windgenerators usually have 2 or 3 narrow blades which turn at a very high speed. For windgenerators, gearing is still needed to multiply the number of revolutions per minute (rpm) up to the range required by a generator. For example, a windgenerator may be charging the batteries at 200 rpm, but only if the gearing has multiplied this to at least 800 rpm at the generator. There are many practical ways to do this "gearing up"; sometimes this dramatically affects the entire design of the windgenerator.

The amount of power available from the wind depends of course on the wind speed. It is a peculiarity of wind power that the energy available increases as the cube of the wind velocity. This means that there is 8 times as much energy in wind moving at 20 mph as there is in wind moving at 10 mph. There are a number of important consequences of this peculiarity; one is that the designer and builder must provide some method of protecting the windmill from the tremendous forces of high winds. There are 3 common methods for this: a "feathering" system for moderately strong winds, in which the angle of the blades is changed so that more of the wind is allowed to pass through the rotor without affecting it; a system which causes the wind rotor to turn sideways out of the wind at still higher wind velocities; and a brake and tying down system for very high winds. In countries that have severe tropical storms sail windmills may be a good choice; the sails can easily be removed, leaving only a skeleton that is not as easily damaged by the wind.

Two other consequences of the power peculiarities of wind as speed increases greatly affect the final positioning of the windmill. Wind speed is generally faster above ground level; for this reason, and to avoid turbulence caused by trees, houses, or other obstacles, windmills are usually placed on top of 20- to 40-foot towers. The wind speed is very much affected by the local geography; this makes site selection important. The top of a small hill will usually have much more wind energy available than the bottom of a hill. (See reviews of **Other Homes and Garbage** and **Build It Yourself Science Lab** for additional information on wind measuring devices to aid in site selection—

pages 42 and 53.)
The wind power available is also determined by the "swept area" of the blades. A 10-foot diameter rotor will sweep an area 4 times as large as that swept by a 5-foot diameter rotor; the larger rotor should be able to capture about 4 times as much power from the wind. As rotors get larger, however, balancing becomes more difficult and vibrations become more of a problem.

The first part of this section is on water pumping windmills, which can be used to provide water for grazing animals or for irrigation of small plots (about 2 acres or 1 hectare). Five of the following entries give complete construction information for water pumping windmills that can be built of locally available materials in most developing countries.

The small-scale generation of electricity using windgenerators is the second major focus of this section. Probably about 500 watts is the practical maximum output to expect from a home-built windgenerator; however, some sophisticated designs are beginning to appear for home-built machines with 2 or 3 times this capacity. This is one of the most active areas of experimentation in alternate sources of energy; the years 1974-1976 saw the publication of most of the best books on the subject, and there is every reason to believe that there will be more to come.

A windgenerator with 3 wooden blades.

Is There A Place For the Windmill in the Less-Developed Countries?, paper, 21 pages, M. Merriam, 1972, free on request from the East-West Technology and Development Institute, East-West Center, 1777 East-West Road, Honolulu, Hawaii 96822.

This is an excellent paper—important reading for anyone seriously considering the use of windmills in developing countries. The author lists the most important considerations in choosing to build a windmill, including the most favorable circumstances for a variety of power needs. Four prevailing types of windmills are briefly examined (the Dutch, American multi-vane, propellor, and Savonius Rotor), and the power and other characteristics of each design are briefly compared. There are several tables, drawings, and appendices with supporting information.

Island applications are particularly recommended. The author includes a series of questions that should be useful in determining whether to build a windmill at all in a rural area. He argues that conventional economic analysis is often too complicated and uncertain and fails to take into account important considerations from the villagers' point of view.

"In places where the average wind velocity exceeds 12 mph, and especially in places where it exceeds 15 mph, windmills should be considered for use as decentralized sources of mechanical and electrical power. Their economic attractiveness is limited to situations where central station power is not available and liquid petroleum fuels are expensive or unsuitable...The greatest problem is that each installation must be engineered to the characteristics of the load and the local wind. The expertise to do this kind of installation engineering is not widely available in the less developed countries.

"The types of loads to which windmills have traditionally been applied and to which they could reasonably be applied now are : 1) pumping water for human or animal consumption, for crop irrigation, for drainage of land; 2) mechanical power for operating machines of the flour milling or small-scale industry type, and 3) generating small amounts of electricity to charge storage batteries, in order to operate radios and other electrical appliances...The amount of electricity required to operate radios...is not large and its value is high."

A Survey of the Possible Use of Windpower in Thailand and the Philippines, book, 74 pages plus appendix, W. Heronemus, 1974, on request from Agency for International Development, Washington DC 20523, USA; or $6.00 from NTIS (Accession No. PB-245 609/3WE, N'74; foreign orders add $2.50 handling charge).

This remarkable book is not the kind of report one has come to expect from a USAID contract. It is easy to read, and the author's emphasis, at least for water-pumping windmills, is on the use of local materials and locally available skills. It answers favorably the question "could windpower be used by the peasant farmer in Thailand or the Philippines to improve the quality of his life?"

"Numbers of six-sail wind machines are currently in use in the salt works around the northern shore of the Gulf of Thailand. The machines are of about 6 meters diameter and use bamboo spars, rope and wire to form a wheel which carries 6 triangular sails, each woven from rush or split bamboo." These machines drive the paddles of the traditional water-ladder low-lift pumps. The author recognizes that while efficiency could be greatly improved, the current machines are "admirably sized to the task they are to perform" and the primary limiting factor is not in the machines but in the land available for salt evaporation.

For use in irrigation, the author makes some stimulating suggestions for improvements in the sail windmill design and for local adaptation of a wooden, 16-bladed fan mill. "The blades would be of molded plywood, made between matched concrete molds in the existing Bangkok plywood factories...Each laminated blade would be inserted into a wood spoke and the spokes would in turn be brought to an iron banded wood hub. The entire wheel would be a timber (plus glue) product, producible by native artisans possessing the same skills and tools required to build the water ladders."

Most of the report is focussed on Thailand, but the contents are of general interest to people in any area where there is a need for low-lift pumps for irrigation. Photos of the sail windmill and water ladder are included.

Considerations for the Use of Wind Power for Borehole Pumping, leaflet, 15 pages, AT Unit Report, 1976, send nominal sum for postage to Appropriate Technology Unit, Christian Relief and Development Association, P.O. Box 5674, Addis Ababa, Ethiopia.

An introduction to the basic considerations for the use of multi-bladed windmills for water pumping. Explains the importance of site selection, rotor design, and the other major components along with the criteria that affect these choices. No plans or detailed information given.

Food from Windmills, book, 75 pages, Peter Fraenkel, 1975, Ł3.55 or US$8.50 surface mail from ITDG.

MATERIALS: pvc pipe, angle iron, steel water pipe, commercial piston pump, steel bar; styrofoam block and half oil drum for float.
PRODUCTION: some welding and metal-cutting.

This book is to be recommended to anyone doing work on the design of low-cost windmills for irrigation. It thoroughly covers the work of the American Presbyterian Mission on adapting the Cretan sail windmill for use in an isolated area of Ethiopia.

The report contains drawings and photos of the necessary components. Much of the text discusses the design, problems, and resulting modifications.

Through the increasingly honored soft-technology approach of 'racing' one design against another (rather than getting involved with expensive monitoring devices), the Mission was able to come up with a windmill that would pump at

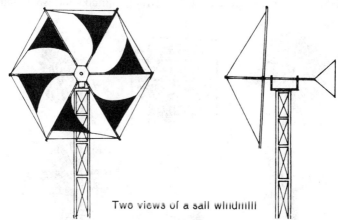

Two views of a sail windmill

almost twice the rate of a commercial American Dempster multi-blade windmill. (This was partly because the sail windmill, due to its relatively light weight, was constructed so as to sweep a larger cross-sectional area. The sail windmill also outperformed 3 Savonius rotor windmills.) The most impressive design had the following characteristics: 16-foot diameter rotor when rigged with four sails, operating at a static head of 9 feet, would pump 1300 gallons of water per hour in a 14.5 mph wind.

The application of this windmill is interesting. Pumping is directly from a river that has a water level variation of 2 meters; a float is used as part of the intake.

The experiments have resulted in a design which has 8 arms. The number of sails actually used depends on the wind at the time. The owner/operators put up the sails in the morning and adjust them while the mill is in use; when work is finished in the fields, the sails are removed for safe-keeping (which also protects the mill from damage in case of a sudden storm and high winds). Thus these windmills are not taking full advantage of the 24-hour availability of wind, though in these circumstances the windmills are in operation during the peak wind velocity period.

A 3-legged tower is about 15 feet high, built of angle iron, and needing no foundation other than impacted soil. 1½'' pvc plastic pipe draws water from the float, which is made of a styrofoam (polystyrene) block fitted into half an oil barrel for protection. There is a foot-valve at the bottom of the pipe to keep the prime. 3'' diameter commercial piston pumps are used. The crank shaft and connecting rod are made of steel bar and water pipe; some of these bearings are hardwood. The sails were made of donated Dacron sail cloth, which was both strong and resistant to the deterioration that comes from continuous exposure to strong sunlight. Cotton is claimed to be not generally strong and long-lasting enough; the kind of cloth sail used in Crete is not identified. Some experimentation was done with detachable aluminum sails, made from surplus roof cappings; these were claimed to be ''readily available and cheaper than Dacron in most areas...more durable than locally-available textile.''

By August 1975, 19 windmills of various types were being used by villagers, and another 5 were operating on the mission grounds. The 11-foot design has a cost estimate of US$250-350, almost all of which goes for the steel, the pvc pipe, and the commercially-purchased pump. This is about 1/3 the cost of a delivered factory-produced model of similar capacity. Costs might be significantly reduced in areas with a supply of strong bamboo and wood materials.

The homemade windmills of Nebraska

The Homemade Windmills of Nebraska, book, 78 pages, E. Barbour, 1898 (reprinted 1976), $3 from Farallones Institute, 15290 Coleman Valley Road, Occidental, California 95465, USA.

Sketches are provided of more than 60 different windmills. They appear roughly in order of efficiency, and the text explains the advantages and disadvantages of each. The books was written with the express purpose of providing good models to copy, so that builders would benefit from the experiences of others.

This is a remarkable little book. Our first reaction was to ignore it—there have been some significant advances in windmill design since 1898. But choice of windmill design involves cost as well as efficiency, and a lot of these windmills could be built for almost nothing—using only local materials. This is a great idea book: many of these designs could be adapted to use bamboo poles and woven bamboo mats for the blades or sails, along with wooden bearings and power transmission arms. In fact, if combined with simple low-lift pumps, a water-pumping windmill could be put together for an extraordinarily small cash outlay in many developing countries. The designs are so simple that any carpenter could put one together just by looking at an existing machine. This is exactly how they spread all over the state of Nebraska in the United States.

The majority of the machines do not have the capability of turning to accept wind from any direction; they were designed for areas with a prevailing wind from a dependable direction. However, some of the machines do rotate to face the wind, and others are vertical-axis machines for which wind direction is not important. J. Baldwin of the CoEvolution Quarterly says this book may result in more working machines than any other. After seeing this book, we think he's right.

"Labor, it is found, is contributed freely to such work, at times when more important work is practically at a standstill." Many of the farmers "put them to work in various ways to save hand labor, such as running the grindstone, the churn, the feed grinder, the corn sheller, the wood saw, and other farm machinery." It is also interesting to note that many of the farmers were wealthy and didn't purchase a shop-made mill (which was more efficient) because they could build a heavier duty, cheaper mill themselves.

The text is full of 'case studies' of the farmers and their mills.

Highly recommended.

Low-Cost Windmill for Developing Nations, booklet with dimensional drawings, 40 pages, H. Bossel for VITA, French edition also available, $2.00 from VITA.

MATERIALS: rear axle and differential of a small car, sheet metal, pipe, steel ribbon/rod/angle iron/channel, and wood.

PRODUCTION: some welding, steel drilling, and sheet metal cutting.

"Construction details for a low-cost windmill are presented. The windmill produces one horsepower in a wind of 6.4 m/sec (14.3 mph), or two horsepower in a wind of 8.1 m/sec (18.0 mph). No precision work or machining is required, and the design can be adapted to fit different materials or construction skills. The rotor blades feather automatically in high winds to prevent damage. A full-scale prototype has been built and tested successfully."

Performance data is included. The windmill is best used to transmit mechanical energy, but also can be connected to a generator.

Sahores Windmill Pump, booklet, 80 pages, J. Sahores, 1975, $6 from Commission on the Churches' Participation in Development, World Council of Churches, 150 Route de Ferney, 1211 Geneva 20, Switzerland.

MATERIALS: bamboo or wood, cloth, nylon strings, inner tube, axle, crank-shaft and bearing supports made of iron and steel

PRODUCTION: some welding and metal work for axle and crankshaft

French language edition only; however, the step-by-step construction plans are so detailed that the unit has been built without a translation of the text.

A group of French engineers has developed a light, simple windmill, mainly using bamboo sticks, cloth and string, which sets in motion a standard water pump (design not included). Only the welded transmission mechanism needs some sophistication for manufacture. This windmill incorporates the primary elements of the American multi-bladed windmill, at perhaps 5% of the cost! One of the most imaginative examples of appropriate technology we've seen.

There are three innovations of particular note: 1) the 3 meter diameter wheel

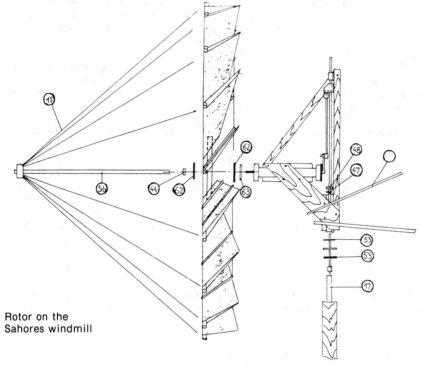

Rotor on the
Sahores windmill

is made of bamboo (or wood) with cloth sails in the shape of the American multi-blade design; its light weight and automatic feathering mechanism mean that the tower can consist only of a pole with 4 cord or steel guy wires rather than a large, expensive (usually steel) structure. 2) The automatic feathering system consists of pieces of inner tube attached so that the blades open more as the wind becomes stronger, thus protecting the windmill from damage while also allowing it to make use of light winds. 3) A counterweight system is employed which enables the pumping action to be adjusted by the owner, for operation at windspeeds from 2 m/sec up to strong winds.

The cost of materials in France was approximately US$85 (this included a purchased pump). The first prototypes have been working for 3 years. 20 of these machines were built in 1974-75 and are being tested in Africa.

Highly recommended.

A Water-Pumping Windmill That Works, article with plans, 7 pages, New Alchemy Institute, in Journal No. 2, 1974 (see page 48).

Dimensional drawings with English measurements, text, and assembly information. A complete parts list is provided.

"This windmill consists of three cloth sails attached to three tubular steel masts which are fastened to a triangular plywood hub. The center of the hub is bolted to the end of an automobile crankshaft, which spins in bearings mounted

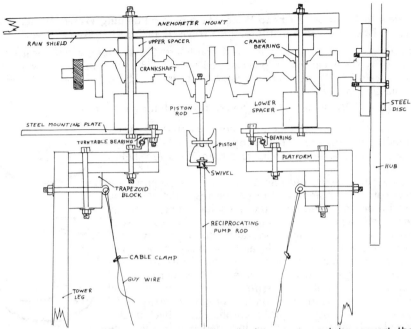

The turntable: an automobile crankshaft and piston are used to convert the rotating motion of the windmill rotor to the up-and-down motion of the pump rod.

on top of a steel ball-bearing turntable. The bearing turntable unit, which allows the windmill to rotate so that the sails are always perpendicular to the wind, is mounted at the top of an eight-legged tower which is firmly guyed and braced. A piston rod connected to the crankshaft transfers power through a reciprocating vertical steel pipe which runs from the top to the bottom of the tower where it operates a high capacity piston-type water pump. This windmill is designed to remain operational and to withstand storm conditions...Water-pumping trials showed a yield of 250 gallons per hour in a 6 mph wind with 18 ft. diameter blades applying power to a 3″ diameter pump through a 3½″ stroke.″ The designers recommend a greater stroke or larger diameter piston so that the full potential of the windmill will be reached.

A version of this sail-wing windmill using a bullock cartwheel and bamboo poles for the rotor has been built in Madurai, India (described on page 101 of the Energy Primer). The ball-bearing turntable is ''the only component that cannot be assembled in an Indian village. A machine shop is required.''

A very promising design.

Wind Power Poster, 1 large sheet, both sides, $3 from Windworks, Box 329, Route 3, Mukwonago, Wisconsin 53149, USA.

Good introductory material on wind power is presented, in the form of a wall poster. Includes single sketches of 17 different windmill designs, giving an idea of what has been tried and the relative sizes of the machines. Shows theoretical potential power and actual performance for each in kilowatts. Formulas and graphs for: available power, some design characteristics, and electrical appliance consumption. Text briefly introduces important considerations for the use of wind power. Annotated references. Summary in French and German.

How to Construct a Cheap Wind Machine for Pumping Water, leaflet, 13 pages, Brace Research Institute, 1965 (revised 1973), $1.25 from BRACE.

MATERIALS: 2 oil drums in good condition, 2 self-aligning ball bearings (flange type), wood frame, plywood, 80 feet of 1/8'' galvanized steel wire, 6 turnbuckles, 1¼'' water pipe for rotor shaft, one ½'' bore ball bearing, 15 feet of plastic pipe.

PRODUCTION: some welding, no critical machining is necessary.

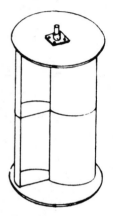

This device is a Savonius Rotor, adapted to water pumping for irrigation where windspeeds are 8-12 mph or more, and water level is not more than 10-15 feet below ground.

Brace has tested the unit to find out its potential for low-cost water pumping. ''From the tests the following conclusions can be drawn: the Savonius Rotor, although not as efficient as a windmill of comparable size, lends itself to water-pumping for irrigation due to its low initial cost, simplicity of materials and construction, and low maintenance cost...The only important points to be observed in erecting such a machine is the proper choice of the site and careful assessment of the average wind speeds. From this information, the proper pump size and stroke can be chosen from the graphs at the back of this pamphlet.'' Another graph is included which gives the output at various wind speeds. One pump designed to operate at 10 mph and lift water 15 feet will have an output of 181 imperial gallons per hour at that wind speed.

The Rotor has been designed in this form for moderate wind speeds and water-lifting up to 30 feet. Brace reports that a fair amount of ''experimentation was needed to determine the best location of the pump relative to both the source and the discharge.'' Design of a simple diaphragm pump is also included.

This leaflet is complete. Shop and plumbing terms are often used. (See also **Wind and Windspinners** in this section.)

Performance Test of a Savonius Rotor, technical report with charts and graphs of the test results, 17 pages, M. Simonds and A. Bodek for Brace Research Institute, 1964, $2.00 from BRACE.

Performance tests were carried out using an 18 sq. ft. rotor on an open site. ''It is concluded that a Savonius Rotor pumping system operates quite satisfactorily and is indeed a practical design of windmill. It is, however, only about half as efficient as the conventional fan mill'' which costs 4 or more times as much. Two rotors would thus have the same output as a conventional fan mill, but the total cost would be less than half that of the conventional machine.

''The system seems best suited for pumping in cases where the well-depth does not exceed 20 ft....the windmill should be designed to look after itself safely in storms.''

This is clearly an important report for anyone who plans to experiment with or build any large numbers of Savonius Rotors. Torque, power co-efficients, and tip speed ratios are examined. (see also **Wind and Windspinners**.)

Simplified Wind Power Systems for Experimenters, book, 80 pages, Jack

Park, 1975, $6 from Helion, Box 4301, Sylmar, California 91342 USA; or WETS.

This book represents another attempt to demystify technology. It is a response to the fact that "most of the information (currently) available requires engineering training or is not complete enough...It is hoped that (in this book) the reduction of complex mathematics into simple graphs and arithmetic problems will allow a greater segment of the innovative public to use the fundamentals an engineer has. To make this book as useful as possible, a page has been devoted to graph reading, and numerous examples are used to illustrate each step in the windmill design process."

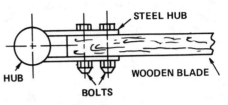

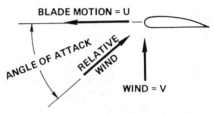

Over 50 illustrations and photos of all kinds of windmachines, and an equal number of simple graphs and minor drawings. It not only gives an excellent overview of the possibilities for small windpower installations; it also comes very close to Park's goal of providing "the reader with the engineering tools necessary to accomplish a respectable job of designing and planning the construction of windmills."

Major topics are power required, wind energy available, windmill efficiency, airfoils, windmill augmentation, structural design, and mechanical design. Very little is actually said about pumping water, electrical systems or direct mechanical conversion; you'll have to go elsewhere for this essential information. But as to the design of the windmill itself, this is the book to have.

Hats off to Jack Park. A significant contribution to the effort to take knowledge of technology out of the sole control of the experts and make it accessible to the public.

Helion also publishes two wind power technical memos: WTM 1—Aerodynamic Layout of Windwheel Blades (a technical method for optimum layout), 10 pages, $1. WTM 2—Hybrid Windmill Notes (a summary of Helion's findings on Darrieus rotor/Savonius rotor vertical-axis hybrid windmills), 8 pages, $2. Plans for an aluminum-bladed 2-5 kw windgenerator, $10.

Electric Power from the Wind, booklet, 29 pages, Henry Clews, no date, $2 from Solar Wind Co., East Holden, Maine 04429 USA; also reprinted in **Producing Your Own Power** (see page 131).

In readable non-technical language, this booklet contains the basics about producing electricity from the wind. Examples are given from Clews' own windgenerator (a commercial unit). A good place to start.

Wind Power, booklet, 17 pages, Syverson and Symons, 1974, $3 from Wind Power, Box 233, Mankato, Minn. 56001 USA.

Large pages with tiny print contain considerable general information on windpower. No illustrations or plans, however. Text includes an overall description of wind-electric systems, design factors, storage devices, site selection, windpower available, maintenance, electricity demand, cost, and sample calculations. No information on water-pumping windmills. A variety of useful charts with kilowatts, propeller diameter, wind speed, wind energy, tower height, etc. plotted against each other. Electricity use statistics are for appliances in energy-gobbling American homes.

Written mostly in standard English; technical terms explained in the back.

Wind and Windspinners (A nuts and bolts approach to wind/electric systems), book, 115 pages plus 24 page supplement, by Michael Hackleman and David House, 1974, $4.25 surface mail to local groups in developing countries, $8.00 surface mail to all other groups, add $2.00 for overseas airmail, from Earthmind, 5246 Boyer Road, Mariposa, California 95338 USA.

MATERIALS: wood, guy wires, steel pipe axis with pipe flanges, (3) 55-gallon oil drums, plywood, flange-type bearings

PRODUCTION: simple handtools

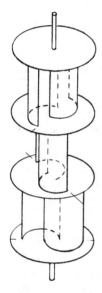

This book was written for people in the U.S. who want to build their own windgenerators. It focuses on the small, owner-built wind/electric system, and "information is provided in such a way as to allow modification of the units we have constructed to fit individual circumstances...The use of wind energy is quite individualistic and because of this, it is difficult for any one system to fit all people and places." So the authors have described the essential factors which affect the choice of a wind/electric system, in order to let the reader make the decisions with his own local circumstances in mind. A very good, practical introduction to windpower; matched only by the wind section in **Other Homes and Garbage** in this respect (see page 42).

The first 5 chapters cover basic information and concepts for any wind/electric system. The last two chapters focus on the Savonius Rotor. The book is written in non-technical language, and is easy to understand (some use of slang may present occasional problems to the non-native English speaker).

The S-rotor has an advantage in that it can use gusts of air coming at a different angle from the main mass of air. A propeller windgenerator can only use wind from a single steady source at any one moment. Also, the S-rotor can begin to charge 12-volt batteries at windspeeds lower than the 7-mph minimum required by a propeller windgenerator.

This is a very comprehensive appropriate technology guide for using an S-rotor wind machine as an electric power generator. For example, it includes a diagram and description of a simple homemade wind-sensing device that will switch on the voltage regulator and alternator when there is enough wind to charge the batteries. (The choice of battery represents something of a problem—an automobile battery, the most obvious appropriate technology unit has two limitations: 1) a small storage capacity and 2) not designed to be repeatedly discharged and charged. A truck battery is a better alternative.)

Good construction information is given (main body of rotor and supports) for all three S-rotor designs that the book covers. The basic design uses three 55-gallon oil drums, cut in half and stacked on top of one another (with plywood endcaps to secure them). A steel rod serves as a vertical axis. The 3-tier S-rotor with its out-of-phase orientation represents an improvement over the single-tier basic S-rotor; it is better able to start up under uneven wind conditions.

This is **the** how-to book on the Savonius rotor in electric systems. No water pumping information is included—but the design details of the body of the rotor can help. For water pumping, the most efficient use of the S-rotor (because mechanical energy is directly used and "storage" can be a water tank), we recommend this book in combination with Brace Research Institute's leaflet, "How to Construct a Cheap Wind Machine for Pumping Water."

The Homebuilt Wind-Generated Electricity Handbook, book, 194 pages, Michael Hackleman, 1975, $4.75 surface mail to local groups in developing countries, $8.00 surface mail to all others (add $2.00 for airmail), from Earthmind, 5246 Boyer Road, Mariposa, California 95338, USA.

Much of this book is not on homebuilt systems at all, but on how to find and rebuild one of the hundreds of thousands of wind-generators that were manufactured in the United States between 1930 and 1950, before the completion of Rural Electrification. But there is a lot more to this book that is valuable to the person building his own windgenerator.

Potentially the most valuable are the 29 pages of simple explanations and drawings of The Control Box. "The point of this chapter is to detail the components of the wind-electric controls—how they work...If you're building a wind-electric system, this chapter will tell you what you must account for and protect, and how you can do it." Covers relays, voltage regulator, current regulator, and other components (ammeters, voltmeters, fuses, etc.) in non-technical language. There is a very simple design for a control box system for units producing less than 400 watts (see below) and a complete wiring diagram and explanation of the owner-built control box for higher wattage systems. Very nice; congrats to Michael Hackleman and friends.

"Let's trace the path of current in this unit. The generator current goes through the heavy coil on the relay but is blocked by the open switch, so it goes through the smaller winding of wire on the relay. When the voltage from the generator is sufficient to begin charging, the current in this part of the relay will be sufficient to pull in the relay and close the contacts. Now the current will flow into the batteries through the ammeter. When the windspeed drops, the windplant will slow; when it's at a lower voltage than the battery voltage, current will flow in a reverse direction

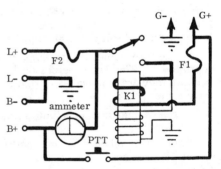

Control box for systems below 400 watts

through the heavy wire winding and this will neutralize the magnetic field of the small wire winding portion of the relay and the contacts will open. If the wind is not present, and you want to be sure that all is okay with the windplant, you can hit the PTT (push to test) switch and this will short the batteries out to the generator and motor the windplant; if it starts turning up there, all is okay. If it doesn't, the batteries are dead or the windplant is frozen up or has a broken connection somewhere."

Also covered in this book is the art of tower-raising (57 pages). These are towers in the 40-foot and taller range, that are fully assembled on the ground. This is a rather delicate manuever, and the text with photos and diagrams seems to cover the do-it-yourself methods nicely. Beats renting a helicopter!

There are also 21 pages on installing the windmachine on top of your tower; again, a delicate manuever. There are 20 pages on auxiliary generating equipment; 13 pages of windmachine design notes (not intended to be comprehensive).

This book complements **Wind and Windspinners** very well.

Homemade 6-Volt Wind-Electric Plants, booklet, 18 pages, H. McColly (Ag. Eng.) and F. Buck (Elec. Eng.), North Dakota Agricultural College Extension Service, 1939 (reprinted 1975), $1.00 from Mother Earth News.

MATERIALS: soft wood for blades, sheet metal, hardwood strip, spring, pipe, strap iron, electric wire, 6-volt lamps, 20 amp fuse and socket, 2 6-volt auto batteries, generator with cut-out and pulley.

PRODUCTION: some soldering

"This publication deals entirely with a homemade wind-driven 6-volt battery charger system which may be used to generate energy to keep batteries charged for radios, autos, and small lighting systems for farm houses and other farm buildings where the energy consumption is not large." The booklet was written for small farmers in the US in 1939, and reprinted in 1975 due to the large current interest in windgenerators.

Dimensional drawings (English units) with text, step-by-step instructions, and many useful hints are given. The blades are hand-fashioned out of wood. This low-cost system charges 2 6-volt batteries and powers several lights, radios, etc. It is designed to charge the storage batteries when the wind velocity is between 15 and 30 mph—probably too high for most situations. (Modification for charging during periods of lower windspeeds would involve either a gearing system, rewinding the generator, or using an alternator.)

Proceedings of the United Nations Conference on New Sources of Energy— 1961, Volume 7 on wind power, 408 pages, $16.00 from United Nations, Sales Section, Room LX-2300, New York, NY 10017 USA.

The seven-volume **Proceedings** were originally printed in 1964, and reprinted in 1974. They are obviously expensive and hard to find; as of this printing they are still available from the above address. Some major libraries have copies.

The relevant material in volume 7 (the only volume dealing with wind power) is as follows:

a) Studies of wind behavior and investigation of suitable sites for wind-driven plants (15 articles).

b) The design of windpower plants (11 articles).

c) The testing of windpower plants (4 articles).

d) Recent developments and potential improvements in windpower utilization (13 articles), including:

"Small Radio, Powered by a Wind-Driven Bicycle Dynamo," by Stam, Tabak, and van Vlaardingen, 5 pages.

"Adaptation of Windmill Designs, with Special Regard to the Needs of the Less Industrialized Areas," by Stam, 9 pages.

"Windmill Types Considered Suitable for Large-Scale Use in India," by Nilakantan, Ramakrishnan, and Venkiteshwaran, 7 pages.

Wind Energy Bibliography, booklet, 66 pages, Ben Wolff, 1974, $3 from Windworks, Box 329, Route 3, Mukwonago, Wisconsin 53149 USA; or WETS.

One of the best wind energy bibliographies available. Topic headings are wind (behavior, measurement), windmills (historic perspectives, developing countries, large scale installations, electrical generators, vertical axis, shrouded and fan type, commercial), aerodynamics, electrical, towers, storage (batteries, compressed air, flywheels), conversion, hydrogen, catalogues. 350+ listings of articles, books, and papers—some of them undoubtedly obscure and hard to find. No annotations, addresses, or prices given (except for 12 annotated general entries).

Most of the materials in the category "windmills—developing countries" are old Brace Research Institute papers.

In addition to the wind energy bibliography and the wind power poster, to experimenters in developing countries Windworks offers full plans of their 25-foot sail windmill. These are $25.00 for one set of plans (we haven't seen them). More information on Windworks' early experiments with various windmills can be found on the back of the wind power poster (reviewed in this section) and in **Energy Book #1** (see page 133); includes some photos and comments.

Energy from the Wind, annotated bibliography, 180 pages, B. Burke and R. Meroney, 1975, $7.50 in USA, $8.00 for foreign orders from Publications, Engineering Research Center, Foothills Campus, Colorado State University, Fort Collins, Colorado, 80521, USA.

"The basis for this bibliography is a systematic search of the major abstracting and indexing tools from 1950 to 1974...In an effort to prepare a comprehensive bibliography useful to many people with varied interests in windpower, all references discovered have been included, regardless of their scope or emphasis. They range from popular review to a technical aerodynamic study, from do-it-yourself homebuilt projects for house or farm to large scale commercial production for power networks." Some annotations are provided. No address or price information is given for the 760 references listed. An annual update service is planned.

We gave this bibliography a test: we looked for everything we knew had been published about homebuilt windgenerators. We did find just about every pre-1975 publication listed. However, most of the best books on homebuilt windgenerators were published in 1975 and 1976. The best of this material on homebuilt windgenerators is already covered in the **Sourcebook**, but you might find **Energy from the Wind** a valuable source of information on other aspects of wind energy.

Wind Power Digest, quarterly journal, 50 pages average length, $6.00 for 4 issues or $2.00 for a single issue, from Wind Power Digest, 54468 CR 31, Bristol, Indiana 46507, USA.

Wind Power Digest is a new and welcome journal on small-scale wind power systems, in non-technical language. It is not a scientific journal but rather a forum for discussion by people experimenting with small wind power systems or simply interested in the subject. Most of the contributors and readers are North Americans.

Contents include how-we-did-it articles by people who use windmills or windgenerators as regular sources of power, ideas from experimenters and notes on new developments from among this informal network, experiences with various home-built and commercially-available windmachines, reviews of new publications and plans for home-built windmachines, brief summaries of developments by the large scientific institutions, and occasional reprints from other sources. The focus is on North American applications of wind power. This journal will be of interest to groups experimenting in developing countries. However, little of the contents so far are relevant to appropriate village-level technology. The editors are planning to add an AT section on non-electric wind power uses.

A good example of a national-level subject-oriented AT journal—a communication tool among a network of ordinary people and experimenters. The plain language, focus on small-scale systems, and the audience make this an important voice in the effort to demystify wind power.

The Generation of Electricity by Wind Power, book, 323 pages, by E. W. Golding, first published in 1955, reprinted in paperback in 1976, ₤4.50 or US$8.00 from Conservation Tools and Technology, 143 Maple Road, Surbiton, Surrey KT6 4BH, United Kingdom.

"First published in 1955...(this book) was soon recognized as the definitive account of the research on wind power undertaken up to that time." With the increasing interest in alternative sources of energy, this classic reference book has been reprinted. Included is an additional chapter outlining the research and technical developments since the book first appeared (brief).

Golding covers: 1) wind behavior and measurement; 2) wind-machines (especially windgenerators); and 3) the economic use of wind power under different conditions. There is a chart of English, French and German terms.

Jack Park's book (see review on p. 146-147) is better on the design and characteristics of wind **rotors**. And many of the conclusions from Golding's book have been widely accepted and reprinted. The part of this book that remains hard to find in other sources is probably the 135 pages given to wind characteristics and measurement (measuring devices have changed a bit).

Recommended for experimenters who want a more detailed reference book.

FURTHER REFERENCES ON ENERGY: WIND

Radical Technology has a very good section on wind power, showing many of the different designs; see review on page 35.

Energy Primer, see review on page 130.

Other Homes and Garbage, especially for small-scale generation of electricity; see review on page 42.

Shelter has just two pages on sail windmills; brief but quite good; see review on page 219.

Alternative Sources of Energy magazine often has articles on wind power; see review on page 282.

Traditional Crafts of Persia has a vertical-axis windmill used for grinding grain; see drawing with review on page 72.

The International Rice Research Institute's agricultural engineering department has been experimenting with an improved Savonius rotor for low-lift irrigation; see drawing and notes on page 102.

LeJay Manual has information on homebuilt windgenerators and how to rewind an automobile generator so that when used with a windmachine it will begin charging at a lower rpm; see review on page 65.

New Alchemy Journal No. 2 also has an article on windmill electronics; see review on page 48.

New Alchemy Journal No. 3 has articles on a new sail-wing for a windmill and a water-pumping Savonius rotor; see review on page 48.

ENERGY: GENERAL, see all the reviews in this section.

ENERGY: WATER

Energy: Water

Water power is one of the oldest forms of power used by man. The most widespread application was in the grinding of grain to make flour, but waterwheels have been used to drive saws for cutting lumber, pump water, and do all kinds of mechanical tasks (see sketch with review of **Diary of an Early American Boy**, page 70).

Water power, where it is available, is in fact a better, more reliable source of electricity on a small scale than wind power.

Small scale water power is attractive both because it can be harnessed by non-engineers and because this can usually be done without much environmental disruption. The same things cannot be said for large scale hydroelectric schemes which also tend to flood agricultural land and displace large numbers of villagers.

It is generally agreed that the slowly turning waterwheel (about 20 rpm) is best suited for direct mechanical applications. The rapidly turning water turbine can be quite small (less than 1 meter in diameter) and still produce significant amounts of electricity. However, we have seen at least one very successful waterwheel driven generator that puts out 2-6 kilowatts of electricity from the flow of a small irrigation ditch (about 5 meters or 15 feet wide) in Indonesia.

The best home-built turbine for generating electricity is probably the Banki turbine, a design which can be built in a small metal-working shop using only steel plate and blades cut from large steel pipe. This design can fit a wide range of heads (the distance through which water falls) and flow rates.

There is a lot of potential for the use of small scale water power in developing countries, particularly those which have wet rice agriculture and extensive irrigation systems. Such small units require only a head of 4 meters (13 feet) and a flow of 400 liters/second (120 gallons/second) to produce 10 kilowatts of electricity—a considerable amount for any village, where people have not learned to waste electricity the way Americans have. Wooden waterwheels can be used directly to thresh and mill rice in these circumstances, and can operate with much smaller flows.

Small waterwheels are now being used in Sumatra, Indonesia to mill rice (see sketch), and an effort is being made in Papua New Guinea to encourage the building of small wooden overshot wheels for a variety of mechanical uses.

This section is light on the "cookbook" plans and heavier on the how-to-design-your-own information. This is probably as it should be, because small water power system designs depend on local circumstances more than most alternate energy systems.

If the **Energy Primer** and **Other Homes and Garbage** are already available as reference materials, a good set of practical material can be completed by combining **Cloudburst 1**, the two VITA manuals, the Banki turbine booklet, and **Leffel Pamphlet "A"**, all for about US$12.00.

Low-Cost Development of Small Water-Power Sites, booklet, 43 pages, H. Hamm of VITA, 1971 (reprinted 1975), Spanish and French editions also available, $2.00 from VITA.

This important booklet is a guide to the desirability, selection, construction, and installation of a small water-power plant. "The manual begins by describing in simple language the steps necessary to measure the head (the height of a body of water) and flow of the water supply, and gives data for computing the amount of power available. Next it describes the construction of a small dam and points out safety precautions necessary...a discussion of turbines and water wheels...Guidelines are given for making the right choice for a particular site...The manual also describes in detail how to make a Michell (or Banki) turbine in a small machine shop with welding facilities, from usually

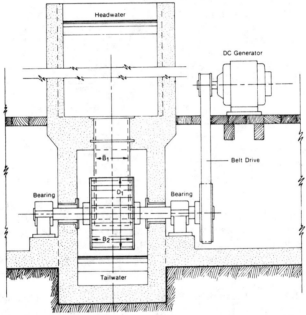

Arrangement for a Michell (Banki) turbine for low-head use without control.

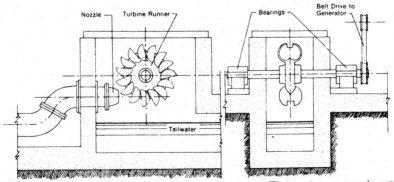

Two views of a Pelton wheel driving a generator. The water comes in under pressure through the pipe at the left, from a source higher than the wheel.

available pipe and other stock material (see **Banki Water Turbine** in this section).

The booklet includes 32 drawings and sketches of different installations and pieces of equipment. The author recommends several companies that manufacture water-power equipment, cautioning that "the hazards accompanying the manufacture of so delicate a machine by do-it-yourself methods and the difficulty of achieving high efficiency should warn the ambitious amateur to consider the obvious alternative of securing advice from a reliable manufacturer before attempting to build his own."

This is the best booklet available.

Reprinted entirely in **Producing Your Own Power** (see page 131).

Your Own Water Power Plant, article with drawings, 16 pages, C. Basset in Popular Science magazine, 1947, reprinted in **Handbook of Homemade Power** (see page 132), **Cloudburst** (see page 43), and **Hydropower** (see review below).

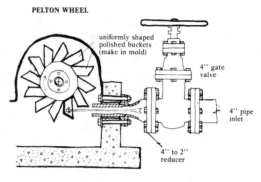

PELTON WHEEL

uniformly shaped polished buckets (make in mold)

4'' gate valve

4'' pipe inlet

4'' to 2'' reducer

This is a classic how-to article, written in simple language and covering much of what you need to know to build your own water power plant. Its usefulness is underlined by the fact that it has been reprinted so many times recently.

The article covers choice of location for a small dam, the measurement of flow and head with simple common tools, small dam construction, making a wooden flume and wooden overshot water wheel, and fabricating a Pelton impulse wheel (Part 4—not included in the **Cloudburst** reprint).

This article **does not** cover the final use of the power produced—neither electricity-generating equipment nor mechanical power are discussed.

Hints on the Development of Small Water-Power—Leffel Pamphlet "A", leaflet, 8 pages, free on request from James Leffel and Co., 426 East St., Springfield, Ohio 45501 USA.

This pamphlet was prepared for those who are thinking of building small water-power plants on small streams to generate electricity. It is intended to give necessary information to people unfamiliar with the general rules and requirements of such developments. Explains the terms "fall" and "head", and how to measure the "head." Includes a simple table for measuring the quantity of water. Discusses the importance of ponds for water storage.

The James Leffel and Co. have been manufacturing water-power equipment for 110 years. The pamphlet is quite useful in itself, and does not require the reader to buy any of company's equipment.

Hydropower, book, 72 pages, £1.70 or US$3.40 from Conservation Tools and Technology, 143 Maple Road, Surbiton, Surrey KT6 4BH, England.

This was published to encourage the use of small-scale water power systems in Britain. Includes reprints of **Your Own Water Power Plant** and **Leffel Pamphlet "A"** (see reviews in this section). One additional 6-page article on water power is included, plus articles on other unrelated subjects. Written with a humorous tone.

Micro-Hydro: Civil Engineering Aspects, paper, 11 pages, by D. Mansell, G. Atkins and S. Kiek, direct inquiries to Prof. Don Mansell, Civil Engineering Dept., PNG Univ. of Technology, Box 793, Lae, Papua New Guinea.

This paper identifies "some of the aspects of small hydro-electric schemes which are of particular concern to the civil engineer, and provides some guidance to non-engineers who wish to build such power sources...(includes) facts, problems and ideas which may be of interest to a person wishing to investigate the feasibility of a small scheme."

Discusses calculations for low flows, flumes and channels (earth, timber, concrete, and steel), and soil problems in small earth dams. The perspective is that of using local materials for small water power schemes in isolated rural areas.

"It is possible to build small dams with reasonable certainty of success with the use of a little simple technology. Such dams should not exceed 5 meters in height."

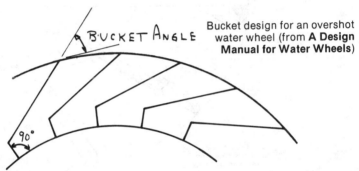

Bucket design for an overshot water wheel (from **A Design Manual for Water Wheels**)

A Design Manual for Water Wheels, booklet, 71 pages, William Ovens, 1975, $4.00 from VITA.

This booklet is a result of a Papua New Guinea University of Technology project involving the development of low-cost machinery (water wheels) to provide small amounts of mechanical power in remote locations. The manual is "for the selection of proper sizes required to meet a specific need and to set out design features based on sound engineering principles" in easily understood language. Wooden overshot wheels were selected as "the most likely choice to give maximum power output per dollar cost, or per pound of machine, or per manhour of construction time." The booklet covers the general principles of bucket design, calculating power output, bearing design (use of wooden bearings recommended), shafts, some information on construction techniques, and water pumping applications. A set of sample calculations for the design of a village water wheel/pump combination are given. No specific plans are provided. 2-page bibliography.

The slow speed of rotation of wooden water wheels (5 to 30 rpm) "is advantageous when the wheel is utilized for driving certain types of machinery already in use and currently powered by hand. Coffee hullers and rice hullers are two which require only fractional horsepower, low speed input. Water pumping can be accomplished at virtually any speed...A usable water wheel can be built almost anywhere that a stream will allow, with the crudest of tools, and elementary carpentry skills." Made of local materials and easy to maintain and repair.

This leaflet's major weakness is the lack of illustrations. There are a variety of graphs, but only 7 drawings—only two of these have to do with the design of the wheel itself. There are 4 good drawings of mechanisms to convert the rotational motion of the wheel into the up and down stroke that a piston pump requires. The piston pump design provided is questionable—it must be cut open for inspection or repair.

Despite the lack of illustrations, we highly recommend this booklet to anyone considering the construction of overshot water wheels. (See also **Oil Soaked Wooden Bearings**, reviewed on page 111).

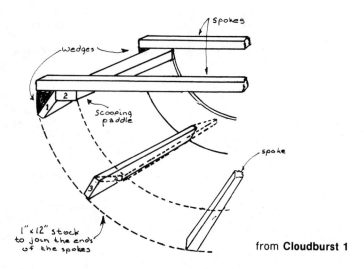

from **Cloudburst 1**

Cloudburst 1 (see review on page 43) has three articles on wooden water wheels in addition to a reprint of 4 of the 5 parts of the article "Your Own Water Power Plant" (also reviewed in this section):

a) "Water Wheel Design," 5 pages including diagrams. This takes a brief look at 4 different types of water wheels. "The overshot wheel takes water in at the top and discharges it at the bottom. The breast wheel takes water in somewhere in the middle of the wheel and discharges it at the bottom. The undershot (Poncelet) wheel both accepts and discharges water at the bottom." And the Pelton impulse wheel is distinctive because it requires a long feed pipe. This article is essentially a very informative discussion of the design characteristics of each of these wheels (though very little is said about the Pelton wheel). No information is included on how to use the power.

b) "A Wooden Overshot Wheel," 3 pages with plans. This design uses an auto rear axle with the end of the drive shaft, an auto generator and batteries, and V-belts. A wood-turning lathe is needed to make the wood pulleys. There is enough information provided to build an overshot wheel. Some design choices are left to the builder.

c) "A Wooden Undershot Wheel," 5 pages with plans. This design uses wood and 2 sets of bearings. It can be built with simple hand tools from the information provided. The dam, trough, and wheel are covered. No specific information on using the power is provided.

Windmills and Watermills, book, 191 pages, John Reynolds, 1970 (reprinted 1975), $8.95 from WETS.

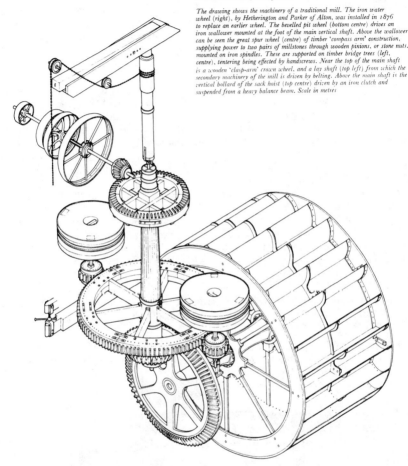

Abbotstone Mill, Hampshire

The drawing shows the machinery of a traditional mill. The iron water wheel (right), by Hetherington and Parker of Alton, was installed in 1876 to replace an earlier wheel. The bevelled pit wheel (bottom centre) drives an iron wallower mounted at the foot of the main vertical shaft. Above the wallower can be seen the great spur wheel (centre) of timber 'compass arm' construction, supplying power to two pairs of millstones through wooden pinions, or stone nuts, mounted on iron spindles. These are supported on timber bridge trees (left, centre), tentering being effected by handscrews. Near the top of the main shaft is a wooden 'clasp-arm' crown wheel, and a lay shaft (top left) from which the secondary machinery of the mill is driven by belting. Above the main shaft is the vertical bollard of the sack hoist (top centre) driven by an iron clutch and suspended from a heavy balance beam. Scale in metres

This book covers the enormous Dutch-style windmills and the large water-powered mills of Europe. Overshot, undershot, breast-shot, floating, tide, and vertical-axis water wheels are examined. Applications include grain grinding, textile manufacture, water-lifting, and pumping. The text follows the evolution of these machines made almost entirely out of wood (even the gears were made of hardwood). Windmills averaged 14 hp and water wheels averaged 20 hp.

This is a very different book from most of those we've reviewed. It is a beautiful picture book, with excellent drawings as well. Looking through it is almost as valuable as visiting the actual machines. You will get a very good idea of how these huge machines worked. Potentially quite useful to anyone considering building wooden water wheels to drive machinery. A glossary explains the terms used.

The Banki (Michell) Water Turbine, booklet, 27 pages, Mockmore and Merryfield of the Engineering Experiment Station, Oregon State University,

1949, $1.00 from Engineering Experiment Station, Oregon State University, Corvallis, Oregon 97331 USA.

This booklet has lots of somewhat sophisticated mathematics and diagrams that explain the theory behind the Banki turbine, filling up most of the text. Oregon State University built an experimental version that worked quite well—a brief discussion of that unit is included.

The Energy Primer claims that the "Michell (Banki) turbine is probably the best choice for most small hydropower installations. It is fairly simple to construct, requiring some welding, simple machining, and a few amenities in the workshop. The steel parts can be cut from stock sheet and standard steel pipe. The design is essentially the same for a very wide range of flows and heads. For installations with variations in flow rates, the rotational speed for top efficiency will remain the same (for a constant head) over a range of flows from ¼ of the flow to full design...The Michell turbine is undoubtedly the best power source (where the head is appropriate—between 15 feet and 100 feet) for the limited budget and those with a desire to be able to do-it-themselves. No other wheel or turbine is quite as versatile, easy to build, and still useful for power generation."

The Energy Primer gives additional information for construction of one of these units—a 12" size. They say about this booklet: "This is apparently the only complete discussion of the Banki or Michell turbine available in the US." (See VITA-"Low-Cost Development of Small Water-Power Sites" for fabrication details and instructions.)

Young Mill-Wright and Miller's Guide, book, 400 pages plus 28 plates (drawings), by Oliver Evans (watermill engineer and inventor), 1850 (reprinted 1972), $21.00 from META.

A handbook written and used during the era when waterwheels were most common. This is a remarkable, classic book on the use of waterwheels to grind

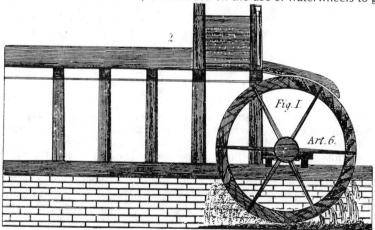

grain into flour and to operate equipment such as saws. The entire book is oriented toward practical applications. The major subjects include the relevant principles of mechanics and hydraulics, descriptions of the different kinds of wheels including tables with proportions and power, descriptions of gears and cogs along with the additional equipment needed for grinding grain into flour, and information for building mills including the wheels and all auxiliary equipment. You can also find short discussions of the strength and durability of teeth of wheels, the bearings and shafts, constructing cogwheels, and mills for hulling and cleaning rice.

"The stones are to be dressed with a few deep furrows, with but little draught, and picked full of large holes; they must be set more than the length of the grain apart. The hoop should be lined inside with strong sheet-iron, and this, if punched full of holes, will be thereby improved. The grain is to be kept under the stone as long as necessary...The principle by which the grains are hulled, is that of rubbing them against one another, between the stones with great force; by which means they hull one another without being much broken by the stones." (From description of "a mill for cleaning and hulling rice.")

This book we mention with a number of reservations. It is the most expensive book we have reviewed. The language used may well prove difficult at times for non-native English speakers; old forms are frequently used which may not appear in current two-language dictionaries. There are fewer drawings than we would like to see; they are grouped at the back instead of appearing with the corresponding text. On the other hand, this appears to be by far the most complete book still in print on large, powerful waterwheels.

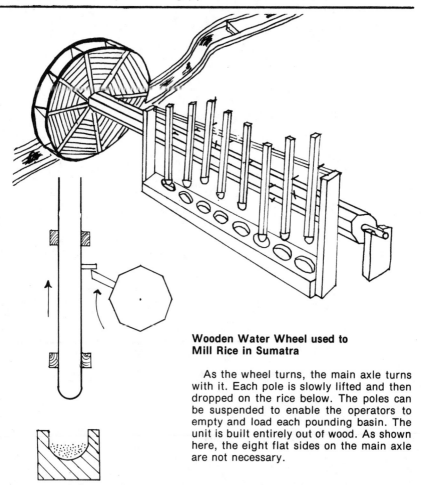

Wooden Water Wheel used to Mill Rice in Sumatra

As the wheel turns, the main axle turns with it. Each pole is slowly lifted and then dropped on the rice below. The poles can be suspended to enable the operators to empty and load each pounding basin. The unit is built entirely out of wood. As shown here, the eight flat sides on the main axle are not necessary.

FURTHER REFERENCES ON ENERGY: WATER

ENERGY: GENERAL, see all the reviews in this section.
Energy Primer, see review on page 130.
Other Homes and Garbage, see review on page 42.
Radical Technology, see review on page 35.
Alternative Sources of Energy magazine, see review on page 282.

ENERGY: SOLAR

Energy: Solar

"I would recommend that anyone interested in solar energy play extensively with such simple things as bubbles, bottles of water, stones, pieces of metal, and thermometers. Our society's approach to problems today is often to leap-frog the simple, obvious solution and land in the midst of computer programs and complicated machines where they are really not needed."

— Steve Baer, America's foremost solar experimenter with small scale systems

Solar energy has many different uses. Of these, home heating, water heating, cooking, water distillation, and food and crop drying are all low-cost systems included in the ATS. Solar distillation (to purify water for drinking) will be found in the section on WATER SUPPLY; solar drying is covered in FOOD AND CROP PRESERVATION AND STORAGE; and the use of attached greenhouses as a low-cost option for home heating at high elevations is presented in **An Attached Solar Greenhouse** *under AGRICULTURE. The other subjects along with general references are covered in this chapter on solar energy.*

Solar water heating for domestic hot water or as part of a home heating scheme is becoming more widely used in industrialized nations as a response to the "energy crisis." It is well suited to temperate regions where the winters are cold, although not to the higher latitudes. A typical system listed here consists of a flat plate collector and storage tank which holds water heated to about 150 degrees Fahrenheit (65 degrees C.).

In tropical regions where home heating is not necessary or desirable, solar water heating systems can be used to provide hot water for bathing, washing clothes and other uses (water heated in a normal flat plate collector does not boil, however, so this is not directly suited to water purification schemes). Solar water heating in these circumstances is probably best used in small health centers and clinics where there is a demand for hot water (the solar heated water needs less fuel to reach the boiling point).

For developing countries, the cost of materials for solar water heaters may make them rather expensive. There are more than a dozen ways to make a basic flat plate collector; there is some potential for very low-cost designs, particularly if a low-pressure [such as gravity-fed] is being used. Such collectors would use metal other than copper, and rely on wire-tying of pipes [instead of welding, brazing, or soldering], replace pipes altogether by using channels. The insulating material behind the collector plate can be local natural fiber such as coconut husks.

Solar cooking is perhaps the most practical application for developing countries besides crop drying. A solar cooker can be in the form of an enclosed box with reflectors to direct the sun's energy inside (a solar oven). It can be in the form of a high-temperature flat plate collector which produces steam (a solar steam cooker). Or it can be a concentrating parabolic dish reflector that focuses a large amount of the sun's energy onto a small area. It should be noted, however, that a concentrating parabolic reflector, if technically well-made, is very dangerous! If the user or a small child is to look into the focusing dish from a position near the focal point (cooking area) of the unit, it is quite possible to permanently blind or severely damage the eyes. Users should wear thick dark glasses, such as welding goggles (not just sun glasses). We think the solar ovens and the solar steam cooker are of more value as appropriate technology because they are not dangerous. All of these devices can be made simply and are readily adaptable to many areas of the world. There is a great potential for solar cooking; hopefully much more work will be done to find safe, low-cost, and effective cookers that use local materials (see review of **UNESCO Source Book for Science Teaching**, page 52; it includes a method for applying a silver mirror plating on glass).

Also included in this section are general reference books on solar energy. The most complete and authoritative review of the subject is Farrington Daniel's **Direct Use of the Sun's Energy**. (At $1.95 it is a bargain!) Another good resource that covers the **design** of solar water heaters and air heating systems very thoroughly is **Other Homes and Garbage** (see review,   page 42). The **Energy Primer** (see review, page 130) also has excellent information on solar energy.

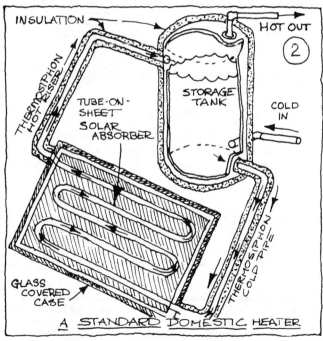

This sketch shows the normal operation of a solar water heater. The storage tank is elevated slightly above the flat plate collector. Cold water descends through the pipe on the right. The water then collects heat from the flat plate collector, and slowly moves up through the pipe until it leaves by the pipe on the left. This is called the 'thermosiphon' effect, because the water will automatically circulate without the use of a pump.

(from **Solar Water Heating for the Handyman** by Paige, the booklet with the best illustrations.)

Direct Use of the Sun's Energy, book, 264 pages, Farrington Daniels, 1964, $1.95 from WETS.

This is still a very current, comprehensive look at possible uses of solar energy. The author discusses how solar energy devices work, and then describes how they are constructed. Very simple drawings and some photos are included, but dimensional drawings from another source would be needed to actually build most of these devices.

There is a discussion of solar cooking devices, including mention of field work evaluating acceptance among villagers. Also, directions are given for the production of simple, low-cost focusing collectors of plastic (see **Capture the Sun** for a method that doesn't require plastic). One 4-foot diameter solar cooker described produces a temperature of 150°C. 'It was found in the field testing that water could be boiled in vessels of clay or earthenware nearly as well as in vessels of aluminum or steel, because the pattern of focused light was diffuse enough that the earthenware vessels weren't cracked by the thermal expansion.'

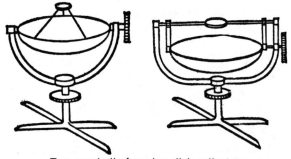

Two parabolic focusing dish collectors.

The author also discusses:the history of solar energy use, solar radiation, solar collectors, heating water, storing heat, agricultural drying, distillation of water, and heat engines. References are given at the end of each chapter.

Steve Baer, a well-known American inventor of solar energy devices for the do-it-yourself handyman, says this is 'the best book on solar energy.'

Capture the Sun—The Parabolic Curve and its Applications, booklet, 46 pages, G. Graham, 1975, $2.75 from Enterprises Unlimited, Star Route, Ferndale, California 95536 USA.

MATERIALS: small pieces of mirror or other reflecting material, small pieces of sheet metal, glue.

PRODUCTION: simple handtools.

A solar collector in the form of a parabolic curve will focus the sun's rays at one point, providing a **large** amount of heat. This booklet covers the design of parabolic focusing collectors as "solar cookers" for boiling water and other uses. Small pieces of mirror are used. There are instructions for making a parabolic shape using graph paper (the ability to use simple geometry is required for this).

The author is interested in small-scale, do-it-yourself devices, and presents the material fairly simply. The many drawings include two different ovens that combine the parabolic focusing collector principle with the solar oven principle. There is also a simple method for small-scale, village level manufacture of solar

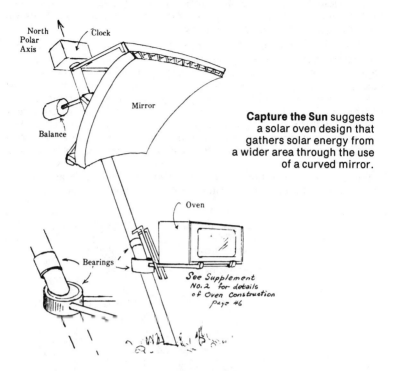

Capture the Sun suggests a solar oven design that gathers solar energy from a wider area through the use of a curved mirror.

cookers (pieces of sheet metal, such as iron or aluminum, are required for this).

This book will most useful to those people who would like to understand the theory behind the parabolic focusing collector.

Solar Science Projects, book, 95 pages, D. Halacy, 1974, $0.85 from Scholastic Book Services, 900 Sylvan Ave., Englewood Cliffs, New Jersey 07632 USA.

This book is a description of several very simple designs that can be built to utilize solar energy. They are mostly of value for demonstrations, although the ideas and designs presented could be used to build larger solar devices. The projects presented include a solar cooker, still, furnace, oven, and water heater. All can be built with very simple materials, and the instructions are very clear. Parts of this book have been reprinted in the **Handbook of Homemade Power** (see page 132).

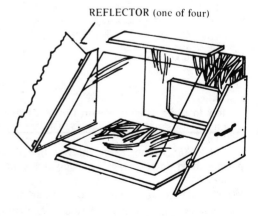

REFLECTOR (one of four)

A SIMPLE SOLAR OVEN

A Floridian's Guide to Solar Energy, book 120 pages, 1975, $1.50 in U.S., $2.75 for foreign orders from Florida Solar Energy Center, 300 State Road 401, Cape Canaveral, Florida 32920, USA.

"This report has been prepared to enable the citizens of Florida to understand the concepts, applications and status of solar energy. It will not show you how to build a solar water heater, but rather will give you some of the background information necessary for determining whether you should consider solar energy, and for which applications...thermal applications of solar energy (water heating, space heating, and air conditioning) are stressed..."

Although this book aimed at people living in the southeastern United States, the theory presented is generally applicable. Solar cooking, crop dryers and distillation are all covered. This information could be adapted to other climates and conditions.

For the price, this book is a useful introduction to solar energy and its applications, although it is limited by its emphasis on American uses.

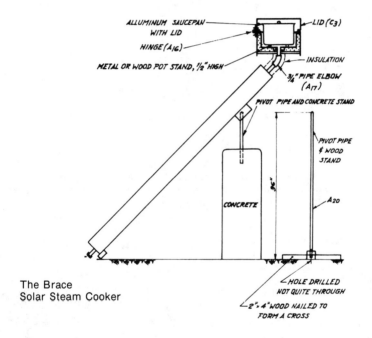

The Brace
Solar Steam Cooker

How to Build a Solar Steam Cooker, leaflet with dimensional drawings and assembly information, 13 pages, Brace Research Institute, 1972, $1.25 from BRACE.

MATERIALS: wood frame, plywood, ¾'' steel pipe, .025'' metal sheet, 26 gauge sheet metal, 1/8'' windowglass, galvanized wire, local dry fibrous insulation.

PRODUCTION: some metal-cutting and soldering.

"This manual describes a relatively simple, yet effective device for steam cooking of food using solar energy." Designed for village use in areas where sunshine is abundant and most food is cooked by steaming or boiling. It is best used for slow cooking at low temperatures, and **cannot be used for frying or baking**.

"The cooker consists of two parts that are rigidly and permanently joined to each other. The first is the solar collector, that is a metal surface heated by the sun causing water to boil and producing steam. The second is the insulated steam cooker, in which the saucepan containing food is placed.

"Steam is produced within an hour of sunrise and will continue to be produced for the rest of the day as long as the sun shines on the collector...thus it is possible to cook both the mid-day meal and the evening meal...the solar cooker is a slow-cooking device and is best suited for foods that require long slow boiling, such as stews, cereals and vegetables.

"The construction of the solar cooker is simple with much margin for adaptation to locally available material, therefore, the fabrication instructions serve mainly as a guide to general proportions."

The information and assembly instructions presented are fairly straight-forward, and could be simplified by an adaptive technology center.

Solar Cooker Construction Manual, leaflet with complete construction and assembly information, 18 pages, VITA, 1967 (reprinted 1975), Spanish and French editions also available, $2.00 from VITA.

MATERIALS: plywood, aluminum foil or aluminized Mylar, wood, iron strip
PRODUCTION: simple handtools; attaching the foil or aluminized Mylar is a delicate operation

This is a concise, complete guide to the construc-tion of a cheap and effective solar cooker. It is designed to give enough heat for the cooking needs of a family with 3-5 children under bright, sunny conditions. However, it cannot eliminate the need for other means of cooking. A broad area the size of the cooking pot is heated, rather than a sharply-focused point. A system of concentric rings rather than a parabolic dish is used. The cost of materials is estimated to be $3.00.

Limitations: "The cooker is not useful for cooking meals in early morning or late afternoon. The cooker must be frequently shifted in position during use to take advantage of the sun's position." It takes some time to learn how to cook effectively using the cooker. Because the application of the foil or Mylar to the plywood is a rather delicate task, the authors suggest that 10 or more cookers be built at one time so that an effective method for this can be developed.

Solar Scotch Oven, dimensional drawings with assembly instructions, 8 pages, J. Rodgers, 1974, $3.00 from J. Rodgers, 125 Yale Ave., Somerdale, New Jersey 08083 USA.

MATERIALS:Corrugated cardboard, plywood, silicon sealant, glass sheet, aluminum sheeting, black paint, aluminum foil, heater duct tape, local fibrous insulation.
PRODUCTION: Uses knife, hammer, and saw.

This solar oven can be easily constructed. The text is simple and straightforward. Dimensions are English units only.

Aluminum foil collectors focus the sunlight into an enclosed box, where the temperature rapidly rises. The black paint on the inside walls, and the insulation keep the heat from escaping, and allow the use of cardboard for the oven exterior walls.

Solar ovens are potentially more practical devices than solar reflector cookers when used in areas where food is commonly cooked in ovens. Temperatures reach over 300°F (150°C.). This unit is easily built and repaired. The same solar oven can also be built using the plans included in **Solar Science Projects** (see page 167).

Solar Water Heating for the Handyman, booklet, 32 pages, Steven Paige, 1974, $5.00 from Edmund Scientific Co, 555 Edscorp Bldg, Barrington, N.J. 08007, USA.

This is an extremely clear and well-illustrated introduction to the subject of solar water heating. There are sections on ''How a Solar Water Heater Works'', ''How the Climate Affects Solar Water Heating'', ''Sizing and Using a Solar Water Heater'', and 3 sample water heating system designs with drawings. The designs are for temperate climates, and are intended to be samples only, without details. They assume a water supply system with plumbing already exists.

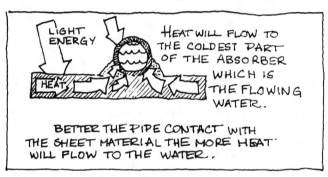

The majority of the book is text that describes collectors and storage tanks, and considerations in installing them, including the thermosiphon principle (to circulate water without a pump), and how to adapt the system to different latitudes. The English is simple and non-technical.

How to Build a Solar Water Heater (Leaflet L-4), leaflet with dimensional drawings/assembly instructions/text, 12 pages, Brace Research Institute, 1965 (revised 1973), $1.25 from BRACE.

MATERIALS: galvanized steel sheet, water pipe, rivets, window glass, rubber strips, oil drum, plumbing float control valve, local fibrous insulation.
PRODUCTION: some soldering and riveting.

'This leaflet describes how to make an inexpensive, yet efficient, solar water heater suitable for domestic or agricultural use in areas enjoying a sunny climate. Although a number of commercial firms manufacture solar water heaters in several countries, these are in the main sophisticated and expensive to buy. The unit described herein has been specially designed to incorporate low-cost materials generally available, even in relatively remote parts of the world.

'This solar water heater can provide from 30 to 40 gallons of hot water per day at a temperature of 130-140 °F. in tropical areas, depending upon the weather. The estimated cost of the materials required for the collector, hot water storage tank and cold water feed tank is the equivalent in local currency of about US$45.00.

'The life of the equipment is about five years with negligible maintenance, after which time it will probably be necessary to spend about $10.00 to replace the oil-drum hot water tank and overhaul the installation.'

Several of these water heaters have been built in Barbados, and Brace has found them to be performing satisfactorily for over seven years.

The leaflet has very complete information. Some plumbing and technical terms used.

Hot Water, booklet, 31 pages, S. and C. Morgan, D. and S. Taylor, 1974 (revised 1975), $2.00 from Hot Water, 350 East Mountain Drive, Santa Barbara Calif. 93108 USA.

''This booklet was written in an effort to combine a variety of materials from diverse sources into an easy-to-follow, technically complete source of information on the construction of home and farm water heating systems.'' The drawings are not to scale.

Drawings, materials lists, and step-by-step construction details are given for 3 kinds of solar collectors, hot-water storage tank connections (pressure and drum), and water heater adaptations for wood and coal-burning units.

The concise, easy-to-read text includes such hints as: ''If you are running a pressure system you must use a storage tank built to operate under pressure. An oil drum and similar units do **not** qualify. They will deform and burst under pressure greater than 10 pounds per square inch.'' And: ''A clean, 30-55 gallon drum will serve as a hot water storage tank for a non-pressure system.''

Of particular interest is the section on water heater adaptations for wood and coal-burning stoves. ''This is a neat system which gives double use every time you light a fire...you get warm and you get hot water too. You can adapt any wood or coal burning unit to include a water heating device. Essentially this is a coil system. A tightly coiled copper tube is inserted into the chimney stack or stove pipe. The water feeds through the coil and into a storage tank. A simple method for coiling the copper tubing is described.'' (A material other than copper might be advised due to cost.)

This remarkable booklet is practical and comprehensive in very few pages.

Water heating using a coiled tube in a stove pipe.

Solar Water Heater, dimensional drawings, 2 large pages, Zomeworks, 1974, $5.00 from Zomeworks, Box 712, Albuquerque, New Mexico 87103 USA.

MATERIALS: copper or steel sheeting, piping, glass and wood.

PRODUCTION: welding and soldering.

Dimensional drawings (English measurements) along with construction ideas and design factors.

The heater is a well-designed flat-plate collector made from tubing placed in a rectangular box that is covered with glass. The inside of the box is painted black. Water flows through the pipes, is heated by the sun, and passes into a storage tank, where it can be used directly. Construction of the tank is not covered. The hot water can be used for washing clothes, bathing, or heating. The plans are straightforward, but experience in working with mechanical drawings would be helpful.

Bread Box Water Heater, (1) 24"X36" blueprint with instructions, Zomeworks, 1975, $2.50 (plus $0.50 postage and handling) from Zomeworks, Box 712, Albuquerque, N.M. 97103 USA.

MATERIALS: wood, possibly aluminum sheeting, insulation, glass, plumbing fittings, silicone or other sealant to keep rainwater out, miscellaneous hardware, 2 old hot water tanks or 30-gallon drums

PRODUCTION: some soldering required, a skilsaw or tablesaw would be useful but not necessary.

Dimensional drawings (English measurements) along with a description of the principles, design, and construction of a simple and effective solar water heater are provided.

Cross section of the bread box water heater

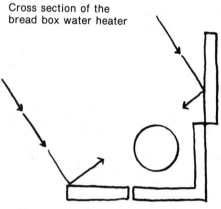

"Two tanks are painted black and placed in a glass-covered insulated box with insulated reflecting doors—the sun shines through the glass onto the tank and also bounces off the reflecting doors onto the tanks...The reflectors on the box serve to wrap the sun around the tanks rather than focus the sun on the tanks...The doors are opened during the day to receive the sun and then closed at night to conserve heat.

"The plans describe the construction of a solar hot water heater using two 30-gallon electric hot water tanks with electric back-up. (30-gallon drums can be substituted for the water heater tanks.) The plans also discuss the principles of the design so that an interested person can vary the construction and know generally what to expect. The plans stress the relative importance of different aspects of the design—where you must be very careful and where you need not be so careful."

Clear and well-illustrated.

Solar Workshops, plans, 4 pages, reprinted from Rain magazine, December 1975, $1.00 plus postage from Rain, 2270 N.W. Irving, Portland, Oregon, 97210, USA.

This is an account of a solar collector that was built as a group demonstration project. The idea of spreading the techniques of building flat-plate collectors through group demonstrations is a very functional part of this reprint.

Instructions on building the collector from wood, iron pipe and corrugated steel using simple construction tools are included. Drawings of the process are provided.

This concept and design could be used elsewhere as a demonstration project for training purposes.

Solar Cooling of Houses in the Tropics

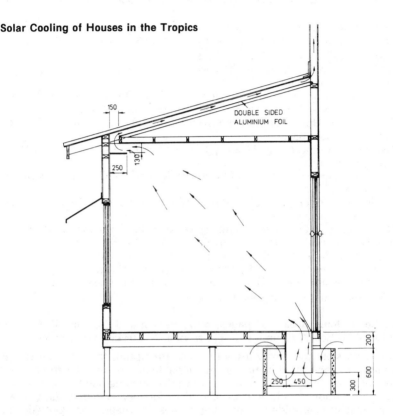

(from UNESCO features)

The sun beating down on the roof of Russell Hill's experimental house in Port Moresby, Papua New Guinea, causes cool air to rise from an air well in the floor. (Dimensions are given in millimeters.)

This house is designed for cooling ventilation by vertical drafts. "The vertical flow of air, creating a steady upward draft (of cooler air from below the house) through the living area, was caused by absorption of solar energy in the roof, and increased by outside air movements...An added advantage is that hot air generated within the building from cooking, washing and lighting, is no longer trapped under the roof but finds ready release through it and even improves the rate of air flow."

"The new system uses similar materials to a normal roof but arranges them differently (the reflective insulation which is normally looped between the timber roof rafters is rearranged to provide air channels between the insulation and a steeper galvanized iron roof.)" Thus the cost is quite small.

Proceedings of the United Nations Conference on New Sources of Energy, Volumes 5 and 6 on solar energy, 423 and 424 pages, $16.00 each from United Nations, Sales Section, Room LX-2300, New York, NY 10017 USA.

The seven-volume **Proceedings** were originally printed in 1964, and reprinted in 1974. They are obviously expensive and hard to find; as of this printing they are still available at the address above. Some major libraries have copies.

The relevant material in volume 6 is a series of 14 articles on the distillation of water. Volume 5 has far more material of interest. The topics are:

a) solar energy for water heating (12 articles);
b) solar energy for space heating (10 articles);
c) solar energy for drying:
  "Use of Solar Energy for Heating Purposes: Solar Drying," by Lof, 8 pages.
  "Drying Crops with Solar Heated Air," by Buelow, 4 pages.
  "Solar Energy Utilization for Crop Drying," by Davis and Lipper, 10 pages.
d) solar energy for cooking:
  "Use of Solar Energy for Heating Purposes: Solar Cooking," by Lof, 11 pages, (excellent).
  "Laboratory and Field Studies of Plastic Reflector Solar Cookers," by Duffie, Lof, and Beck, 6 pages.
  "Design and Performance of Folding-Umbrella Type Solar Cooker," by Lof and Fester, 5 pages.
  "Report on Tests Conducted Using the Telkes Solar Oven and the Wisconsin Solar Stove over the period July to Sept. 1959," by FAO, 6 pages.
  "A Cylindro-Parabolic Solar Cooker," by Prata, 11 pages.
  "Cheap But Practical Solar Kitchens," by Stam, 11 pages.
  "Practical Solar Cooking Ovens," by Telkes and Andrassy, 5 pages.
e) solar energy and heat storage (3 articles).

The Solar Home Book, 293 pages, by Anderson and Riordan, 1976, $7.50 from Cheshire Books, Church Hill, Harrisville, NH 03450, USA; or WETS.

This is possibly the best American book attempting to make the design principles of solar-heated homes understandable and useable for the average person. Stresses 'passive' systems (in which the building itself acts as a solar collector and storage unit, without special circulatory systems). Also covers systems that can be added to existing homes. A chapter on do-it-yourself methods includes insulation, window box heaters, and attached greenhouses. Altogether, there are about 40 pages on the design of solar water heaters.
  "Homes can be designed to respond to local climates...Simple low-technology methods are cheaper and more reliable than the many complex, high-technology devices being employed to harness the sun's energy...Anyone with good building skills and a knowledge of materials can take advantage of these simple methods..." Highly recommended for Americans and other people in temperate climates interested in building a solar-heated home.

FURTHER REFERENCES ON ENERGY: SOLAR

ENERGY: GENERAL, see all the reviews in this section.

Other Homes and Garbage has a very good section on active solar energy systems; see review on page 42.

Energy Primer, see review on page 130.

Radical Technology, see review on page 35.

Alternative Sources of Energy magazine, see review on page 282.

ENERGY: WOOD, SAWDUST AND RICE HULL STOVES

Energy: Wood, Sawdust and Rice Hull Stoves

*Wood is the most commonly used and oldest fuel in the world. Eric Eckholm, in a widely published article which has now been included in the book **Losing Ground** (see review, page 76), identifies the shortage of firewood as the most important fuel crisis now facing much of the developing world. Some of the publications listed here are thus intended to promote the more efficient use of wood as a fuel; stoves are more efficient than open fires, for example, and they can be simply made. If stoves are already used, the designs included here will not necessarily be an improvement; this is one area that needs considerably more attention from appropriate technologists.*

Many of these publications cover how to make wood burning stoves from used oil drums. Some are for space heating (home heating) in cold climates, while others are for both heating and cooking. It is relatively easy to convert a heating stove into one that could be used for cooking, but remember that such a stove will also continue to heat the kitchen area, something that may or may not be desirable. The methods of making a stove out of an oil drum are not difficult, as can be seen from the drawings in this section. Welding is desirable but not always necessary, and usually the rest of the fabrication can be done locally.

The most interesting stove designs we've seen are those built to use sawdust or rice hulls as fuel. Normally these materials do not burn well. These suggested designs create a constant flow of oxygen next to the outer burning surface of the compressed rice hulls or sawdust. We've had tea made from hot water boiled in just a few minutes on one of these (see sketches).

Stoves can also provide hot water. A coil of metal pipe placed inside the stovepipe will heat water that is circulated through it. (If using copper tube, be sure to fill it with sand before coiling it, to prevent it from breaking.). There is a drawing illustrating such a coil system on page 171. (For other methods of heating water, see ENERGY: SOLAR).

Rice Hull Stove

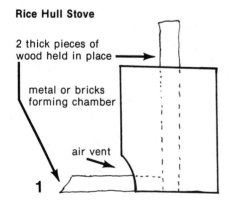

2 thick pieces of wood held in place ➞

metal or bricks forming chamber

air vent

1

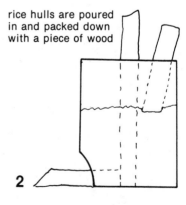

rice hulls are poured in and packed down with a piece of wood

2

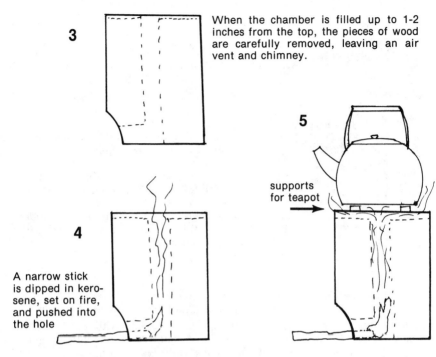

3 When the chamber is filled up to 1-2 inches from the top, the pieces of wood are carefully removed, leaving an air vent and chimney.

5

supports for teapot →

4

A narrow stick is dipped in kerosene, set on fire, and pushed into the hole

This is a stove found in parts of Bali that uses rice hulls as the fuel. Sawdust could also be used. The burning stick should be slowly pushed into the opening, as the end of it burns up. It is important that this stick is no more than 1/2 the diameter of the thick sticks used to form the air openings; otherwise it will block the essential flow of air through the system. A one-meter length of wood 2cm in diameter and a full chamber of rice hulls is said to provide a usable cooking flame for 2 hours. Such units could be of different sizes—the exact dimensions are not important.

The Woodburner's Handbook, booklet, 94 pages, David Havens, 1973, $2.95 from WETS.

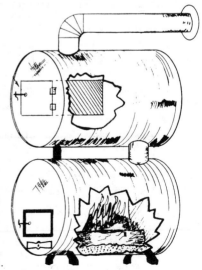

This book covers both wood heating and cooking. It includes sections on cutting wood, techniques of cooking on a wood stove, and a very good chapter on "How to Build Practical Wood Stoves" from 55-gallon oil drums. Chimneys are also covered. Other sections include fireplaces and wood stoves for heating. Many practical ideas and tips are to be found in this very complete "compilation of skills" for woodburning. The book is suitable anywhere wood can be used as a fuel for cooking, and places with colder climates where wood heating is appropriate.

The most complete woodburning book.

Yukon stove

The Working Woodburner, booklet, 31 pages, D. Dahlin, 1976, $1.65 from WETS.

This book contains an overview of wood heaters, how to use and select firewood, cooking and heating stoves, cooking in fireplaces, smoke ovens, and fireplace water heating. Explains many general techniques for efficient woodburning.

The individual designer should find this book helpful in providing general guidelines for building and installing stoves, even though there are no specific plans included. (Much of this information is included in the **Energy Primer**.)

The Complete Book of Heating with Wood, book, 123 pages, Larry Gay, 1974, $3.95 from Garden Way Publishing, Charlotte, Vermont 05445, USA.

The author covers many different aspects of heating with wood, concentrating on ways to burn wood efficiently. The chapters include information on choosing the proper type of fuelwood, log splitting, cutting enough wood without destroying forests, woodlot management, efficient stove designs, tips on ventilation, and using heat exchangers in the chimney to heat water. There are quite a few drawings of stoves, intended as ideas, not detailed designs.

Some parts of the book are aimed at American uses, such as a section on choosing fuelwood that includes North American trees and climate considerations. In general, though, there is much in the way of general techniques for burning wood efficiently; there are few specific details, so this book's usefulness is limited to an introduction to wood-burning techniques.

How to Build an Oil Barrel Stove, booklet, 24 pages, Ole Wik, $1.95 from Alaska Northwest Publishing Co., Box 4-EEE, Anchorage, Alaska 99509 USA.

MATERIALS: oil drum, sheet metal
PRODUCTION: metal cutting tools, anvil, hacksaw.

This wood burning stove is primarily for cooking. Whereas most oil-drum stove designs retain the round shape of the drum, this design is a rectangular shape which provides the user with a fairly large cooking surface.

''The author has provided simple directions for making this stove...requiring shaping and assembling 12 pieces of metal cut from a discarded oil barrel, entirely without welding equipment or power

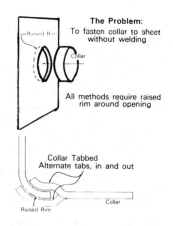

The Problem:
To fasten collar to sheet without welding

All methods require raised rim around opening

Collar Tabbed
Alternate tabs, in and out

tools." Very well illustrated with photos and dimensional drawings.

The author is experienced at metal-working with simple tools, and includes many helpful suggestions, such as how to make a metal-cutting tool out of a scrap piece of metal. A good set of plans.

Oil Drum Handicraft, article with plans, 7 pages in The Mother Earth News magazine #22, July 1973 (see PERIODICALS), by Gary Brooks.

This article covers some of the different uses the author has found for used oil drums, among them the Yukon Stove, developed in Alaska, for cooking and heating with wood. The article is more descriptive than detailed, covering other things such as a drum water heater,

The design is simple. It also is somewhat original in that it has a flat surface for cooking. Some welding is required for this, however.

Oil Drum Stove, article with plans, 3 pages in Alternative Sources of Energy magazine #21, June 1976 (see PERIODICALS), by John McGeorge.

MATERIALS: oil drum, sheet iron, tin pan
PRODUCTION: simple hand tools

The author discusses making a wood-burning stove out of a grease barrel or oil drum. Includes information on the damper (which regulates air flow) and chimney. Photos are included.

This stove is for space heating only. The individual builder could modify it for cooking, however. No special wood is required for fuel. The article contains clear but not detailed instructions.

The $1.50 Woodburning Stove: this stove is made out of a small oil drum. It can conserve possibly as much as 1/2 the wood that would be used in open fire cooking.

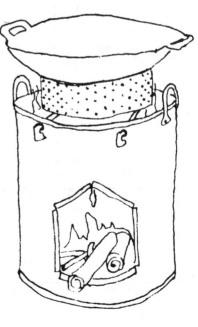

The Chula Stove (Technical Bulletin #8), booklet, 26 pages, D. Brett, 1970, free to serious groups, from DTWS.

"The purpose of this bulletin is to act as an information guide to the history and development, construction and usage of the Chula Stove...Basically this stove consists of a firebox leading into a clockwise flue duct having four circular openings. The first three holes serve as pot seats for cooking while the fourth opens to the chimney."

The unit is cast in four sections, for easy handling and replacement of damaged parts. There is a removable hotplate directly over the firebox. Alternative uses are described. Concrete is the construction material; wood is the fuel. Photographs, drawings, and exploded views are included. English measurements. Clear instructions for making the molds and building the oven.

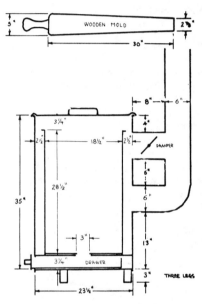

Figure 2.—Design of the experimental double-drum stove.

Double Drum Sawdust Stove (Research Note #NE-208 and Photo Story #30), leaflet, 7 pages, J. Wartluft, 1975, free from Northeastern Forest Experiment Station, 6816 Market St., Upper Darby, Pennsylvania 19082, USA.

MATERIALS: one 55- and one 30-gallon oil drum, 6-inch stove pipes.

PRODUCTION: some brazing and metal drilling.

This is a brief description of experiments done with a sawdust burning stove, which consists of an inner drum filled with packed sawdust, and an outer drum used to channel updrafts. Rice hulls could also be used as the fuel. Photos are included as well as a simple dimensional drawing of the original design (reproduced here). Installation and operation are also described.

These two papers are short but concise, providing enough information to enable someone to build a stove using this design. Although designed for space heating, this stove could easily be adapted for cooking.

Sawdust-Burning Space Heater Stove, dimensional drawings with text, 9 pages, D. Huntington, 1975, $2.00 from META.

MATERIALS: 55- and 15- gallon oil drums, steel pieces, bolts and stovepipe.
PRODUCTION: some welding desirable but not essential.

This is a stove very similar to the one above, which can be used for heating or cooking. The plans are easy to understand. Welding facilities are recommended but not necessary for construction. The stove provides a steady heat output. Ideas are given for using the stove as the basis of a forced air heating system in colder climates, where it may be placed in a room apart from the area to be heated. Rice hulls can be used as a fuel in both this design and the preceding design.

ENERGY: METHANE GAS

Energy: Methane Gas

The use of methane gas plants as a source of fuel and fertilizer is a practice only recently introduced in this century. The process of bacterial decomposition has occurred in nature since life began—plants and animals die and are recycled to sustain life on the planet. In the presence of oxygen, organic material 'composts' (undergoes aerobic decomposition). When decomposition occurs in the absence of oxygen (anaerobic conditions), methane gas is produced, and the liquid remainder is rich in nitrogen and other nutrients.

The natural occurrence of methane (the bubbling gas seen in ponds where animal manures have been dumped), can be duplicated. Water- and air-tight containers (called 'digesters') are built, either as pits lined with bricks, concrete or stabilized earth (if this can be waterproofed), or as steel, concrete, or brick tanks. Manures and other organic wastes (after being suitably diluted) can be stored and processed by either the 'batch' or 'continuous' methods. Premixing chambers, digestion tanks, and effluent discharge ponds are linked by pipes. The gas is collected in storage tanks and distributed by smaller gas pipes to serve as a fuel for cooking, lighting, or operating small engines. There are important factors to control in operating an effective methane plant—temperature, pH, detention time, loading rate, carbon/nitrogen ratio and other variables. Different designs and techniques based on local environmental factors and cultural practices have evolved over the last 30 years.

The books in this section as a whole adequately cover the fundamentals and practical design and maintenance considerations associated with building methane plants for communities and farms. Besides the work of two important pioneers, India's Ram Bux Singh and South African L. John Fry, we have included sources which provide information and advice free of charge, although not in as detailed fashion. All sources agree that methane plants are not to be isolated projects, but linked with the total development scheme. The emphasis is on 'integrated systems' in which the digesters are combined with livestock production (pigs, chickens, or cows), and the effluent provides a rich environment for aquaculture (algae, fish, eels, shrimp, etc.) and a fertilizer for agriculture, when applied dried or diluted to the soil.

At the present time many myths and misconceptions have been generated about the methane digestion process. Those who see it as a panacea for solving the interrelated problems of waste treatment, fuel shortages, environmental health, and food production, are often disappointed when results do not measure up to expectations. It is still a risky proposition, for example, to use digesters as a method of handling human waste—only regular composting, when properly controlled, will kill the pathogens found in human excreta (the composting temperature is 60°C, while digesters average only 35°C). Quite often the smooth functioning of 'integrated systems' is interrupted when algae is destroyed by rains, scum builds up inside the digesters, fish are killed by overly acid effluent, and so forth.

As is true so often in the field of appropriate technology, the major considerations are generally not engineering problems. Obstacles to widespread public acceptance of methane schemes in many developing countries are a combination of lack of: information, designs and materials appropriate to the area, and financial support from government and private sources, among other reasons. India, due to an active village extension and credit process, and the enthusiastic involvement of groups such as the Khadi and Village Industries Commission, has over 10,000 methane plants in operation. Reports indicate that China is proceeding rapidly with methane plant construction schemes.

There are few, if any, small-scale working digesters in the United States, despite a great deal of recent interest. The digester seems best suited for use with dairy farms and perhaps community waste treatment. In temperate climates, as indicated in the Energy Primer's Methane section, much energy is lost in heating the digester and compressing the gas, and the benefits may not warrant the expense.

The digester still has a great potential in hot climates, but we still do not know of a simple, low-cost design suitable for a poor farmer. A family really needs at least 2 penned large animals (about enough manure for 2 cubic meters of digestion space) to successfully operate even a small digester. The highly-publicized large numbers of digesters in India and Taiwan are to our knowledge mostly owned by rich farmers, and usually cost at least $250—a very large sum for most poor farmers. This high price seems to be primarily for two reasons: 1) the high cost of materials to build the main tank (cement, bricks) and air-tight cover (some kind of metal that does not corrode easily); and 2) experimenters have concentrated on the elegant 'Cadillacs', and neglected the development of less impressive, lower capacity designs that could cost significantly less.

It is clear that there is much room for improvement in the literature on methane applications in developing countries. An impartial, practical, and readable book containing essential information and drawings from various successful sources, is in order. Community Aid Abroad, the Australian affiliate of OXFAM, has undertaken to produce such a publication. That effort will be coordinated by a former VIA volunteer who worked on methane projects in Indonesia. The book will also deal with the important problems of scale, safety precautions, and low-cost but effective designs, and suggest directions for further experimentation. This book will be available free of charge or at cost to concerned groups in developing countries. Readers are encouraged to send inquiries to Mr. Neil O'Sullivan, 75 Brunswick Street, Fitzroy, Victoria 3065, Australia.

Methane: Proceedings of a One-Day Seminar, booklet, 51 pages, Dr. Leo Pyle and Peter Fraenkel, 1975, L1.10 or US$2.25 from ITDG.

This summarizes the presentations given at a seminar organized by the Methane Panel of ITDG. Present were individuals active in the research, development, and operation of methane digesters both in England and the developing countries. Valuable as a secondary reference for those who have had experience with methane or would like more advanced background information on various digester schemes. Two excellent articles included are "Food, Fuel and Development" (which describes an integrated methane homestead system concept) and "Costs and Benefits of Methane Generation in Poor Countries." Addresses of people who would be able to provide help on specific aspects of methane production are included.

Methane: Planning a Digester, book, 150 pages, Peter-John Meynell, 1976, $4.50 from META.

This is a well-balanced book surveying the current and historical uses for the methane digestion process. It realistically assesses the potential of digesters as sources of fertilizer, fuel, and income. Written from a practical planner's point of view, with excellent treatment of the subjects of safety, economics and field developments. While intended for conditions in England, much of the information is valuable throughout the world. This book does **not** address the conditions facing poor farmers in developing countries, nor does it provide a design. It does cover basic principles, requirements, problems and advantages, making it a valuable general reference book.

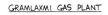

GRAMLAXMI GAS PLANT

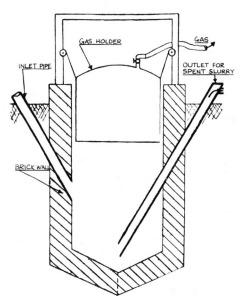

Bio-Gas Plant: Generating Methane From Organic Wastes, and Designs with Specifications, book, 90 pages, Ram Bux Singh, $10.00 from WETS.

This is a very thorough treatment of the possibilities and uses of methane. What makes this book extremely useful is that it is not too academic—just a practical look at methane that includes illustrations and technical drawings of various types and sizes of digesters. The book combines two booklets that were originally available separately.

The first half of the book is a general discussion of how methane digestion works, what factors to consider in the design of a methane plant, how to use the gas that is produced, construction techniques and suggestions (including detailed instructions for building a few different types of digesters—even one for using vegetable scraps and waste). Also included are descriptions of various experiments with bio-gas in India and the U.S., along with a short economic analysis of the relative production costs of different sizes of digesters in both of these countries. These range from small, one-family units (100 cubic feet of gas per day) to large industrial facilities (2,000 cubic feet per day).

The second half of the book is devoted to drawings of 20 different types of digester designs, with English measurements. The drawings are fairly detailed, with a range of sizes being represented in the designs. Drawings are also presented for gas storage tanks. The construction materials required range from cement, bricks, and sand, to steel tanking, iron angle bars, and piping. The materials necessary for each project are clearly indicated.

One point should be emphasized. To build a digester from these plans assumes a prior knowledge of the materials and construction techniques to a small degree. Being an expert in the field is by no means a prerequisite, but at least some ability in reading technical drawings and familiarity with construction techniques is recommended. The instructions in the first half of the book give the general steps to be followed in a clear fashion, but are not overly explicit.

This book would be very useful to anyone with access to the necessary materials. Very complete.

We believe essentially the same published material is still available in the form of two booklets, with the above titles, from the Gobar Gas Research Station, Ajitmal, Etawah (U.P.), India. We do not have price information on this, however.

Small-Scale Bio-Gas Plant in India, 19 pages, Case Study #6 in the Canadian Hunger Foundation's **Appropriate Technology Handbook**, 1976, (see review page 32).

This is one chapter in the above book, but it deserves special mention. This case study survey of bio-gas plant theory and practice (covering the Indian circular sump digester designs) is the best introduction and summary on the subject currently available, to our knowledge. Clearly worded and backed by straightforward illustrations and facts, this chapter covers more ground in less space than any other source, including Fry and Ram Bux Singh.

Two designs for methane gas burners for cooking

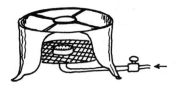
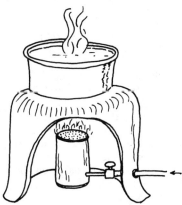

From the information presented in the case study, one could conceivably proceed with the construction of a methane plant geared to specific needs (if the builder has sufficient general construction experience). A few points not covered include adequate design features for regulating pressure on the gas covers (included in the WHO monograph on **Composting**—see page 85), flametrap and scum controlling devices (Fry's **Practical Building of Methane Power Plants** thoroughly deals with them), and more precise drawings on gas appliances. The reader should be advised that control over air-intake can be achieved by simple means, such as sliding valves over control air inlets (inclusion of a 1/16'' gas jet at the gascock and several 1/4'' holes bored in to the pipe between the gascock and the burner, covered by the adjustable slide—usually a piece of sheet metal soldered as a tube to cover the pipe.)

"The bio-gas plants that were developed by this research were ideal for farms with 4 or 5 cows and also for communities with a minimum population of 50. A larger system simply requires larger numbers of the same basic unit. Construction of the plants is labor intensive, and almost all of the necessary skills and resources are available in rural areas. The local farmers own, manage, maintain and control their bio-gas plants."

"The initial capital outlay is relatively high. The plant described in more detail cost approximately Rs. 2000 (U.S.$300) in 1973. However, study of the operation of bio-gas plants over the last 10 years indicates that the initial cost is recovered within 6 years in the form of fuel, fertilizer and improved crop yields. Maintenance and operating costs are negligible."

Gobar Gas Scheme, informational leaflets, 1975, free to serious groups from Khadi & Village Industries Commission, "Gramodaya", 3, Irla Road, Vile Parle (West), Bombay 400 056, India.

This very valuable package of information on methane comes from the Directorate of Gobar Gas Scheme, a division of the Khadi and Village Industries Commission of Bombay. Continuing in the Ghandhian tradition of village self-reliance, this active group has been promoting gobar (cow dung) gas plants for many years with a great deal of success in India. Their work includes research, documentation, and extension work throughout the country.

The Commission also provides an invaluable service crucial to promoting methane gas plants on a mass scale: they arrange for low-interest, long-term loans as starting capital for small farmers. We highly recommend this packet of information, and suggest donations or book exchanges to those who can afford it.

The designs presented are those of the Indian circular sump digester models (see drawing in this section). Very helpful itemized cost analyses are presented. The basic design has been adapted for capacities from 2 to 85 cubic meters, simply by adjusting the dimensions proportionally as needed. This is a versatile scheme suitable for conditions in India and other nations. The information package includes:

a) Gobar Gas—Why and How: a concise 17-page booklet explaining the basics, and where to go for further information inside India;
b) Gobar Gas—Manure for Farm and Fuel for Cooking: a small idea leaflet comparing the energy and fertilizer values of methane gas and effluent to other materials;
c) History of the Development of the Gobar Gas Scheme in India: a 10-page paper summarizing the value of methane plants in India's overall development effort;
d) Details of Efficient Gas Appliances Used for Gobar Gas: a small illustrated flyer showing the burners, stoves and lamps available commercially in India for effective use of the gas; (we suggest that interested parties in other countries either ask for more detailed plans for these devices or import samples so that they can be adapted and duplicated cheaply by local cottage industries);
e) A set of 4 dimensional drawings with the overall design and various details such as gas covers, pipe parts, inlet and outlet, accompanied by a list of materials required for a 3 cubic meter (106 cubic foot) capacity vertical gas plant.

Methane Digesters for Fuel Gas and Fertilizer, booklet, 44 pages, R. Merrill and L. John Fry, New Alchemy Institute Newsletter #3, 1973, $3.00 from WETS.

MATERIALS: inner tubes, plastic tubing, 3-5 gallon containers, oil drums.
PRODUCTION: some welding.

This is a condensed version of Fry's larger book, boiling the design and operation of digesters down to a shorter form. Includes practical information on how to determine your particular gas requirements. Also included are instructions on how to build a sump digester (batch loading with oil drums), and

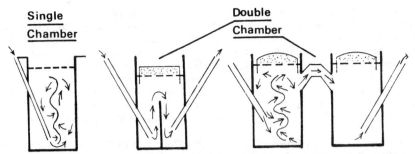

Single Chamber

Double Chamber

Three different designs for the main tanks, showing the motion of the slurry

detailed instructions on an 'inner tube' digester. The latter design apparently does not produce a practical volume of gas. It could, however, be utilized as an experimental/demonstration model.

This publication is shorter and briefer than the two preceding publications, but it covers essentially the same material.

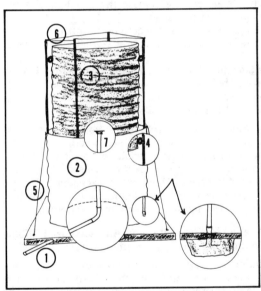

Figure 18: Gas holder. 1) *Gas flow in and out.* 2) *Water tank.* 3) *Gas holder tank.* 4) *Roller on guide pipe.* 5) *Stay wires on guide pipe.* 6) *Cross bracing.* 7) *Top of gas pipe with protective plate.*

Practical Building of Methane Power Plants for Rural Energy Independence, book, 96 pages, L. John Fry, 1974, $12.00 from WETS.

Fry is a pioneer in digester designs—he owns a large pig farm (1000 pigs) in South Africa. This book grew out of his 20 year's experience in experimenting with the production of methane gas. For Fry, methane digestion is valuable because it can provide energy for cooking and lighting, as well as solving the problem of disposing large amounts of pig manure by converting it into fertilizer. It should be noted that the installations Fry discusses range in size from a large farm to industrial applications in digesting sewage.

Approximately half the book is devoted to recounting the author's experiences in experimentation with various types of digesters. For example, he discusses how to mix the manure for digestion; clogging due to scum; sludge; gas holder design; and more. The second half of the book deals with each of these areas in detail. Topics include: Biology of Digestion, Raw Materials, Digester Design and Operation, and Gas and Sludge Usage. Finally, one chapter is devoted to suggested plans and the construction of three different types of digesters.

Throughout this book, Fry is continuously giving hints, suggestions, and hard facts based on his experience in every phase of digester designing and operation. The book is very useful not for step-by-step instructions, but for someone who can use the ideas and go on to design his own methane installation. An excellent guidebook for someone who is somewhat familiar with construction techniques and materials. This book covers many of the fine points such as temperature, safety precautions in burning methane mixtures, and the entire methane-sludge-algae pond-fertilizer cycle. More of these obscure fine points are covered here than in the Ram Bux Singh book, while the latter is more instruction-oriented. Fry's book is a good general reference.

Process Feasibility Study: The Anaerobic Digestion of Dairy Cow Manure at the State Reformatory Honor Farm in Monroe, Washington, book, 119 pages, 1976, $8.00 from ECOTOPE Group, Non-Profit/Research, P.O. Box 618, Snohomish, Washington 98290, USA.

This is a thorough account of a large-scale digester project using dairy cow manure (now in operation). The system has two huge agricultural storage tanks of 378 cubic meter capacity, gas compressor, propane tanks to hold the compressed gas, heat exchangers between effluent and input lines, and a novel gas recirculation system which is claimed to eliminate the problem of scum accumulation, due to the agitation effect of the gas.

The project cost $70,000, a huge sum in most developing countries. Some of the information might still be useful for a dairy cooperative methane scheme.

The Anaerobic Digestion of Livestock Wastes to Produce Methane: 1946 to June 1975, A Bibliography with Abstracts, 103 pages, G. Shadduck and J. Moore, 1975, $2.00 surface mail from Department of Agricultural Engineering, University of Minnesota, St. Paul, Minnesota 55108, USA.

This annotated bibliography surveys the anaerobic digestion process literature. The authors have described the contents and evaluated each entry. Intended to give a broad overview of all available resources, so that readers' questions may be answered, as well as additional questions raised. Addresses are given only for the more popular books. There is an excellent scientific analysis of fuel and fertilizer results from different animal manures. Recommended for those already familiar with methane or research techniques.

Methane Generation by Anaerobic Fermentation: An Annotated Bibliography, 64 pages, by Freeman and Pyle, 1977, price unknown, from ITDG.

This "bibliography is intended for people directly involved in building, designing and improving methane generators in the Third World...The majority of the literature available relates to large municipal systems...(The authors) had to include many sources which do not apply directly to the sort of wastes to be treated, or the size of the facility, but which nevertheless give sound information on the process and its fundamentals...(They have tried) to include at least one sound and basic reference on each problem area."

The booklet has a description of the process with diagrams, and a glossary of terms. Topic areas are: general background reading, factors affecting the performance of digesters, use of slurry as a fertilizer, and factors in the design of digesters. There is an address list of journals, publishers and institutions. Nothing is included on the use of family-size digesters in China, which has rapidly become the world leader in this field (1.3 million units built in 1976).

FURTHER REFERENCES ON ENERGY: METHANE GAS

ENERGY: GENERAL, see all the reviews in this section.

ENERGY: PEDAL-POWER

Energy: Pedal-Power

The bicycle is in many respects the most efficient machine ever developed by man. Bicycling is a more effective use of human energy than walking. Motorized vehicles, which multiply the speed of a bicycle by 2-5 times, do this at a greatly increased cost in initial capital, complexity, maintenance, and petroleum consumption.

Pedaling is probably the most efficient use of the muscles of the human body. The stationary use of pedal power is particularly appropriate when relatively small amounts of power are needed at irregular intervals, or when a light, mobile power source is desirable (such as pedal threshers and winnowers which can be easily carried to the fields and used there.) Pedal-power, using either a bicycle-like pedal arrangement or a treadle mechanism, can be used to power a variety of agricultural equipment, shop tools, water pumps, grain grinders, and electric generators.

The 'dynapod' consists of a stationary bicycle frame, seat, handlebars, and pedals which drive a series of chains or belts. The number of revolutions per minute (rpm) can be adjusted by changing the pulleys or gears used. Such a unit can in fact be built almost entirely out of wood.

Many pieces of equipment have the bicycle chain drive or treadle mechanism built as part of the unit. Usually it is necessary to add a heavy circular flywheel to the system. This smooths out the high and low power portions of a person's natural pedaling rhythm, making it possible to maintain constant speed and power. A flywheel can be made out of concrete poured in a flat circular mold (with a strong bearing in the center); a bicycle wheel that has the inner tube filled with water (an extra valve must be added to let the air escape); a bicycle wheel that has had cement poured between the spokes; or a large wooden or metal wheel or gear. A flywheel used on a potter's wheel would serve quite well.

Three-wheeled rickshaws (pedi-cabs) and carts can be improved with the addition of a low-cost 3-speed gearbox (see article below entitled **Pedal Power**). This would enable easier starting when loaded, facilitate hill climbing, and make the operation of the vehicle less wearing on the driver. Another innovation for 3-wheeled machines with 2-wheeled rear drive is a bicycle differential, which enables the two wheels to rotate at different speeds as the machine goes around corners. This makes the machine more stable, and allows wider versions to be made.

In addition to the pedal-power articles listed in this section, there are about 20 designs for tools that use pedal-power that can be found in other parts of the Sourcebook (see FURTHER REFERENCES at the end of this section).

Pedal Power, article, 18 pages, S. Wilson, 1975, in **Lectures on Socially Appropriate Technology** (see review on page 34).

This is the most valuable article on pedal-power we've seen. 26 drawings and photos. The author discusses the energy efficiency of the bicycle compared to other modes of transport; and we discover that a person on a bicycle is the most energy efficient moving thing that exists (measured in calories per unit of weight per unit of distance). By measuring the energy output of a bicyclist, Wilson has found that "the normal cyclist has an expenditure of about 75 watts—roughly 0.1 horsepower...the fullest sustainable output of the human body, using the right muscles, right motions, and the right speed."

The author gives consideration to stationary pedal-power, used to operate pumps, for example. A rotary pump is shown with pedal attachments. "It is such a simple type of pump and suitable for direct pedaling for heads of 3 to 8 meters that it is, I think, worth developing." Wilson notes that some traditional water-lifting devices in India require 4 men to raise the same volume of water that one man on a pedal-power pump could lift.

An optimum stationary pedal-power unit, called a 'dynapod' is described. "It takes the drive forward and you can gear it down for something like a winch or gear it up for a winnowing fan...One of the requirements in a stationary application is a flywheel to steady out the torque, and here the flywheel is made from a bicycle wheel with cement filling in between the spokes."

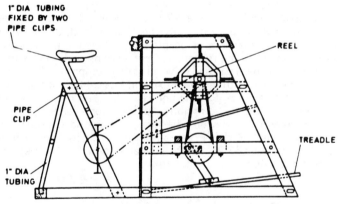

Peanut thresher showing options for either pedal-drive while seated or treadle-operation while standing

Other pedal-powered machines shown are the traditional Chinese square pallet chain pump (also called the 'water ladder'); a two-man powered milling machine; a hand-driven winnowing machine which could be adapted to use pedal-power; a peanut thresher (see drawing); and a cassava grinder.

Notes on an improved cycle rickshaw (three-wheeled pedicab) are included, explaining how two bicycle 'freewheels' are combined to form a differential—a device that allows a rickshaw with two rear wheels to turn corners with the two wheels rotating at different speeds. The author suggests a design for local production of bicycles in developing countries, relying on sheet steel and angle iron instead of imported steel tubes; he has built prototypes. The 'Oxtrike,' a rickshaw using these materials, also has a very low-cost 3-speed gearbox to allow easy starting and climbing hills.

Highly recommended.

Cycling Toward Energy Efficiency, article, 5 pages, Diana Branch, in May 1976 issue of Organic Gardening & Farming Magazine, reprint available (price unknown), from Energy Cycle Reprint, Rodale Press, 33 E. Minor Street, Emmaus, Pa. 18049, USA.

This is an account of experiments using pedal-power to drive a variety of equipment. Some drawings and photos are included. OG&F's Research and Development department found that the following equipment was well-suited to pedal-power: grinding food scraps for fish ponds, grinding grain into flour, grinding meat, and operating a potter's wheel, jewelry lathe, sharpening stone, buffer, and corn sheller.

Potentially the most valuable application was running a water pump that they claim will pump 3,500 gallons per hour when used with a 1½-inch inside diameter hose (a garden hose will only carry 420 gallons per hour). This was used to fill the fish tanks, presumably lifting the water only a couple of feet. "It's a job that takes all the rider can give—but what satisfaction to see that stream of water gushing 5 or 6 feet! With a nozzle he could send it 30 feet, showing that a pedal-powered pump could easily irrigate a garden from a pond or creek."

The pedal-power unit seemed to save about ⅔ of the time normally required to do a task such as grain grinding. "Just as important, the bike gives people a big edge in endurance. On a hand crank, the stronger arm does most of the work."

The most recent prototype was designed to be switched from one task to another. A small platform table can be raised, lowered, or swiveled, according to the tool to be used. A flywheel was added, and its momentum eliminates "the unevenness most people have in their rate of pedaling and makes work smoother." The researchers are working on a device to allow an ordinary bicycle to be harnessed to drive all of this equipment. This would save some of the expense of cutting up an existing bicycle to build the unit.

When attached to a generator, the unit could be used by an average person to put out about 75 watts for 10 minutes, and less for a longer period of time.

The author notes that "it won't be long until we have refined the cycle enough to offer plans." Rodale Press is working on a pedal power book; it will be about 150 pages, cost $5.95, and be available in mid-1977. (See page 196.)

Highly recommended.

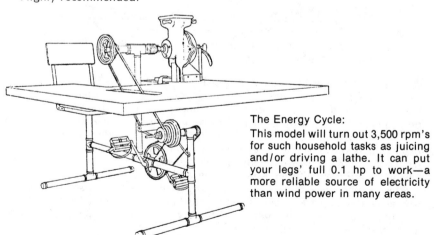

The Energy Cycle:
This model will turn out 3,500 rpm's for such household tasks as juicing and/or driving a lathe. It can put your legs' full 0.1 hp to work—a more reliable source of electricity than wind power in many areas.

Bike-Generator Plans, drawings with text, 13 pages, A. Andersen, 1975, $2.00 from Homestead Industries, Ananda Village, Nevada City, Calif. 95959 USA.

MATERIALS: auto generator, voltage regulator, and battery; (2) small rubber wheels; ½'' steel rod; ball bearings; 6'' pulley.

PRODUCTION: simple hand tools.

This unit can be used as a 12-volt emergency power source, a remote area permanent power source, a mechanical power source (to operate grinders and threshers directly), or an automobile battery charger.

The text is straightforward, with dimensional drawings using English units only. Those who wrote the text are confident that anyone with simple mechanical and carpentry skills can build it.

The bicycle can be quickly connected and disconnected to the bike-generator, so normal use of the bicycle is not affected, and the cost of the bicycle need not be included in the cost of the unit. "For about one hour's pedaling a vigorous person could store enough energy in the battery to light a 15-watt fluorescent tube (equivalent to a 45-watt incandescent bulb) for about 8 hours, or a small TV or record player for about 8 hours, or a radio for several weeks." This unit might be of great interest in rural areas where motorcycle or car batteries are used to operate radios.

Foot Power (**Bike Generator Plans**), 2 pages, 1976, $1 from North Shore Ecology Center, 3070 Dato, Highland Park, Illinois 60035 USA.

These are non-detailed drawings, with very little text. They show mechanical setup, and electrical wiring; the general idea of using a bike to run a generator. Three different designs. Materials required are the same as the preceding plans.

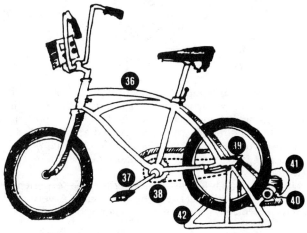

The system provides a 12-volt power source and can be used to charge auto batteries. The bike can also be used to operate grinders and pumps.

Note: It is generally said that human beings can produce about 75 watts when pedaling at a comfortable speed that can be maintained for an hour or more. Also, 12-volt electricity requires very large diameter wires if carried over any distance; otherwise there will be large losses of electricity due to the resistance of the wire.

Transport Bicycle, dimensional drawings with text and photos, 17 pages, free to serious groups (we suggest you send one of your publications in exchange), or $2.00 airmail outside Africa, from the Dar es Salaam Liberation Support Group, P.O. Box 2099, Dar es Salaam, Tanzania.

MATERIALS: bicycle, angle bar, tubing, wood strips.

PRODUCTION: some welding and machining.

This leaflet describes a metal frame that can fit onto an existing bicycle for carrying large loads (up to 200 kgs.). The operator walks alongside the bicycle. The intent was to design a transporter that could be used on rough terrain where cars and trucks can't go, yet could carry loads much heavier than humans can carry. These objectives appear to have been met.

The parts of the transport bicycle
·(see also photo at the end of this section)

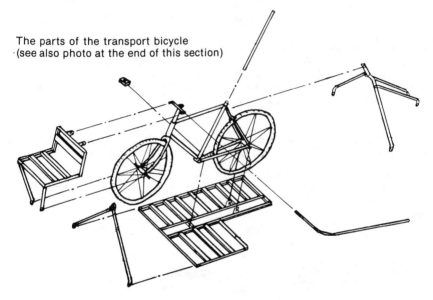

The plans include photographs of the prototype model, with dimensional drawings showing the construction quite clearly. The frame is welded and bolted together, then attached to the bicycle. It is the authors' intent that this design be adapted to different areas, not copied exactly. "As the bicycles on which the transporter is based will be of different origin, it is not possible beforehand to give a definite set of measurements...the exact size is to be determined from case to case."

Construction is straightforward, although some experience machining, welding, and working with metal will be necessary. A very practical design, particularly for narrow paths where a cart cannot be used.

Bicycles: A Case Study of Indian Experience, book, 87 pages, UNIDO, 1969, $1.00 (Sales No.: E.69.II.B.30) from United Nations, Sales Section Room LX 2300, New York, N.Y. 10017, USA; or UNIDO (United Nations Industrial Development Organization), P.O. Box 707, A-1011 Vienna, Austria.

For anyone interested in the idea of making bicycles on a national or regional level, this is a fascinating book. Much of it is technical; for example, it lists the specifications of each of the different parts for the chosen model (a single speed, heavy-duty design). The book certainly does not provide all the information needed to begin bicycle manufacture, but it does give a good idea of what might be required.

There is a comparison of manufacturing requirements and costs in small and large-scale production units in India. Describes tests made for each of the major components. Lists conventional equipment required and costs. Describes the manufacturing and assembly operations, including those for a small-scale plant producing 15,000 bicycles yearly. Discusses manufacturing of specialized components by small subcontractors.

The conclusions and recommendations include the following: A) A bicycle industry can be started with the manufacture of only a few simple parts and components and the rest imported. B) Complete bicycles can be manufactured by units making only a few parts themselves and obtaining the rest from co-operating small-scale units. C) Gradually imports can be reduced with a view to reaching self-sufficiency. Under a 3-phase program, the imports would be: Phase 1—free-wheels, BB shells, hubs, rims, chains, spokes, and nipples, tires and tubes, steel balls; Phase 2—only free-wheels, BB shells, hubs, tires and tubes, and steel balls would be imported; Phase 3—only BB shells, tires and tubes, and steel balls would be imported. After this all components would be produced within the country.

If the reader were to combine what is provided here with S. Wilson's 'Oxtrike' idea (making use of sheet steel and angle iron instead of tube steel for the frames) a much smaller scale and lower cost method of production might be possible.

The Tanzanian Transport Bicycle: for use in rugged areas where cars and trucks can't go, and carries much more weight than a human can carry.

Pedal Power News Notes, several pages each, irregularly issued, from Stuart Wilson, Department of Engineering Science, Oxford University, Oxford, England.

These are short papers with sketches covering a variety of potential uses for pedal-power. They are produced by Stuart Wilson (author of the first article reviewed in this section) and report on his work. He is testing the designs discussed in the newsletters. Past subjects include the Oxtrike (an improved pedicab that can be built locally—see description in the first article in this section), a pedal rover (four-wheeled vehicle pedaled by four people, for rough terrain where cars and trucks can't pass), a pedal-powered winch, and pedal-powered pumps for use with deep boreholes. If you are interested, we suggest you send a small contribution or exchange information about pedal-power work you are doing or know of.

LATE ADDITION

Pedal Power: In Work, Leisure and Transportation, book, 144 pages, edited by James McCullagh, 1977, $5.95 from Rodale Press, 33 E. Minor St., Emmaus, Pennsylvania 18049, USA.

This book "examines the past, present, and future of the bicycle and other pedal and treadle machines...(and) explores the potential for pedal-driven devices in the workshop, kitchen, on the farm, and for transportation." There are 72 photos and 65 illustrations. Included are building instructions for the Rodale Energy Cycle (a stationary pedal-drive unit with adjustable RPM that can power a wide range of devices) and designs for new pedal-power inventions.

FURTHER REFERENCES ON PEDAL-POWER

Farm Implements for Arid and Tropical Regions has a drawing of a Japanese treadle-powered rice thresher; see drawing with review on page 95.

Treadle-Powered Thresher for Rice and Other Small Grains, see review on page 97.

Treadle-Operated Peanut Thresher, see review on page 97.

Pedal-Powered Thresher and Winnower, see review on page 97.

Diaphragm Pump designed by the agricultural engineering department of the International Rice Research Institute is operated by a person standing and rocking back and forth; output of 190 liters/minute at 1 meter lift; see drawing and description of this unit on pages 102-103.

Cassava Grinder (ITDG Agricultural Green Leaflet #27), see drawing and review on pages 108-109.

Foot Powered Thresher (ITDG Agricultural Green Leaflet #37), see note on page 110.

Selection and Maintenance of Logging Hand Tools includes a drawing of a treadle-operated grinder for sharpening tools; see drawing and review on page 114.

Chinese Chain and Washer Pumps includes many designs for pumps which are or can be pedal-powered; see drawings and review on page 203.

A Foot Powered Saw, see drawing and review on page 67.

Treadle-Powered Wood Turning Lathe, see drawing and review on page 66.

Invalid Carriage, Bush Wheelchair, and **Bush Ambulance** are all pedal-powered pieces of health care equipment; see drawings and reviews on pages 256-8.

Liklik Buk includes pictures of a pedal-powered thresher and winnower; see review on page 50.

First Steps in Village Mechanization includes a hand-cranked corn (maize) sheller that would be better operated by pedal-power; see drawing and review on page 44.

Simple Working Models of Historic Machines includes drawings of two different foot-powered lathes; see drawing with review on page 45.

WATER SUPPLY
AND WASTE DISPOSAL

Water Supply
and Waste Disposal

A supply of potable (drinking) water is a basic necessity all over the world; it should be a prime consideration in village development planning. The water supply books listed here deal with two concerns: how to get water (using pumps) and how to purify water once you've got it. Taken together, these areas are crucial to the planning and design of water supply systems. Equally crucial is the matter of waste disposal; how this is done dramatically affects the quality of the water supply and therefore the health of the community.

The pumps included here are both hand pumps and hydraulic ram pumps (powered by falling water). Most use metal parts and often require machine shop and/or welding facilities. However, there are a number of different ways to build pumps using wood, bamboo, discarded rubber or other local materials; examples can be found in **Chinese Chain and Washer Pumps**. Piston pumps can be made entirely of wood except for a piece of rubber tire as a flap valve; these, while not as efficient as metal pumps, will lift water a surprising 10-20 feet (see sketches). Local materials and skills can often be substituted, and people should experiment with and improve on the designs presented in these publications. For information on the use of windmills to pump water, see ENERGY: WIND.

The methods of purification include solar distillation (for small scale water needs), sand filtration, and chemical/biological methods of treatment. One topic that isn't covered due to a lack of information is the use of iodine for water purification. Chlorine is often added to water supplies to purify them, but recent work suggests that iodine **may** be a more effective method, with fewer side effects. However, this method has not yet been widely tested, and further study is needed on techniques for use wherever pathogens cannot be removed by simple filters.

Solar distillation is an elementary process: salt water or polluted water is placed in a container under a transparent cover. This cover traps solar energy which heats the water. The water evaporates and then condenses on the inside of the cover, and the impurities are left behind. This condensed water can be collected and used for drinking and cooking. However, only small quantities of water are produced (about 25-30 gallons per square foot of still per year), and so this method is suitable only for small community applications where other sources of water are not available.

Sand filtration can be used on a larger scale. Passing water slowly through a tank filled with sand purifies water in two ways: the sand acts as a screen to trap large particles, and it holds the bacteria that digest fecal matter naturally so that it will be harmless to humans.

Bamboo water pipes are used in many parts of Java, sometimes for carrying water over relatively long distances. They can be used as the distribution pipes from a main steel pipe line. They should be full of running water at all times, or they will quickly rot. The VITA **Village Technology**

Handbook *provides details of the simple connections between pieces of bamboo. Pieces of bamboo are sometimes split to form open channels for water. Such systems in places run for 100 meters or more. Similarly, in Mexico poles are sometimes split in half and hollowed out to form water channels. One water supply system in the mountains of Mexico uses old pipes from an abandoned gold mine. The pipes are propped up by trees and sticks, and the connections are sealed using old rags and pieces of plastic sheet. While not elegant, this system was built by the villagers and is maintained and continues to function for this reason; many more expensive systems have failed in other parts of the world because the local people were not involved.*

Composting privies provide one of the most promising options for human waste disposal; safe compost is produced which can be used as fertilizer. Another possibility is the simple pit latrine: when the pit is full, a fruit tree is planted and the latrine structure is simply moved a few feet, over a new pit.

All of the methods listed here (with the exception of the bamboo pipes) can be adapted for use in both rich and poor countries. There are two excellent general books on the broad subject of water supply and sanitation: the ITDG book **Water Treatment and Sanitation** *is the best low-cost guide, while the WHO monograph* **Water Supply for Rural Areas and Small Communities** *is the most comprehensive reference book. And we have to recommend* **Stop the Five Gallon Flush** *as a remarkable survey of human waste disposal alternatives.*

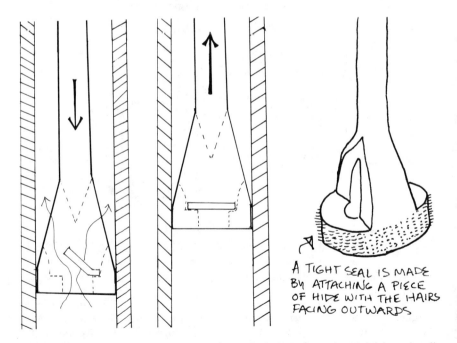

A TIGHT SEAL IS MADE BY ATTACHING A PIECE OF HIDE WITH THE HAIRS FACING OUTWARDS

This is a water pump with a piston made entirely out of wood, except for a small piece of old rubber tire that serves as a flap valve. The outer cylinder can be steel or iron pipe, bamboo, or a hollowed out log. This kind of pump is used on the small boats operated by the Bugis sailors of Sulawesi, Indonesia. The pumps are about four inches in diameter, and are used to pump water out of the hulls, a distance of 3 to 4 meters. We have no figures on the volume of water this kind of pump can lift in an hour, but they are surprisingly effective.

Water Treatment and Sanitation: Simple Methods for Rural Areas, small book, 60 pages, H. Mann and D. Williamson, 1973, Ł1.80 or US$4.15 surface mail from ITDG.

''The purpose of this handbook is to put together in a simple and logical form various aspects which must be considered when investigating the development of a water supply and sewage disposal scheme for a small community, and to make known the possibility of applying low-cost techniques. It is not intended as a textbook for engineers, although they may find some sections useful for rapid reference, but is intended for technicians, leaders of rural communities, administrators of schools or hospitals and others who wish to develop a water supply and sewage disposal scheme for their own use.

''Many of the methods in this handbook are based on the standard practices used in developed countries. They are, however, adapted to suit rural tropical conditions, and much material has been included which has been derived from experience in tropical areas drawn from a variety of sources, and is not normally found in standard temperate-zone practice.''

Includes chapters on selection of source and simple water testing; water supply; water treatment; excreta disposal; sewage treatment; temporary and emergency treatment. Charts, graphs and simple methods for roughly calculating water demand, flow measurement, and pump heads are included, as are simple drawings of a variety of water system equipment: sand filters, pumps,

THE UPWARD FLOW SAND FILTER

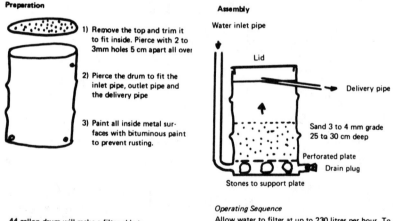

Preparation

1) Remove the top and trim it to fit inside. Pierce with 2 to 3mm holes 5 cm apart all over

2) Pierce the drum to fit the inlet pipe, outlet pipe and the delivery pipe

3) Paint all inside metal surfaces with bituminous paint to prevent rusting.

Assembly

Water inlet pipe

Lid

Delivery pipe

Sand 3 to 4 mm grade 25 to 30 cm deep

Perforated plate

Drain plug

Stones to support plate

44 gallon drum will make a filter able to treat 230 litres (50 gal) per hour

Operating Sequence

Allow water to filter at up to 230 litres per hour. To backwash stop flow, remove drain plug, allow dirt to flow out. Replace drain plug and restart flow.

privies, water seal toilets, and simple sludge treatment ponds. A glossary of technical terms is included, as are drawings and a bibliography.

One weak point is that some of the chemical and biological analysis suggested to determine water quality may be difficult to perform in some areas where litmus paper and similar testing equipment are not available. Red cabbage, for example, turns one color when water is basic and another color when water is acidic. There is a need for identification of a range of fruits and vegetables that change color under these conditions (see review of **Build It Yourself Science Laboratory** on page 53 for some additional examples); and the development of similar techniques for testing water quality in isolated areas.

This is still one of the two best books on the subject. Highly recommended.

Water Supply for Rural Areas and Small Communities (**WHO Monograph #32**), book, 327 pages, E. Wagner and J. Lanoix, 1959 (reprinted 1971), available from World Health Organization regional offices; or WHO, Distribution and Sales Service, 1211 Geneva 27, Switzerland (30 Swiss Francs); or $17.60 from WETS.

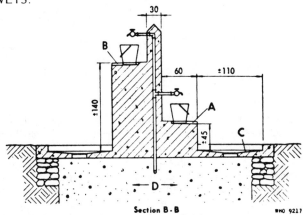

Section B - B   WHO 9217

Measures are in centimetres.

A = Platform level at about knee height
B = Platform level at about shoulder height
C = Hard-surface floor
D = Soakage pit : length may extend beyond limits of fountain
E = Control valve

Public fountains should be constructed of the most durable materials possible because no part of the water system will be required to take so much abuse. It is usually possible to construct the platform and faucet support so that only the most excessive abuse will damage it. The weakest part is the faucet itself. This should be the strongest available.

This is a very important reference work on water supply. It deals with both supply sytems and sanitation considerations. It focuses on the development of a water-supply program, installation, operation, maintenance, and management of water supply systems.

"An effort has been made to discuss the problems of rural water-supply in a clear and realistic manner and to avoid nebulous concepts which cannot possible apply to most of the rural underdeveloped areas of the world at the present time." Includes drawings of the equipment and systems discussed; many of them are sufficient for local construction.

From the experience of one of us working out in the field, **Water Supply for Rural Areas** is an essential book, despite its high price. Besides thorough coverage of rural sanitation, a significant part of the book is devoted to guidelines for effective management of water supply systems after their installation, and efforts to create and sustain community awareness and participation. Most importantly, an entire small community's water supply can be thoroughly planned with the use of this book—taking into consideration all major aspects such as geological formations, topography, needs analyses, flow, distribution, storage systems, and the vital human component—what happens when people accustomed to crossing ravines and climbing down steep slopes have potable water flowing from a tap.

FIG. 1. DIAGRAM OF A SLOW SAND FILTER

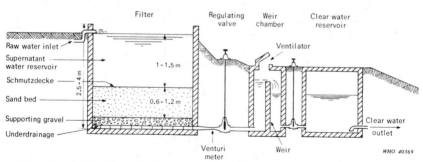

Slow Sand Filtration, book, 115 pages, L. Huisman and W. Wood, 1974, $7.40 from WHO regional distributors; or from WHO Distribution and Sales Service, 1211 Geneva 27, Switzerland.

The slow sand filter is one of the best means of treating a raw water supply where specialized chemical technology is not available. Far from being an old-fashioned technology, the authors feel that the slow-sand method can be the cheapest, simplest and most efficient method of water treatment.

Several scales of design are discussed and illustrated, although knowledge of basic engineering mathematics would be helpful. The last part of the book discusses the use of sand filters for recharging ground water, an important consideration for arid areas. In areas of known biological contamination, however, the use of chemical treatment (chlorine or preferably iodine) along with sand filtration would provide a very safe water supply .

Slow sand filtration methods are also very simple to operate: "Provided that a plant has been well designed and constructed there is little that can go wrong as long as the simple routine of operation is carried out."

A very valuable book for those involved with planning water supplies for small to medium size communities.

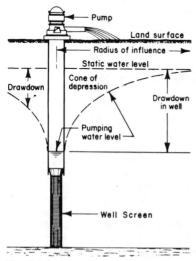

Fig. 2.11 CONE OF DEPRESSION IN VICINITY OF PUMPED WELL.

Water Wells Manual, book, 156 pages, U. Gibson and R. Singer, 1969, $7.00 from Premier Press, Box 4428, Berkeley, Calif. 94704 USA; or WETS.

This is a "simplified, small wells how-to" manual. A good knowledge of English is necessary. It is intended as a "basic introductory textbook" and to "provide instruction and guidance to field personnel engaged in the construction, maintenance, and operation of small diameter, relatively shallow wells used primarily for individual and small community water supplies." ("Small" used here means up to 4" in diameter.)

Topics include: background information on water cycles, geologic formations, water quality, ground-water exploration, well design, well construction and maintenance, sanitation and wells, and a review of various types of pumping equipment and energy sources including a discussion of the advantages and disadvantages of each.

This book would be useful for a community development worker who reads English well but has no formal training in water supply and/or well design. It is, however, oriented toward more technically-minded people, even though it is described as 'simplified.' Nevertheless, it is useful as a background reference.

Hand Pumps for Village Wells, booklet, 14 pages, C. Spangler, 1975, $1.50 from VITA.

This publication reviews the principles of operation of piston and diaphragm hand pumps used in many parts of the world. Deep and shallow well types are included. There are clear drawings of the various types that show the general features and method of operation. Although detailed designs are **not** given, the design principles are simple and clear.

Materials such as metal castings and PVC pipe are recommended, but simpler locally available materials such as wood could be used. Adaptation to fit local conditions will be necessary.

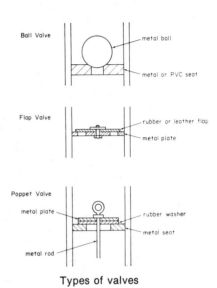

Ball Valve — metal ball — metal or PVC seat

Flap Valve — rubber or leather flap — metal plate

Poppet Valve — metal plate — rubber washer — metal seat — metal rod

Types of valves

Chinese Chain and Washer Pumps, booklet, 49 pages, S. Watt, 1976, Ł1.25 or US$2.90 surface mail from ITDG.

"This publication contains 21 versions of the chain and washer water lifting device, displayed at the 1958 Peking Agricultural Exhibition, in China. Each version of the pump was designed and built by separate communes, using local materials, skills and tools. A description of each pump with performance figures was written up in the simple information sheets that have been literally translated for this publication. The drawings presented are on the information

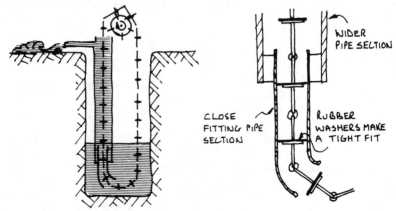

WIDER PIPE SECTION

CLOSE FITTING PIPE SECTION

RUBBER WASHERS MAKE A TIGHT FIT

sheets, and have been copied to allow anyone with a basic understanding of mechanics to build one of the devices; construction details are not included in this publication.''

Each pump design listed has information on the rate of pumping and a summary of the construction method and materials. The introduction describes the principles of operation of chain and washer pumps, components of the pumps, design factors, and power sources available for water pumping (human, animal, wind, solar, and electric). The appendix includes 5 more pump designs, from India, France and Britain.

An excellent book.

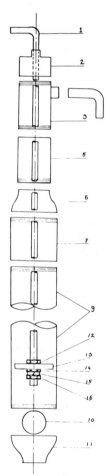

Shinyanga Lift Pump, plans, 4 pages, 1973, free from CCPD, World Council of Churches, 150 Route de Ferney, 1211 Geneva 20, Switzerland.

This is an easy to construct hand pump, used in villages in Tanzania. Made of 2-inch water pipe, with minor plumbing fittings. A length of ½-inch rod with a steel ring is the piston. A 1 1/8-inch steel ball and plastic ring make up the foot valve.

The design is simple, but perhaps too simple—see **The Salawe Pump** (below).

The Salawe Pump, plans, 8 pages, $1.25 from TOOL.

This is another village-built pump introduced into Tanzania—almost exactly the same design as the **Shinyanga Lift Pump**. The step-by-step drawings with instructions are clear and easier to understand than the Shinyanga pump leaflet. The pump is made of 2-inch water pipe, with plumbing fittings including several reducers. A 1 1/8-inch steel ball and plastic ring or reducer serve as the foot (bottom) valve. A ½-inch steel rod with a steel ring serve as the piston (the ring is 3mm smaller in diameter than the pipe).

There are problems with this design, however. Making the piston ring 3mm smaller to fit inside the pipe is difficult without machining facilities. The fact that water flows around the outer edges of the piston rather than through a valve on the down-stroke of the pump means that it will do the same thing on the up-stroke. For this reason the pump may not be able to lift water more than 6 feet or so. Also, the handle is simply a vertical rod that must be pulled up and down—a horizontal pump handle would be a great improvement.

Further work with this pump design could eliminate the drawbacks; hopefully this kind of improvement work will be done in the field to adapt the pump to local materials.

Solar Distillation as a Means of Meeting Small Scale Water Demands, book, 86 pages, 1970, $2.00 from United Nations, Sales Section Room LX 2300, New York, N.Y. 10017, USA.

Solar distillation is a method of providing water in small communities in dry areas where no other water source is available. It is particularly suited to areas that do have a supply of brackish or sea water. About 25 to 30 gallons of drinkable water per square foot of still can be expected every year in areas with a reasonable amount of sunshine.

An excellent manual on all sizes of solar distillation plants, for providing fresh water in small communities. The purposes of the manual are: "to review the current status of solar distillation, outline the general situations where it may be the best solution to water supply problems, provide a method for potential users to estimate performance and costs of current still designs in their area, to note practical problems of solar still design and operation, and to recognize possible changes in solar distillation technology and economics which may affect the applicability of the process in the future."

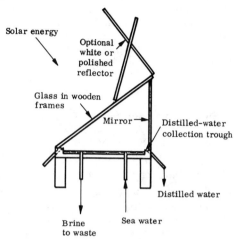

Very good information on the design of stills is included, requiring a knowledge of basic mathematics. There is a lack of detailed plans, but construction of stills using the ideas and drawings in the book is possible. The major requirements for a solar still are simply a basin of cement or other material to catch water, and a clear covering (glass or plastic).

We recommend this book.

How to Make a Solar Still (plastic covered), dimensional drawings with text, 13 pages, Brace Research Institute, 1965 (revised 1973), $1.25 from BRACE. MATERIALS: plastic sheets and bricks.
PRODUCTION: simple hand tools.

"This leaflet permits the user to make a relatively inexpensive solar still, primarily out of plastic sheets and bricks. It is not what might be recommended for a long-term installation. However, this plastic covered unit can certainly be adequately used for temporary installation."

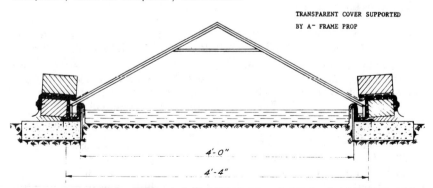

"It has the advantage of being suitable for units producing anywhere from 1 gallon to 1000 gallons per day, and will operate for long periods in isolated locations without attention. No auxiliary power source is needed, other than

means for feeding water into the unit...12 square-feet of solar still area are needed to produce one gallon of water daily." A 400 square-foot still in the West Indies cost US$228.00 for materials.
To really use this leaflet well, one would have to improvise considerably. The size they chose is 100 feet long, with a concrete base—hardly a temporary enterprise—yet the plastic sheeting will last only 6 months to 2 years even though it represents ½ the cost of the materials. The task of replacing it is easy.
These instructions are thorough.

Simple Solar Still for the Production of Distilled Water: Technical Report T17, 6 pages, T.A. Lawand, 1965 (revised 1967), also available in French and Arabic, $1.25 from BRACE.

MATERIALS: galvanized steel sheet, wood shavings, wood, copper tube, plastic tubing, caulking, aluminum paint, metal primer.
PRODUCTION: soldering, possibly some riveting.
This unit was "designed primarily for use in service stations with the object of providing distilled water for automobile batteries." Distilled water is very necessary for battery maintenance, especially in arid regions. This still will produce an average of 3 liters per day.
Clean fresh water (can be collected on roof during rainy season) is added to the still each day--distilled water is drained off. Users must be careful with the storage of the distilled water to avoid contamination.
The drawings are simple. The materials required are listed with the dimensions given. "The total cost of materials should be about $8.00-10.00."

Plans for a Glass and Concrete Solar Still: Technical Report No. T58, 8 pages of text plus 2 large blueprints, by T.A. Lawand and R. Alward, 1972, $4.50 from BRACE.

"This report contains a series of plans and specifications for a solar distillation plant designed by the Brace Research Institute for a site in Haiti." The average output is 200 gallons of distilled water per day. "The units are simply built and, apart from plumbing, are composed of four components: concrete curbs, a butyl rubber basin liner, glass panes for the transparent cover and a silicone glass sealant." This system is actually a series of solar stills connected together.

Installation of a Solar Distillation Plant on Ile de la Gonave, Haiti: Internal Report No. I67, 10 pages plus 10 photos, R. Alward, 1970, $1.25 from BRACE.

This report covers the actual installation of the glass and concrete solar still for which plans are given in the above **Technical Report No. T58**. Illustrates point by point the problems encountered in the actual construction, and the solutions that were found. There are 10 excellent photographs showing the method and stages of construction.

A Manual on the Hydraulic Ram Pump, booklet, 37 pages, S.B. Watt, 1974, £1.30 or US$3.00 surface mail from ITDG.

The hydraulic ram is a device that makes water pump itself. It pumps only a small percentage of the water that flows through it, but it does so to a level that is much higher than the source. It can, for example, be used to pump water to a house on a small hill above a creek. The power source is the water moving through the pump!

ITDG Hydraulic Ram Pump

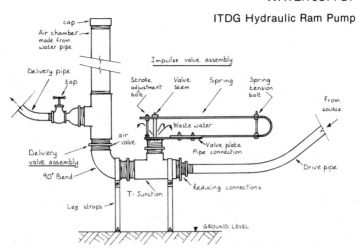

"We have written this manual primarily to show field workers how they can design and construct a simple ram pump from commercial pipe fittings, how to choose a suitable site for the ram, how to install and adjust the ram, and the sort of maintenance the pump will need during its working life. We have tried to write the manual in non-technical language so that it can be used by people with little or no technical training; this information makes up Part I. In Part II, we describe in greater detail the range of operation of ram pumps, and the different materials that have been used to make them." This part of the

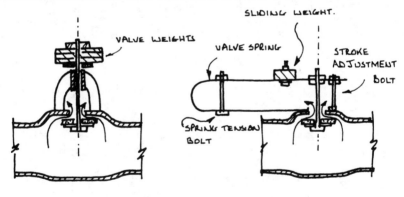

a) SIMPLE CLACK VALVE   b) CLACK VALVE WITH SPRING

Two designs for the impulse valve on a hydraulic ram pump

manual will be of interest to those who have a basic understanding of engineering materials and simple mathematics, as it explains the calculations necessary to design a ram.

"In places where this ram can be used, it has many advantages over other pumps powered by hand, animal, wind or motors, despite the fact that a lot of water passes through it without being pumped:
a) it does not need an additional power source and there are no running costs,
b) it has only two moving parts, and these are very simple and cheap to maintain,

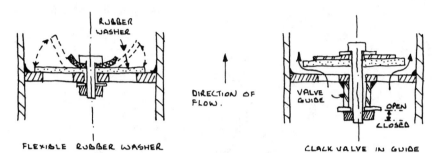

FLEXIBLE RUBBER WASHER   CLACK VALVE IN GUIDE

Two designs for non-return delivery valves on a hydraulic ram pump, which ensure that the water in the delivery pipe only moves in one direction

c) it works efficiently over a wide range of flows, provided it is tuned correctly,
d) it can be made using simple workshop equipment.''

This design is an improvement on the original **VITA Hydraulic Ram** design (see below)—it is described more thoroughly and is adaptable to different water flows and heads. There appears to be no way to avoid the necessity for pipe fitting equipment, drilling, and a little welding in any good ram design.

Dimensional drawings (metric units) with assembly information are given. The best hydraulic ram publication available.

A Hydraulic Ram for Village Use, booklet, 11 pages, Ersal Kindel, 1975, French and Spanish editions also available, $1.00 from VITA.

This manual consists of ''working instructions and drawings on how to construct a small, simple hydraulic ram from commercially available water pipe fittings. The ram described has a supply head of 6.5 meters, a delivery head of 14 meters, with a delivery of 7 liters/minute. It is thus only used for small water supplies.''

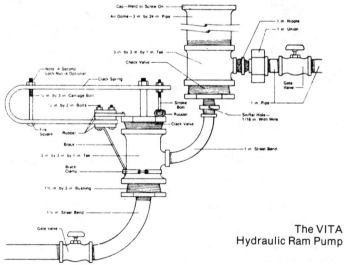

The VITA
Hydraulic Ram Pump

Although less detailed and thorough than the **Popular Mechanics** article, this information is more adapted to village resources. The operating principle is a bit simpler than the **Popular Mechanics** designs, but both should work equally well. If possible, it would be helpful to look at more than one of the designs listed here (**ITDG, Popular Mechanics and VITA**) before building a ram.

Popular Mechanics Hydraulic Ram—Reprint #X346, article with plans, 11 pages, C.A. Crowley, $2.25 from Popular Mechanics, Dept. CO, Box 1014, Radio City, N.Y. 10019, USA.

MATERIALS: standard plumbing parts and pipe.
PRODUCTION: welding, drilling, some machining.

This reprint from **Popular Mechanics**, a magazine, has two parts. The first explains the operation of a hydraulic ram, simplified methods enabling anyone to determine how much water can be lifted from a stream to the place where it will be used, how to measure the amount of water flow in the stream, and where and how to install the pump.

The second part describes a design for an actual ram pump made from standard plumbing parts. The drawings and construction are clear, and the design is quite good. The materials and production processes required may not be locally available everywhere; however, it would be possible to convert this design to a village resource base.

Manual of Information—Rife Hydraulic Rams, booklet, 14 pages, 1975, free from Rife Hydraulic Engine Manufacturing Co, Box 367, Milburn, N.J. 07041, USA.

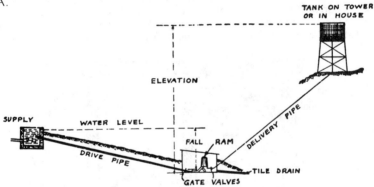

This pamphlet covers the information you need to install a ram: where to place it, how to estimate the water output, how to measure the flow, choosing the size for the drive and delivery pipes. Describes the operation of a ram, but does **not** describe a ram design. The information is aimed directly for use with rams manufactured by Rife, not any ram, so this booklet's usefulness is limited. It does, however, provide an introduction to the subject of hydraulic rams.

A Bibliography of Low-Cost Water Technologies, annotated bibliography, 39 pages, G. Bateman, 1974, £1.30 or US$3.00 surface mail from ITDG.

This bibliography was assembled for the following reason: developing countries ''have the greater proportion of their populations living as farmers in scattered communities, and the technologies for the services we are considering which have evolved for dense populations, prove to be prohibitively expensive for most rural areas. These facts suggest that we should not overlook alternative methods of collecting, treating, and distributing water, or different techniques of waste disposal, that were once used in one form or another throughout most of the world.''

This bibliography is a good annotated listing of the literature. Sections include sources of water, access, storage, transport and distribution, lifting and pumping, purification and treatment, and standards. ''The references in this bibliography are mainly concerned with water supplies for domestic and agricultural use—we have included only a few references to sewage and waste water disposal.''

Notes on the publications are grouped in a very readable, organized fashion. Unfortunately, perhaps most of the items listed will be difficult to obtain for people in developing countries—many are out of print. Still, this is an excellent bibliography.

Stop the Five Gallon Flush, booklet, 82 pages, 1973, $5.00 from Minimum Cost Housing Group, School of Architecture, McGill University, P.O. Box 6070, Montreal H3C 3G1, Canada.

This report is an extensive survey of human waste disposal systems, ranging from the $7.50 Chiang Mai (Thailand) squatting plate, to the $7,000 high-tech Cycle-Let system. There are explanatory illustrations and text, which would enable the reader to construct the simpler systems on his own. 66 waste disposal systems from 14 countries are covered.

Systems are divided into the following categories: Infiltration (absorption and dispersion of excreta in the soil and groundwater, as in pit latrines or aqua privies); Manual or mechanical removal (buckets, vacuum units, or sewage pipe networks); Destruction (incinerating toilets); and Decomposition (where

Two chambers of the Vietnamese composting privy

microbiological action destroys pathogens and creates fertilizer, as in compost privies or methane digesters). Included is the Vietnamese composting privy—an effective device with widespread applications (see drawing above).

''It should be clear, at this point, that water-borne waste represents a (relatively recent) answer within a particular set of economic and physical conditions, and not clearly the least wasteful answer at that. Flush toilets should not be considered as 'advanced' compared to the pit latrine. Under certain conditions the latter is ecologically sound, cheap and quite safe.''

Septic Tank Practices, booklet, 75 pages, Peter Warshall, 1976, $3 from Box 42, Elm Road, Bolinas, California 94924 USA.

This informative and inspirational manual comes from a small California community which successfully implemented alternative waste ''disposal''

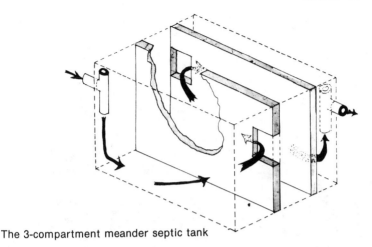

The 3-compartment meander septic tank

systems by public initiative, thus preventing its waterways from becoming a sterile sewage lagoon. Systematically presented are accounts of life-giving resource recyling schemes (and where to procure plans, as in the case of the effective Farallones Institute **Composting Privy**—see review, this section). The focus is on septic tanks, emphasizing the natural ability of the soil to purify and absorb "waste water." This volume complements ITDG's **Water Treatment and Sanitation** and the privy options included in **Cloudburst 1** and the VITA **Village Technology Handbook**. Excellent sections on biology and maintenance, although it lacks the concise working details and plans of WHO's **Excreta Disposal for Rural Areas and Small Communities**.

"Homesite treatment is cheaper, pollutes less, recycles more, slows or controls urban sprawl, has fewer health hazards and remains personal and intimate with the necessities of water, nutrients, and the lives of other creatures. Centralized sewage disposal, shielded by public authorities, has kept citizens unaware of sewage costs, inadequate treatment and disposal as well as their own natural responsibility for recycling their own wastes and keeping other plants and animals productive and healthy."

Composting Privy (Technical Bulletin No. 1), leaflet, 17 pages, Farallones Institute, 1974, $2 from Farallones Institute, 15290 Coleman Valley Road, Occidental, California 95465 USA.

MATERIALS: cement, concrete blocks or bricks, wood, plywood, wire screen, steel reinforcing bar, plastic (or other) piping
PRODUCTION: simple handtools

The Farallones Institute Composting Privy has proven successful in its rural California trial sites. Human waste is aerobically composted in twin chambers for a 1-year period—then it can be safely used in a garden. The elegant design is straightforward, virtually odor-free, low-maintenance, of simple yet durable construction, and can be built by amateur builders for less than $100 (in the U.S.—certainly less in developing countries). Uses common tools and materials. This system requires a few minutes each month to turn the compost pile.

By providing on-site treatment of human waste and organic household waste without the use of water or plumbing, the flush toilet, septic tank and garbage can are eliminated, and valuable nutrients and humus are returned to the soil. Besides the hygienic factors, this composting privy allows the use of the

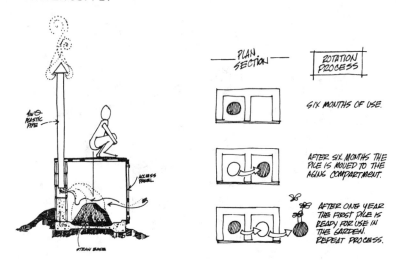

PLAN SECTION

ROTATION PROCESS

SIX MONTHS OF USE.

AFTER SIX MONTHS THE PILE IS MOVED TO THE AGING COMPARTMENT.

AFTER ONE YEAR THE FIRST PILE IS READY FOR USE IN THE GARDEN. REPEAT PROCESS.

4in Ø PLASTIC PIPE

ACCESS PANEL

STRAW BASE

squatting position, long considered the most comfortable and healthy posture for defecation.

A note of caution: this design is intended for aerobic conditions (that is, where there is free circulation of air through the pile). It cannot deal with an overload of moisture. Thus a modification must be found for conditions in Southeast Asia, where anal cleansing by water is the standard cultural practice.

This composting privy is most similar to the Vietnamese composting privy. Both can be found in **Stop the Five-Gallon Flush** (see review in this section).

Excreta Disposal for Rural Areas and Small Communities (WHO Monograph #39), book, 176 pages, E. Wagner and J. Lanoix, 1958 (reprinted 1971), from World Health Organization regional offices; or WHO, Distribution and Sales Service, 1211 Geneva 27, Switzerland (28 Swiss Francs); or $11.20 from WETS.

This is a solid reference work on the disposal of human wastes. 100 pages are given to various privy methods of waste disposal; advantages and disadvantages are given for each method considered. Water-carried methods and considerations are similarly treated with 35 pages.

The book is full of drawings that include enough information for local construction; dimensions and principles of operation are given for these drawings.

Much of the material presented in this excellent but high-priced manual is covered by other sources (**Village Technology Handbook, Stop the Five Gallon Flush, Septic Tank Practices**) which cumulatively give more information. We recommend discretion on the part of the prospective buyer.

LATE ADDITIONS

The Jensen Hand Pump (A.T. Unit Report #6), leaflet, 8 pages, small charge for postage, from Appropriate Technology Unit, Christian Relief and Development Association, P.O. Box 5674, Addis Ababa, Ethiopia.

This report introduces a remarkable, easily-built hand pump being tested at the National University of Ethiopia. It consists of a length of pipe with a foot valve, but no inner moving piston. The upper end of the pipe hangs on a spring, and has a handle attached. As the pipe is pushed up and down the water comes out the top.

The pump is self-priming and high lifts are theoretically possible. Construction is simple, requiring only basic plumbing and sheet metal work. "A simple foot valve appearing to give satisfactory service is a rubber disc (minimum of 2mm thick) seated against a steel plate in which 5-10mm diameter holes have been drilled." This foot valve is easily locally made.

In a test, a 4-inch diameter pipe pump operated by one man at a lift of 6.4 meters and 75 strokes a minute had an output of 245 liters/minute. Under roughly the same conditions, a 2-inch diameter pipe pump with a commercial foot valve could only lift 45 liters/minute (demonstrating that the home-built valve is better adapted to the design).

A good description of the pump, but no drawings are included. A fascinating idea.

Bamboo Piping: An Experiment in Mezan-Teferi, Ethiopia (A.T. Unit Report #5), leaflet, 16 pages, small charge for postage, from Appropriate Technology Unit, Christian Relief and Development Association, P.O. Box 5674, Addis Ababa, Ethiopia.

This is a very good overview of the necessary conditions for the use of bamboo piping. Much of the information has been reprinted from the VITA **Village Technology Handbook** section on bamboo water pipes; but the additional material here and the case study information make this a valuable addition to that section.

The authors did not have much success with a circular punch tool for knocking out the inner dividing walls of the bamboo. They developed a simple drilling bit which can be easily made by a blacksmith (drawings and photos of this bit are provided). With this tool 3 workers could easily bore out twelve 7-meter bamboo poles in one hour. The experimenters also developed a unique joint sealing system in which soaked cow-hide is wrapped around the joint twice and sealed tight with two pieces of galvanized wire. The authors note that bamboo piping can be expected to serve for 3-4 years; and that the pipes can take up to 2 atmospheres of pressure before bursting. The pipes were used to carry water for irrigation as well as for domestic human use.

Recommended.

Hand Dug Wells and Their Construction, book, 234 pages, by S. Watt and W. Wood, 1976, £4.05 or US$8.10 surface mail from ITDG.

"This manual describes hand dug shaft wells and their construction by relatively unskilled villagers. Modern concepts, methods and designs are incorporated, but in such a way that those who will carry out the actual work do not require a high degree of education, training or supervision. Much of the equipment can be made locally and costs (especially the cost of imported materials) can be kept to a minimum. The simple directions are based upon proven methods and satisfactory results gathered from various parts of the world. Wells constructed by the methods indicated need be in no way inferior to those produced by mechanical equipment at many times the expense."

"The first part of the book deals with the general principles of ground water storage, hygienic sources, and some notes on the preparatory work. Part II deals with the actual construction, and Part III with alternative methods and techniques. Part IV details the standard equipment and materials used, and

Part V provides additional information and sources.'' There are many drawings and photographs.

The best book on low-cost wells. Highly recommended.

A Footnote on Waste Disposal: The Water Seal Toilet

The water seal on this toilet removes all problems of fly and mosquito breeding and all possibility of odor nuisance from the contents of the pit to which it is connected. The volume of water used for flushing (by bucket) may be as low as 1½ liters. The use of a water seal system makes it possible to install the toilet in the house, connected to the pit by a 100-150mm inside diameter pipe running in a straight line with a slope of at least 5% (1 in 20).

(From **Water Treatment and Sanitation**—see review on page 200)

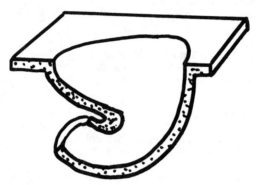

FURTHER REFERENCES ON WATER SUPPLY

VITA Village Technology Handbook has information on developing water resources (such as well-digging), water lifting and transport, and water storage; see review on page 41.

Simple Working Models of Historic Machines includes drawings of a variety of machines for pumping and raising water, including the Archimedes screw, chain pump, suction pump, and diaphragm pump; see review on page 45.

Rainwater Catchment Tanks and Micro-Irrigation in Botswana, see review on page 89.

A Diaphragm Pump for low-lift irrigation using human power has been developed by the agricultural engineering department of the International Rice Research Institute; it is more durable than the widely-reported bellows pump that IRRI developed earlier; see drawing with notes on pages 102-103.

A grey water soak pit is shown on page 47.

ARCHITECTURE, HOUSING AND CONSTRUCTION

Architecture, Housing, and Construction

''It is not so much 'how to build' as 'how to choose techniques and materials appropriate to a given situation.' ''

—letter from a volunteer in Papua New Guinea

Some of the listings here contain information on specific skills and techniques, while others deal with architectural philosophy. Together they provide a broad view of the options available to individuals and groups who are designing and building homes.

The 'how-to' books cover construction materials and techniques for houses, other buildings, and roads, with emphasis on simple methods using wood, bamboo, and stabilized earth. The principal advantages of these methods are twofold: they are inexpensive and they can be used by people to build their own homes.

For developing countries, some very interesting and relevant publications come from the Department of Transport, Works and Supply in Papua New Guinea. They have compiled their own ''appropriate technology sourcebook'' identifying published information in PNG (see **Technical Information Handbook**, reviewed on page 47); some of the publications they list we have obtained and reviewed here. These provide information on how to use various construction techniques and materials that fit conditions in Papua New Guinea—good examples of what is immediately applicable and appropriate to a particular area and culture.

There is a world-wide housing crisis, most sharply felt in the slums on the fringes of cities in the developing countries, where masses of people live in make-shift shelters that fall far below the standards of traditional housing in the rural areas. With no access to building materials and only the high-rise steel and glass 'modern' styles to aspire to, the only dim hope for such people has been that they may someday enter one of the sterile, expensive government 'low-cost' housing projects. Even people in the rural areas are beginning to be convinced that the only good house is one made of industrialized materials. In response to this there has arisen a movement of designers and planners (inspired by 78-year-old Egyptian architect Hassan Fathy) developing 'no-cost' housing that stresses available local materials such as mud/earth bricks and bamboo, and restores to people the ability to shape their living environment.

We feel that the ideas of Fathy and others are among the more important architectural concepts in the development of appropriate technologies for housing (see **Architecture for the Poor**). The emphasis is on making use of ingenious 'indigenous systems' of community shelter design, which have tended to evolve to fit local conditions. ''Far from being backward or illogical as is often supposed, many traditions do in fact have an underlying rationale or system'' which has developed in response to local climatic conditions and *availability of materials, states Iran's Development Workshop. Appropriate technologies for housing should begin with and extend these indigenous systems. Self-help, owner-built housing, says John Turner, ''is very much a process, intimately related to the user's needs and finances, and very much in the user's control. The idea of housing being the production and distribution of a number of units by the government or a private institution to a passive, recipient population is one of the misleading models set up by Western countries.'' The Development Workshop adds: ''Control, participation and culture emerge more easily in an operation that uses local resources, is labor intensive, is small-scale, and has continuity with local traditions.''*

There are some interesting lessons in all of this for the United States, which has moved away from owner-building in the past 30 years—and is now experiencing a 'housing shortage.' Industrialized housing materials, hired labor, and land are rapidly becoming extremely expensive. And the owner-builder who attempts to skirt all of these by building himself with low-cost materials in an area where land values are still reasonable comes up against another obstacle: The Building Code. Appropriate technologies for housing in the United States can not be considered apart from the legal battles to provide more flexibility in the building codes.

Hopefully, the ideas and techniques in the publications reviewed here will gain more acceptance world-wide for both urban and rural areas. These publications present effective ways of providing housing and helping people provide their own housing.

This section is divided into three parts: Philosophy and General Books, Earth Construction, and Wood and Bamboo Construction.

Philosophy and General Books

Architecture for the Poor, book, 350 pages, Hassan Fathy, 1973, $5.95 (paperback) from WETS.

Hassan Fathy is an Egyptian architect. He strongly feels housing should be based on traditional forms of architecture, not those forms imported from the West. The people themselves should be intimately involved with the design, building and ownership of their own housing. When the government or private contractors step in and build **for** the people, the result is often housing and planning which is vastly out of touch with local social, cultural, economic and environmental conditions.

''This book describes in detail Fathy's plan (during the 1940's) for building the village of New Gourna, Egypt, from mud bricks, employing almost

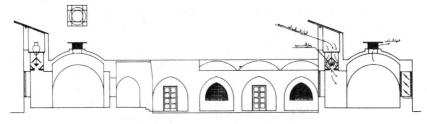

Ventilation system at girls' primary school

exclusively such traditional Egyptian architectural designs as enclosed court-yards and domes and vaulted roofing. Fathy worked closely with the people to tailor his designs to their needs; he taught them how to work with the mud bricks, supervised the erection of the buildings, and encouraged the revival of such ancient crafts as claustra (lattice designs in the mudwork) to decorate the buildings...In addition, Fathy worked out an economic and organizational base, so that the production in the village derived from local crafts and organizational patterns.''

Although bureaucratic and other problems prevented the completion of New Gourna, Fathy argues convincingly for the necessity of simple, traditional housing in developing areas that can be built by the people themselves. They would use local materials and adapted traditional building methods. Today Fathy's ideas are becoming more accepted as rural development becomes more of a priority throughout the world.

There are more than 100 photographs and some design sketches included. An important book. Highly recommended.

Indigenous Building and the Third World, booklet, 44 pages, $5 from the Development Workshop, Building & Housing Research Center, P.O. Box 15-1114, Tehran, Iran.

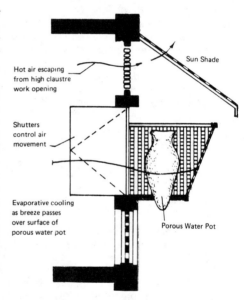

Water jar coolers make use of free energies to cool air before it enters the room.

''Indigenous planning and building methods are most evident in villages, traditional city quarters and the more recent 'squatter' settlements in Third World countries. The architecture of these indigenous settlements has evolved over thousands of years. They reflect a country's accumulated expertise on how to build appropriately to local social and economic conditions. Furthermore, the majority of people live in these settlements. Thus the approach to both understanding shelter needs and improving them in a Third World country is through first using and developing the indigenous methods reflected in these settlements.''

The authors, four architects with Iran's Development Workshop, stress views on housing very similar to those of Hassan Fathy. This book is an attempt to compare and contrast traditional and modern/industrialized methods of construction, design, local and regional planning, cooling systems, environmental designs; all in a wide variety of places and countries. The authors explain why they feel the traditional patterns of housing are generally superior to government housing projects which borrow heavily from the industrialized nations. Using photographs and sketches from Iran, Egypt, Oman, Turkey, Pakistan and India they illustrate both the problems caused by unnatural and foreign forms of design and organization, and circumstances where traditional forms can be usefully adapted. As with **Architecture for the Poor**, this book represents a view of architecture and design that is becoming more important throughout the world. It is aimed primarily at architects and planners in the Third World, encouraging them to use and improve upon indigenous methods in their own cultures. Full of practical ideas. Highly recommended.

Shelter, large format book, 176 pages, edited by Lloyd Kahn, 1973, $6.00 from WETS.

"This book is about simple homes, natural materials, and human resourcefulness. It is about discovery, hard work, the joys of self-sufficiency, and freedom. It is about **shelter**, which is more than a roof overhead."

Shelter is a big beautiful book with unlimited vision and ideas. Filled with photographs and drawings, it is a tribute to native, traditional, rational, and recent innovative building styles. Included are articles on a variety of structures from animal dwellings to a survey of human habitats; from the so-called 'primitive' to the futuristic.

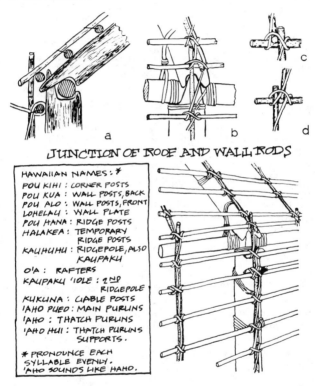

JUNCTION OF ROOF AND WALL RODS

HAWAIIAN NAMES: *
POU KIHI : CORNER POSTS
POU KUA : WALL POSTS, BACK
POU ALO : WALL POSTS, FRONT
LOHELAU : WALL PLATE
POU HANA : RIDGE POSTS
HALAKEA : TEMPORARY
          RIDGE POSTS
KAUHUHU : RIDGEPOLE, ALSO
          KAUPAKU
O'A : RAFTERS
KAUPAKU 'IOLE : 2ND
              RIDGEPOLE
KUKUNA : GABLE POSTS
'AHO PUEO : MAIN PURLINS
'AHO : THATCH PURLINS
'AHO HUI : THATCH PURLINS
          SUPPORTS.

* PRONOUNCE EACH
SYLLABLE EVENLY.
'AHO SOUNDS LIKE HAHO.

The authors echo a growing feeling among builders: "We now realize that there will be no wondrous new solution to housing, that our work, though perhaps smart, was by no means wise. In the past year, we have discovered that there is far more to learn from wisdom of the past: from structures shaped by imagination, not mathematics, and built of materials appearing naturally on the earth, than from any further extension of whiteman technoplastic prowess (Western technology—ed.)."

A highly recommended and stimulating book, **Shelter** has some precise working drawings on basic designs, such as hipped, gabled, or shed roofs, concrete floors, wooden framing, windows and doors. At the back of the book, there happen to be some brief but very good drawings, photos, and text on sail windmills.

For those seeking design inspiration, **Shelter** is required reading.

The Owner Built Home, book, 367 pages, Ken Kern, 1975, $6.95 from WETS.

''**The Owner Built Home** is intended to be a how-to-think-it book. Alternatives to the professionally executed, contractor built home are presented in text and through non-detailed sketches.'' It is mostly concerned with design considerations for all facets of home building.

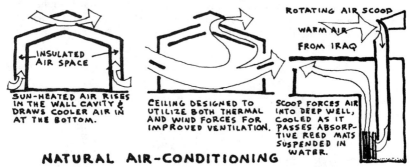

SUN-HEATED AIR RISES IN THE WALL CAVITY & DRAWS COOLER AIR IN AT THE BOTTOM.

CEILING DESIGNED TO UTILIZE BOTH THERMAL AND WIND FORCES FOR IMPROVED VENTILATION.

SCOOP FORCES AIR INTO DEEP WELL, COOLED AS IT PASSES ABSORPTIVE REED MATS SUSPENDED IN WATER.

NATURAL AIR-CONDITIONING

The areas covered include heating and natural ventilation, living space design, floor, wall, and roof design. One-third of the book covers how to work with different kinds of building materials—adobe blocks, rammed earth, concrete, wood frames, pole frames, stone masonry. This is perhaps the most useful, practical information contained in the book; it gives a good view of the principles and techniques of building with rammed earth, for example.

The rest of the sections on general design are somewhat directed towards Americans building their own homes. However, the materials sections provide a very good practical overview.

This book does not tell you how to **build** a house—it tells you all the things to consider in **designing** a house.

The Owner-Built Homestead, book, 265 pages, Ken Kern, 1975, $5.00 from WETS.

This book is a supplement to **The Owner-Built Home** (see review above). It covers how to develop the land **around** a home—a garden, orchard, pasture, woodlot, water supply, wells, fish-culture ponds, fencing, barn, shop and outbuildings. Also included are an oil drum stove design, an adobe barn and silo (for grain storage) design, animal shelter and feed management, waste disposal methods such as composting privies, and nutrition.

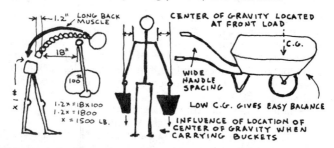

LOW C.G. GIVES EASY BALANCE

INFLUENCE OF LOCATION OF CENTER OF GRAVITY WHEN CARRYING BUCKETS

Like **The Owner-Built Home**, this book is an overview of the great many topics included, and a broad compilation of skills and techniques. There is again a slant towards American applications, but the book is extremely complete. For their value as very complete skills, ideas and methods guides, we feel Ken Kern's books are extremely useful, and lend themselves very well to adaptation in other countries.

The Ecol Operation, book, 128 pages, by the Minimum Cost Housing Group, 1975, $5 from MCHG, School of Architecture, McGill University, P.O. Box 6070, Montreal, Quebec H3C 3G1 Canada.

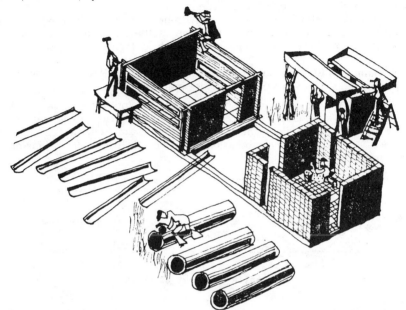

''This report describes the work done in the McGill program of Minimum Cost Housing...in which the main activity has been the construction of a self-sufficient, habitable low-cost house. This house was built as a test of ideas and a demonstration of how much can be done with unusual materials and methods of construction, and inexperienced builders.''

Two structures were built: one from sulfur concrete blocks and the other from logs. The roofing is made of sections of asbestos cement (sewer) pipes.

There is a very good section on sulfur blocks for building, which describes how to make sulfur concrete and then mold it into blocks—perhaps the most useful part of the report. The interesting characteristic of these blocks is that they are designed for mortarless, interlocking construction, so that walls can be built by anyone just by fitting the blocks together. This system is meant to simplify wall construction to encourage self-help building, and to be earthquake resistant without the need for reinforced concrete.

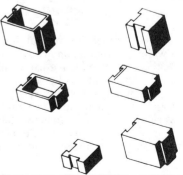

A system for notching and grooving logs to form load-bearing walls without cement or mortar is also described. The tools used are simple—from hand pliers and hacksaw to hammer and masonry tools. Photographs of the construction are included.

The water, solar energy and wind energy systems were designed in cooperation with Brace Research Institute. The designs used are presented with drawings, with emphasis on the water supply and waste disposal systems that conserve water. The appendix covers solar distillation (including a simple design with drawings), and a short discussion of relatively new efforts to obtain water from the air through condensation.

An excellent model for low-cost, easy-to-build, self-help housing. A provocative example of what might be done in the slums of large cities in developing countries to enable people to construct their own homes.

A Manual on Building Construction, book, 360 pages, Rev. H. Dancy, 1948, reprinted 1973, Ł2.05 or US$4.70 surface mail from ITDG.

This book was originally published by the Sudan Interior Mission, in 1948. The ITDG reprinted it in 1973 because they felt that it had "exceptional value as a practical field building manual." Written for missionaries as amateur builders/supervisors, the text occasionally reflects the paternalistic thinking of the time.

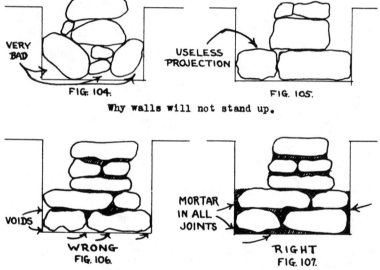

VERY BAD

USELESS PROJECTION

FIG. 104.　　　　FIG. 105.

Why walls will not stand up.

VOIDS

MORTAR IN ALL JOINTS

WRONG
FIG. 106.

RIGHT
FIG. 107.

A comprehensive manual, it deals with the essential elements of permanent dwelling construction, relying on block, brick, adobe, or stone walls. The author makes effective use of illustrations. The book does, however, reflect only Western ideas of proper house construction and design. It does not draw on the building methods, designs and experience of other cultures, nor does it touch on the innovative new building techniques such as ferro-cement and the various methods for making stabilized earth blocks.

In short, this book will be useful until someone writes a true, international appropriate technology handbook of small building construction to replace it.

How to Build a House Using Self-Help Housing Techniques (Como Fabricar Una Casa Usando Tecnica Ayuda Propia), illustrated book, 50 pages, 1974, free to serious groups, from Dept. of Housing and Urban Development, Office of

International Affairs, Washington, D.C. 20410, USA.

"This manual is designed as a graphic means of demonstrating the basic methods and techniques used in building a home, whether it be a one room cabin or a more complicated dwelling. It has been conceived as a basic technology handbook for use by either individuals or groups who have the goal of building, or adding to, a home of their own, and for those involved in self-help home building projects."

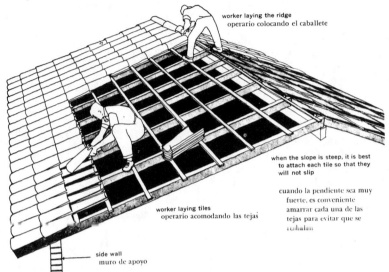

worker laying the ridge
operario colocando el caballete

when the slope is steep, it is best to attach each tile so that they will not slip

cuando la pendiente sea muy fuerte, es conveniente amarrar cada una de las tejas para evitar que se resbalen

worker laying tiles
operario acomodando las tejas

side wall
muro de apoyo

The usefulness of this manual is that it is primarily drawings, with captions in English and Spanish. Each drawing presents a complete idea, so a knowledge of English or Spanish is actually unnecessary. The drawings are clear and simple.

This manual is intended to be an idea book, to show the reader different methods of constructing each part of a house. For example, there is a section which illustrates methods of making floors using either wood, concrete or stone. There are also sections on walls, roofs, windows and doors, water supply systems, sewage disposal systems, how to measure and lay a foundation, and a comparison of house designs appropriate to different climates: rainy, hot, hot and humid, and temperate areas.

Although this book is attractive due to the excellent illustrations, the designs are distinctly Western.

Lime and Alternative Cements, book, 164 pages, compiled by Robin Spence, 1974, Ł4.05 or US$9.30 surface mail from ITDG.

The proceedings of a recent ITDG seminar on low-cost materials having the properties of cement. Excellent reference book on small-scale manufacture of alternative cements. Photos, discussion, references, papers.

Shaft Lime Kiln (Technical Bulletin #13), leaflet, 11 pages, S. Mason, 1974, Papua New Guinea, free to serious groups, from DTWS.

This kiln is appropriate "where only small quantities of lime are required for building purposes, stabilization of soils and lime washes." The bulletin assumes that limestone is locally available.

"The shaft lime kiln is a vertical circular opening cut into the side of a hill. The lining can be large boulders of limestone, which are replaced as they burn out, or bricks made from clay in the area. The capacity of the kiln is three tons of hydrated lime per burn, which requires one week to produce."

Brief instructions are provided, covering testing for limestone, construction, and operation of the kiln. The lime that is treated in this kiln is usable as a stabilizing agent for soil construction. There are very clear, dimensional drawings with English measurements. Bricks are needed for construction.

Technical Research Bulletin, booklets, Volume 1: 29 pages, Volume 3: 48 pages, by the Dept. of Public Works in Papua New Guinea, free to serious groups from DTWS.

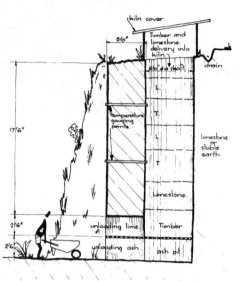

"The Dept. of Public Works has for some time been engaged in research into technical and other aspects of architectural and engineering works. This programme is currently undergoing a rapid expansion with a strong emphasis on the use of local resources and ways of producing efficient engineering and architectural works within a limited economy.

"This is the first of a series of bulletins through which it is intended to convey to local Government Councils, Missions, and other interested bodies information resulting from the research work which they may find useful." Each volume has a few drawings.

Volume 1 has articles on stabilized bricks (including brickwork in earthquake areas), plain earth and stone construction, lime stabilization and production, and the treatment of organic materials against fire, decay and insect attack. In Volume 3, the emphasis is on the technical, rather than the practical, aspects of soil engineering. The contents are: a review of building foundation practice on swelling soils, cement requirements for soil cement bricks, and further notes on lime stabilization of soils.

Roofing in Developing Countries — Research for New Technologies, National Academy of Sciences Report, 56 pages, 1974, $4.75 from NTIS (Accession No. PB-234-503/AS; foreign orders add $2.50 handling charge).

"The most serious obstacle to low-cost housing in the developing countries, regardless of setting or sophistication, is the lack of a low-cost roofing material that will provide satisfactory performance for a reasonable time under many adverse conditions...In many developing countries roofing alone represents more than 50% of the total construction cost of a low-cost house."

An attempt is made here to identify materials that would last longer than thatch/fired clay and yet be cheaper than imported corrugated iron. The use of plastics, foam composites, sulfur, carbonized plant materials, asphalt, hydraulic cement binders, agricultural and wood wastes, and ferrocement is discussed. The qualities and research needs for each of these are pointed out. The work of the Central Building Research Institute of India is briefly described. This is an overview only of promising new technologies—useful primarily to research institutions and universities. Expensive for what you get. No illustrations.

Ferrocement: Applications in Developing Countries, summary booklet, 69 pages, by the National Academy of Sciences, 1973, $5.25 (#PB 220-825) from NTIS (foreign orders add $2.50 handling charge).

"Ferrocement is a highly versatile form of reinforced concrete made of wire mesh, sand, water, and cement, which possesses unique qualities of strength and serviceability. It can be constructed with a minimum of skilled labor and utilizes readily available materials. Proven suitable for boat-building, it has many other tested or potential applications in agriculture, industry, and housing.

"Ferrocement can be fabricated into almost any shape...is more durable than most woods and much cheaper than imported steel, and it can be used as a substitute for these materials in many applications...Ferrocement construction does not need heavy plants or machinery; it is labor-intensive."

The report examines the use of ferrocement for construction of boats in a Chinese commune, food storage silos in Thailand and Ethiopia, and water tanks in New Zealand. "The report considers the potential for further use of already discovered application, such as boats and silos, and identifies promising new application, such as roofs and food-processing equipment."

"Deliberately scant in technical language and brief in documentation, the report is detailed enough to provide a clear understanding of what ferrocement is and what it can do. In particular, this report seeks to convey a sense of ferrocement's wide-ranging potential to readers in developing countries—government officials, technical assistance representatives, and technical experts—who are becoming more curious about this increasingly discussed technology." Summaries are provided in French and Spanish.

This is a good overview, and the booklet was at one time available free; unfortunately, it is now very expensive for what you get.

Construction with Surface Bonding, booklet, 18 pages, B. Haynes and J. Simons, 1972, $0.45 (Stock Number 0100-03340) from Superintendent of Documents, U.S. Government Printing Office, Washington DC 20402 USA.

MATERIALS: blocks of uniform dimensions, cement, hydrated lime, calcium chloride, calcium stearate, glass fiber filament.

PRODUCTION: simple handtools, including some kind of water-spraying device.

"Normally, concrete blocks are laid in mortar. Contrary to popular belief, the mortar does not act as a 'glue' to hold the blocks together. It serves mainly as a bed to aid in leveling the blocks...Surface-bonded concrete block walls are stronger and tighter than conventionally-laid walls.

"Surface bonding is both a material and a technique for erecting concrete-block walls without mortar joints. The bonding material is a cement-glass fiber mixture that is troweled on both sides of the stacked blocks to hold them together. No mortar is used between blocks...The surface bonding mixture becomes a waterproof coating for the walls."

This booklet shows how to construct buildings with this method from start to finish. Blocks must be very uniform in all dimensions, to form a straight wall without mortar when stacked. Steel reinforcing rods are used over windows and doorways. Mixture: 78 parts cement, 15 parts lime, 1 part calcium stearate, 2 parts calcium chloride, and 4 parts glass fiber. 25 pounds (dry weight) of this mixture will cover 30 square feet of wall on both sides.

Waterproofing Soil Construction, booklet, 11 pages, J. Boatwright, French edition also available, $1.00 from VITA.

"This manual is concerned with the methods of waterproofing all types of soil construction. The basic intent is to show people how to use all forms of native vegetation to produce gums, resins, and oils that are useful waterproofing agents." The techniques are simple, requiring only locally produced small tools which are described. No effort is made to identify the various plants. Some of the more common ones are listed as examples of what might be used. The booklet is written as if the author were describing these techniques to villagers, in English.

We hesitantly include this pamphlet because of its lack of specifics. It may inspire countless haphazard trial and error experiments. On the other hand, the information and ideas contained within are undoubtedly valuable to people who have **no** source of waterproofing agents. (We suggest consulting **Underexploited Tropical Plants with Promising Economic Value**, reviewed on page 90. It lists various plants with oil, seed, and resin potential, such as the wax-secreting Jojoba or the Babassu Palm.)

Rural Roads Manual (Simple English Edition), book, 128 pages, by the Papua New Guinea Dept. of Public Works, 1976, free to serious groups, from DTWS.

Papua New Guinea's Dept. of Public Works, recognizing the importance of well constructed and maintained roads, has published this manual in an attempt to promote self-help road construction all over PNG. Written purposely in very simple English (the national language), it is a complete guide to road design, construction and maintenance using low-cost local materials and tools, and local skills. Covers subjects such as surveying, laying out a road, drainage, building in swampy areas, maintenance and upgrading, plus information on building bridges, culverts and low-level crossings. Metric measurements.

Illustrated with drawings on almost every page, this manual is intended for fieldworkers and local government councils in PNG, so that road building and maintenance can become a decentralized process. While specific to conditions in PNG, this manual is valuable as an example for adaptation to other areas.

Earth Construction: Adobe, Rammed Earth, and Soil-Cement

The following books all have information on adobe/mud brick-making:
Making the Adobe Brick, book, 88 pages, Eugene Boudreau, 1971, $2.95 from WETS.
Adobe Craft, book, 72 pages, Karl Schultz, 1974, $5.50 from WETS.
Earth for Homes, (see review on page 228).
Handbook for Building Homes of Earth, (see review below).

All of these books cover the basic operations in making adobe bricks, such as testing and choosing the proper soil, mixing the soil with a stabilizing agent (emulsified asphalt, oil, clay or other materials), molding and drying the bricks, usually using wood molds. Information on making walls with mud bricks is also included, although the emphasis is sometimes on Western architectural forms.

Both **Making the Adobe Brick** and **Adobe Craft** cover the same material; emulsified asphalt is used as the stabilizer. **Making the Adobe Brick** is written by a American who built his own home using adobe. The basic brick-making information is all there in a relaxed style, although without as much detail as **Adobe Craft**—it is a good, basic introduction. **Adobe Craft**, in addition to having more complete information and detail, contains information on both brick-making **and** reinforced poured adobe, a process which eliminates the need for bricks. The appendix contains a very good explanation of adobe construction methods, as well as how to use oil drums to make both a soil sifter and a mixer. **Adobe Craft** also costs more, but you do get more information. If funds are limited, we recommend **Making the Adobe Brick**, which does give an adequate introduction to the subject.

Earth for Homes and **Handbook for Building Homes of Earth** are both general soil construction manuals; both contain good sections on adobe/mud bricks, again covering all the basic operations as well as many different types of stabilizers (for the specific use of portland cement as a stabilizer, see **Soil Cement**, page 229). **Handbook for Building Homes of Earth** is the more complete and detailed of the two, with more pictures, drawings and detailed discussions.

Handbook for Building Homes of Earth, book, 158 pages, L. Wolfskill, $6.25 from NTIS (Accession No. PB-179-327); or free to serious groups from Office of International Affairs, Dept. of Housing and Urban Development, Washington D.C. 20410, USA.

This is a very complete, all purpose manual covering **all** types of earthen housing construction, including adobe, rammed earth, and pressed blocks. The manual covers many areas: different types of soils, testing soil, soil stabilizers, building site preparation, foundations, roofs, and preparing soil. In addition, each of the three major types of earth construction (adobe, rammed earth and pressed blocks) are covered separately and extensively. There are detailed chapters on how to make different kinds of blocks, and how to build structures with them. (continued on next page)

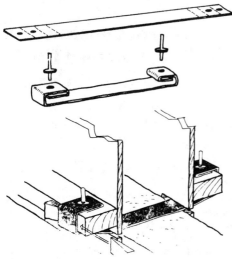

Figure 75. Thin metal strips such as these can be used instead of bolts to tie rammed earth forms together.

This is an extremely comprehensive book, useful in many different climates and regions—for example, there is information on soil cements applicable to humid, tropical climates where protecting earth structures from the rain is important. This book is comparable to **Soil Cement: Its Use in Building** in the amount of useful information it has about soils. However, this book covers many types of stabilized earth in addition to soil cement.

Recommended as a very complete book on all forms of earthen housing. Photographs and illustrative drawings are included.

Earth for Homes, book, 70 pages, HUD Ideas and Methods Exchange #22, free to serious groups, from Office of International Affairs, Dept. of Housing and Urban Development, Washington DC 20410 USA.

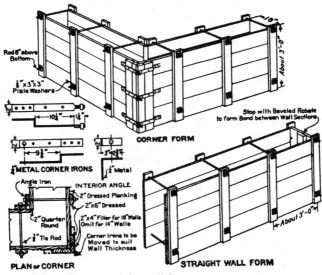

Corner and straight wall forms for rammed earth

This book is very similar to **Handbook for Building Homes of Earth** (see listing); it covers almost all of the same material but is not as detailed. For example, all the different methods of earth wall construction are covered in one chapter here. Soil stabilizers, earth floors and roofs, and general wall design considerations. There are only a few drawings and photographs.

Although not as detailed as the **Handbook**, this book appears to be also very useful.

Soil Cement: Its Use in Building, book, 126 pages, Augusto A. Enteiche G., 1964, also available in Spanish and French editions, publication #E.64.IV.6, $6.00 from United Nations, Sales Section Room LX 2300, New York, N.Y. 10017, USA.

"The compound of soil, cement and water, mixed in the proper proportions and compacted to the proper degree, constitutes "soil-cement." This paper shows how soil-cement may be used at various stages in the construction of a house, together with a number of examples which may be helpful to anyone wishing to use this material for building purposes.

"**Soil Cement** is divided into chapters, dealing with basic facts and practical application on: knowing soils, soil as a construction material, the preparation of soil-cement, the use of soil-cement for housing, and accomplishments in soil-cement. The order of presentation, the terminology used, and the large number of illustrations, are all designed to make the instructions more readily understandable with a view to the greatest possible circulation and impact."

The author is a staff member of **CINVA** (Inter-American Housing and Planning Center) in Colombia, South America, where the CINVA-Ram was developed (see **Making Building Blocks with the CINVA-Ram**, page 230). **Soil Cement** also covers the use of the CINVA-Ram for making building blocks.

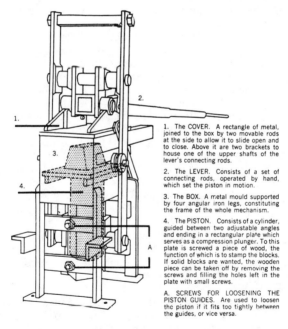

1. The COVER. A rectangle of metal, joined to the box by two movable rods at the side to allow it to slide open and to close. Above it are two brackets to house one of the upper shafts of the lever's connecting rods.

2. The LEVER. Consists of a set of connecting rods, operated by hand, which set the piston in motion.

3. The BOX. A metal mould supported by four angular iron legs, constituting the frame of the whole mechanism.

4. The PISTON. Consists of a cylinder, guided between two adjustable angles and ending in a rectangular plate which serves as a compression plunger. To this plate is screwed a piece of wood, the function of which is to stamp the blocks. If solid blocks are wanted, the wooden piece can be taken off by removing the screws and filling the holes left in the plate with small screws.

A. SCREWS FOR LOOSENING THE PISTON GUIDES. Are used to loosen the piston if it fits too tightly between the guides, or vice versa.

Fig. 36 CINVA-RAM moulder for the production of soil-cement blocks: explanatory sketch.

This book covers the subject of soils and soil-cement **very** completely; it is comparable to **Handbook for Building Homes of Earth** (see listing, page 227) in the amount of useful information it has; the difference is that it concentrates on the use of cement as a soil stabilizer, rather than including all forms of stabilized soil construction. Recommended.

Mud Brick Roofs, booklet, 16 pages, HUD Ideas and Exchange Series #42, 1957, free to serious groups, from Office of International Affairs, Dept. of

Housing and Urban Development, Washington DC 20410 USA.

This short booklet describes the use of mud bricks for vaulted roof and dome construction, as used in traditional Egyptian architectural styles. It uses as a specific example Hassan Fathy's design for New Gourna (see review of **Architecture for the Poor**). The design of buildings using traditional vaulted arch construction is summarized; photographs of the process of building the arches are included. An appendix summarizes the technique for making mud bricks as done in Egypt.

The emphasis in this booklet is to illustrate what **can** be done in housing using locally available materials and traditional construction techniques that are updated and improved. It is clear that in different areas, mud brick construction may be impractical, but other local methods may be very useful.

Mud Brick Roofs, which describes the construction techniques used in New Gourna, could be used along with **Architecture for the Poor**, which concentrates on the social, economic and administrative aspects of Fathy's experience.

Making Building Blocks with the CINVA-Ram, instruction manual, 21 pages, 1966, Spanish edition available, $1.50 from VITA.

"The CINVA-Ram is a simple, low-cost, portable machine for making building blocks and tiles from common soil. The press, made entirely of steel, has a mold box in which a hand-operated piston compresses a slightly moistened mixture of soil and cement or lime." Blocks made with the CINVA-Ram are easier to make than concrete blocks, are low-cost, and can be made on a building site and so avoid transportation costs.

"This manual combines the experience of four people who used the CINVA-Ram and figured out answers to the inevitable problems of detail as they came up day after day." It is intended as a manual for field workers and supervisors, giving instructions on how to use the Ram, including: testing and mixing the soil, operating the Ram to make blocks, curing the blocks, and construction using pressed blocks.

Subtitled "A Supervisor's Manual", this book is intended as an instruction manual on how to **use** the CINVA-Ram. As far as we know, there are no publications available on how to **build** a CINVA-Ram; it can, however, be purchased for about US$250.00 from METALIBEC Ltda, Apartado Aereo 11798, Bogota, Colombia, S.A. Write to them for further information on the Ram. It is an excellent machine for making earth blocks, and this manual is a valuable companion.

(See review in this section of **Soil Cement: Its Use in Building** and the accompanying drawing of the CINVA-Ram.)

Selection of Materials for Stabilized Brick Manufacture (Technical Bulletin #5), leaflet, 6 pages, by S. Mason and J. Kent of PNG Building Research Station, 1970, free to serious groups, from DTWS.

"The purpose of this bulletin is to provide instruction in the preliminary identification of suitable material for the manufacture of stabilized bricks." The soil combinations described are to be used with an earth ramming machine, such as the CINVA-Ram. Tests to determine soil composition are described.

Manufacture of Stabilized Bricks Using Ramming Action Brick Machine (Technical Bulletin #6), leaflet, 12 pages, by S. Mason and J. Kent of PNG Building Research Station, 1970, free to serious groups, from DTWS.

"The purpose of this bulletin is to act as an instruction manual in the operation" of a brick ramming machine developed in Papua New Guinea, similar in principle to the CINVA-Ram. Basic steps in soil testing and preparation, and operation of the machine are provided, with photographs.

Selection of Materials for Burnt Clay Brick Manufacture (Technical Bulletin #7), leaflet, 5 pages, by Papua New Guinea's Building Research Station, 1970, free to serious groups, from DTWS.

"The purpose of this bulletin is to provide instruction in the preliminary identification of suitable materials for burnt clay products." Burnt clay bricks are made from clay, and then fired in a special oven (kiln). Simple tests to determine whether a material is suitable for use in burnt bricks are described. (See next entry).

Small-Scale Manufacture of Burned Building Brick, booklet, 14 pages, D. Thomas, also available in French, Spanish, and Portuguese, $1.00 from VITA.

MATERIALS: sheet metal to control draft; fuel: wood, coffee husks, coconut husks and hulls, dung, olive pits have all been successfully used.

PRODUCTION: very simple methods for local brick production.

"The purpose of this manual is to outline, in as simple a manner as possible, the details of making and burning clay brick suitable for domestic building. The scope of the manual is confined to 'cottage industries'...the author has had personal contact with such brickmaking plants in both Central Mexico and Honduras."

The booklet "explores the establishment and operation of a building-brick plant wherein nothing but 'on-hand' materials and labor will be utilized."

This is a step-by-step guide that also covers important considerations such as the location of suitable clay deposits and the firing and cooling of the finished bricks. Includes illustrations of the kiln and the brick-loading patterns.

1000 to 3000 Capacity Brick Kiln, leaflet, 18 pages, Papua New Guinea's Building Research Station, 1973, free to serious groups, from DTWS.

"A 1000 to 3000 capacity brick kiln has been devised by the Building Research Station, to meet the needs of small scale intermittent production of a durable material at the village level. The kiln is a rectangular construction with an internal dimension sufficient to stack to a predetermined pattern of a maximum of 3000 bricks within its walls."

According to the authors, "the design has been made as simple as possible, eliminating the need for skilled labor in its construction." Their design appears to be an efficient one capable of creating uniformly durable bricks; significant if this characteristic is an important one in the reader's area. This kiln is more complex than the one described in VITA's **Small Scale Manufacture of Burned Building Brick** (see review). Also, this design doesn't employ a flue system, and the firebox construction seems less flexible than in the VITA design (which could be easily enlarged to whatever capacity is desired).

A well-illustrated leaflet with excellent features such as a glossary of terms and detailed drawings.

Wood and Bamboo Construction

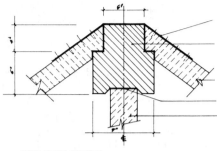

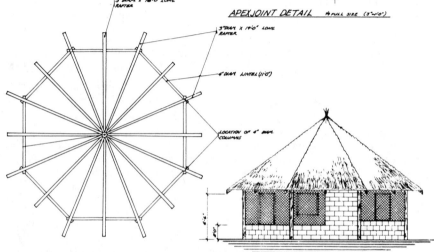

Pole Buildings in Papua New Guinea, booklet with design drawings, 41 pages, Peter Lattey, 1974 (to be revised), $3 from the Forest Products Research Centre, P.O. Box 1358, Boroko, Papua New Guinea.

This book describes work with traditional designs from PNG using wooden poles to build houses, schools, and meeting centers. 12 designs are presented, with drawings and photos. Also covered are details of how to connect poles at joints, and how to join the poles to walls using galvanized iron strips.

The designs are based on the author's actual experience in building in PNG. He used traditional building techniques, updating and improving them. The methods and the designs should be applicable to many places where wood poles are available for housing, if an effort is being made to use low-cost local materials, local labor, and simple construction techniques.

Manual of Rural Wood Preservation, booklet, 27 pages, Forest Products Research Center, 1975, $3 from Office of Forests, FPRC, P.O. Box 1358, Boroko, Papua New Guinea.

This is a practical manual for wood preservation techniques, useful in any tropical area where wood rots quickly or is eaten by termites. The areas covered include sections on: wood-destroying insects and fungi, building practice, materials (including poles and woven bamboo), treatment methods for rural areas (including sap replacement, use of C.C.A. and Octabor chemical preservatives). This last section is very useful, as it outlines the various

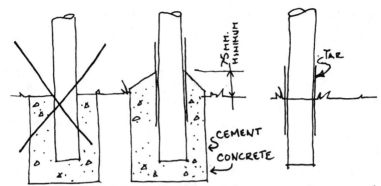

treatment methods in detail. The building techniques are also very useful for designing wooden structures to last longer.

Both this book and **Pole Buildings in Papua New Guinea** could be very useful to someone who is designing low-cost, simple housing in rural areas.

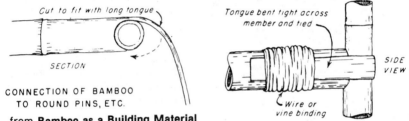

CONNECTION OF BAMBOO TO ROUND PINS, ETC.

from **Bamboo as a Building Material**

Bamboo as a Building Material, booklet, 52 pages, F. McClure, 1953 (reprinted 1972), available free to serious groups from U.S. Dept. of Housing and Urban Development, Office of International Affairs, Washington DC 20410 USA.

The how-to material and many of the photos in this booklet have been reprinted in the VITA **Village Technology Handbook**. Shows techniques of fastening bamboo without the use of nails, and various uses of bamboo in building construction around the world.

In addition, there is a rather general 5-page discussion of the use of bamboo in housing. Another section is given to bamboo reinforcement of concrete; this is a reprint of a technical summary of conclusions from tests on concrete beams. Problems included bond between bamboo and concrete, and swelling that occurs when seasoned bamboo absorbs moisture from wet concrete.

While many houses have been built with only a machete, more refined or elaborate structures might require some of the handtools briefly described (no illustrations). The booklet also includes a lengthy list of bamboo types used around the world, and a 60-entry list of selected references up to 1953.

Palms—Their Use in Building, booklet, 26 pages, 1964, free to serious groups, from Dept. of Housing and Urban Development, Office of International Affairs, Washington DC 20410, USA.

This article reviews the uses of the palm all over the world, both as a building material and for other products, such as sugars, starches, oils and waxes. In buildings, the uses for walls, floors, and roofing are detailed. Suggestions are made to improve the use of palm wood, through preservation and other means.

Grasses—Their Use in Building, leaflet, 5 pages, 1964, free to serious groups, from Dept. of Housing and Urban Development, Office of International Affairs, Washington DC 20410, USA.

This is a very brief survey of the world-wide uses of grasses, primarily for thatching. Scientific names for the grasses are given, along with the regions in which they are used. In addition, there is a discussion of the simple tools and methods generally needed to make thatched roofs.

Low Cost Housing: Prefabricated Panel System (Technical Bulletin #14), booklet, 39 pages, D. Brett of Papua New Guinea's Building Research Station, 1974, free to serious groups, from DTWS. .

''To assist in providing accommodations for low income earners in PNG this bulletin outlines economies possible by using a prefabricated panel construction technique. Prefabricated building can maximize returns in material, labor and money. This bulletin explains a simple technique through which reductions in materials and construction time can significantly reduce other building costs.''

Contains construction techniques using these prefabricated walls (made from wood), assembly drawings for making the panels themselves, and photographs. The panels can be made locally using only hand woodworking tools.

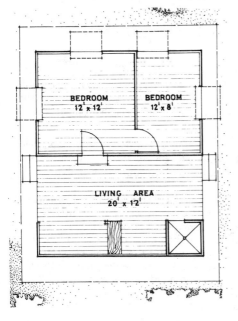

Experimental Low Cost Housing, booklet, 23 pages, by the Building Research Station in Papua New Guinea, free to serious groups, from DTWS.

This is a compilation of 11 low cost building designs developed for use in Papua New Guinea. A photograph and floor plan is included for each; the designs range from 321 to 910 square feet. Prefabricated panels (see **Technical Bulletin #14**) and stabilized earth bricks are used in the designs.

''Detail sheets (dimensional drawings) at the conclusion of the book indicate the form of construction used. This booklet is good as an illustration of the types of low cost homes that are being experimentally built in PNG. The designs are not new or novel—they are simply attempts to fit PNG's resource and economic conditions.

The Jalousie—An All Wood Louvre Window, plans, 4 pages, Forest Products Research Center of Papua New Guinea, Technical Note No. 3/1975 from Office of Forests, FPRC, P.O. Box 1358, Boroko, Papua New Guinea.

''For many years all-wood louvre windows called 'Jalousies' have been used to advantage in the Philippines. These windows...are attractive, secure, and can be fabricated using the simplest of tools and wood.''

"The window is an arrangement of overlapping wooden boards or slats. The slats are nailed on side frames which are cut in half. Each board is nailed with two nails on each end, one nail on one half of the frame and the other nail on the other half. This allows free movement of the boards or slats to be in the closed or open position as desired."

A useful design idea for inclusion in any type of housing.

The Yurt, plans, 1 large fold-up sheet, W. Coperthwaite, $3.50 from the Yurt Foundation, Bucks Harbor, Maine 04618, USA.

MATERIALS: wood planks, plywood, glass, glue, paint, 2x¼ inch steel bar, insulation, (4)-3/8 inch cable clamps, 2-3/8 inch steel cables 60 feet long.

PRODUCTION: simple hand tools; the steel bar is welded into a ring.

Well-illustrated dimensional drawings with text and assembly information. The Yurt is a circular dwelling that originates in Mongolia "where the prototype has for thousands of years been found to withstand the severe cold and violent winds of the steppes...The purpose of this design is to reduce the skills needed in building to a minimum and still have a beautiful, inexpensive, permanent shelter...The design of the contemporary Yurt is the result of 10 years' effort to develop techniques that make it possible for children and unskilled adults to participate in a major way in the creation of their own shelter."

Bill Coperthwaite created this particular design for North Americans. It remains simple in both materials and tools required, although some of the materials may be expensive in other parts of the world. It can be built by several people in just a couple of days.

Coperthwaite's solid board Yurt design (drawing by Charney in **Build a Yurt**)

The Yurt has a ten-sided plywood floor. The overlapping boards forming the exterior wall slope outward as they go up. They are held together at the top through the principle of the tension band (such as is often used in wooden buckets) with a 3/8-inch cable. The roof slopes gently to the center of the structure, where a steel band forming a skylight keeps the roof from collapsing inward. This structure is evidently remarkably strong, and requires no complicated, expensive supporting beams. A very good design.

Build a Yurt, book, 134 pages, Len Charney, 1974, $3.95 from WETS.

This book presents a Yurt design based on the author's own experience. Charney began with the Yurt Foundation's design, and incorporated many of

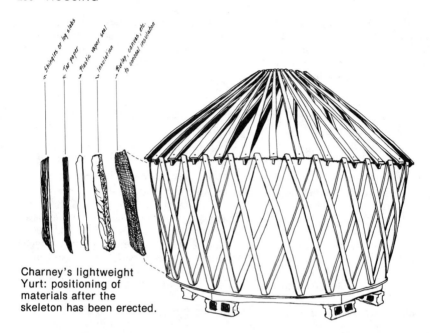

Charney's lightweight
Yurt: positioning of
materials after the
skeleton has been erected.

the original elements from the Mongolian Yurt back into it. The walls and roof
are made from 1x2 inch wood strips arranged in a lattice network, rather than
the solid boards used by the Yurt Foundation. The positioning of the wood
strips in combination with a 3/16 inch steel cable provides for an extremely
stable, strong structure.

The book has both text and drawings/photographs. The author describes in
detail the construction steps, including building a wooden floor, using canvas,
burlap, tarpaper and/or wood shingles to cover the framework. The explanations are clear and easy to follow. Another good design.

LATE ADDITION

Chawama Self-Help Housing Project, Kafue, Zambia, book, 80 pages,
American Friends Service Committee, 1975, $3.00 from American Friends
Service Committee, 1501 Cherry Street, Philadelphia, Pennsylvania 19102,
USA.

"Between 1968 and 1973, a project to improve the conditions of life of
squatters in Kafue was conducted jointly by the Government of Zambia, the
Kafue Township Council and the American Friends Service Committee. The
objective of the project was not only to provide acceptable housing with
suitable amenities but also to develop patterns of cooperation among the
residents which would create the conditions of a viable and harmonious
community."

The report contains a foreword by Dr. Kenneth Kaunda, the President of
Zambia, stressing the national priorities and ongoing impact of the project.
Well-illustrated and documented with photographs, drawings, charts and
tables, the report covers all aspects of the project design, planning, and
construction. The book shows how the successful effort in community-building

at Chawama was the result of thorough surveys of the origins, nature and needs of the squatter settlement. Included is a good review of CINVA-Ram block construction, the building method the Chawama community finally chose.

''The project may be seen as an instance of productive collaboration between a foreign voluntary agency and an African government as they joined together to meet a pressing social need. The AFSC found that it could respond to the government's explicit request for assistance with a flexible and informed approach, as well as with a philosophical outlook in respect to self-reliance which was in harmony with the government's. Zambian participation in all aspects of the project, from planning to actual construction, was central to the philosophy underlying the program's development. Thus the AFSC played a catalytic and facilitating role, not a controlling one.''

Recommended.

FURTHER REFERENCES ON HOUSING AND CONSTRUCTION

Design of Medical Buildings is a remarkable book on the use of local building techniques and architectural styles for low-cost medical buildings; see review on page 253.

'Thailo' Ferrocement Rice Bin booklet includes some solid information on the art of ferrocement construction; see review on page 122.

Small Farm Grain Storage also includes some information on ferrocement construction techniques; see review on page 124.

HEALTH CARE

Health Care

Leading off this section are three very good annotated bibliographies on the subject of low-cost rural health care in developing countries. There are also practical books to be used by doctors and other highly trained personnel, and books to be used by lesser-trained locally-recruited health auxiliaries. The classics **Medical Care in Developing Countries** and **Pediatric Priorities in the Developing World** should be required reading for all expatriate medical personnel, and there is much in them to be recommended to nationals in developing countries. Half a dozen books are to be found on the Chinese experience with health care—of considerable relevance to other developing countries attempting to meet the health care needs of large dispersed populations under conditions of limited resources.

One concept that emerges strikingly is the need for wider use of health auxiliaries—non-professional health workers. In developing countries doctors are trained at great expense in national manpower and resources, yet generally prefer to remain in the urban areas where they service the small proportion of the population that can well afford the customary fees for service. Even if this were not the case, there are simply not enough doctors and not enough of the supporting facilities they are trained to depend on; nor is there any possibility of training enough doctors to fill the enormous need for health care that exists. Wider use of medical auxiliaries is essential if there are to be any available health services in many areas.

The need for more medical auxiliaries is also acutely felt in the United States, a country which 'imports' many thousands of graduates from the poor countries that can least afford it. This is no less than a national disgrace. We too need larger numbers of lesser-trained health workers to become self-sufficient in health care. Such people are quite capable of treating most common health problems. Doctors are probably universally over-worked, whether in the halls of 'Mass. General' or in the rural areas of Central America. Even self-less service in a needy area, however, does not even begin to meet the longer term health care needs of the people unless it involves training members of the community so that they can begin to tackle their own health care problems. In developing countries the vast majority of health problems are relatively simple ones, often avoidable through the application of basic principles of preventive medicine, and usually compounded by a poor level of nutrition and a lack of access to prompt treatment.

A villager whose main qualifications are the ability to read and write (3 to 6 years of primary education) and a sense of responsibility and compassion for his/her fellow human beings can be trained in two months to diagnose, treat and prevent 95% of the health problems commonly found in developing countries. Often these local health workers have proven themselves to be more effective in diagnosing and treating common local problems than a small, overburdened professional staff. They live among the people they treat and charge what people can afford. Because they have grown up in the community, they know the socio-economic and family history of their patients, and they are sensitive to local concepts of health, disease, and treatment. For these reasons, they frequently have insights into the causes of local health problems and their advice is more likely to be understood and followed.

In many of the programs that do use medical auxiliaries, these people are given almost no responsibility; their role is limited to dispensing aspirin and cough syrup, and referring anyone who really needs care to the medical professionals. This represents a sad failure to develop the full potential of this approach which has, where carried out properly, involved the community for the first time as 'promoters', not just 'recipients' of good health.

Another emerging principle is the necessity of integrating health care with community development. Good health must be based on an agriculture that produces an adequate diet for all the members of the community; it must be based on a self-conscious populace that can organize itself to tackle the communal problems of water supply and sanitation. The seeds of good health must be planted and allowed to grow and multiply, given the careful attention that only the people themselves, with their knowledge of local culture and circumstances, can give.

The demystification of medicine is an essential corollary to these other principles. This does not mean that everything about medicine can be learned without extensive training—there will always be complicated health problems requiring university-trained professionals. But much can be accomplished by presenting the basic principles of health care in language that is understandable to the non-professional. We are very pleased to be able to review **Donde No Hay Doctor***, a manual in basic Spanish for village health workers, and two books, **The Well Body Book** and **The Tooth Trip**, which provide the English-speaking North American with the basics of health and preventive dental care.

*to appear in English in early 1977.

Low-Cost Rural Health Care and Health ManpowerTraining, annotated bibliography, 164 pages, Shahid Akhtar, 1975, free to libraries, researchers, institutions, etc. in less-developed countries (others Canadian $5.00), from the International Development Research Center, Box 8500, Ottawa, Canada K1G 3H9.

This is the best of the annotated health bibliographies, with 700 concise entries. Publisher information is given where possible—no price information.

"This bibliography is an attempt to coordinate information of nontraditional health care delivery systems in remote regions of the world, especially in developing countries. The literature abstracted focuses primarily on new models of health care delivery, and on the training and utilization of auxiliary health workers. (Very little information is included on the economics of low-cost rural health care.) The bibliography is intended to be of use to: a) persons who are involved in planning, operating, and evaluating systems to provide rural health services; b) persons concerned with the training of auxiliary health workers to staff such systems; and c) organizations that are supporting research into the problems of organizing and staffing health care delivery systems."

The IDRC will attempt to supply a copy of any publication abstracted in the bibliography if it is impossible to find elsewhere.

The Training of Auxiliaries in Health Care, annotated bibliography, 110 pages, compiled by K. Elliott, 1975, £1.80 or US$4.15 surface mail from ITDG.

This is a good annotated bibliography with an extensive list of contacts. "The medical auxiliary concept was explored in the ITDG's publication in 1971 **Health Manpower and the Medical Auxiliary** (see review in this section) which also included an annotated bibliography about auxiliary use and training. We have tried to contact as many sources as possible for information about texts and other teaching aids. The quality of material received varies greatly and almost every reply emphasized the need for more and better manuals for auxiliaries, oriented to local conditions and written in the local language."

"Resources of medical and paramedical professionals are inadequate to meet Third World needs—nor are such expensively trained personnel necessarily as efficient at the village level as people recruited and trained locally... Today's emphasis is on the health team. To this auxiliaries can contribute at various levels from the village health aide, possibly just literate, up to the highly trained medical assistant who can diagnose and treat most pathological conditions."

The book is divided into 5 sections: Contacts (people who in some way contributed to the bibliography; names, organizations, and addresses numbering more than 600); Materials for Auxiliaries (books and publications)—13 pages; Materials for Direct or Indirect Absorption into Auxiliary Teaching Courses (publications)—15 pages; General Background Material (publications)—25 pages; and List of Training Centers and Contacts Country by Country—30 pages. There is also an appendix with journals and publishers listed.

Reference Material for Health Auxiliaries and Their Teachers, annotated bibliography, 41 pages, 1973, free from REMAHA, World Health Organization, 1211 Geneva 27, Switzerland.

This reference work is WHO's response to "the shortage of suitable reference material (textbooks, manuals, course guides, etc.) for health auxiliaries and their teachers and a nearly complete lack of such material in the local language spoken by these auxiliaries. In the delivery of health care the biggest need is for health auxiliaries working in rural and 'ultrarural' areas, i.e., medical assistants, auxiliary nurses, midwives, nurse-midwives and auxiliary sanitarians. Therefore REMAHA decided to concentrate its attention on reference material for these categories..."

"It was also agreed that by first giving priority to reference material suitable for the use of **teachers**—both groups, teachers and students, would be served. The main long-term objective however should be to promote production at national and local level of reference material for students—in other words to compose a kind of 'do-it-yourself kit' for teachers which should include a set of good examples of existing reference and source materials, a guide on the writing of manuals, and illustration material. This could enable them to undertake the local production of reference material for students which would meet the local requirements better and may be written in the local language."

208 references were selected from those gathered. This list has been divided into general subject categories. Within each category three further divisions are made: Recommended Material, Potential Source Material, and Other Material. The annotations are brief but concise. Publisher and price are given where possible. An updated version is in progress.

Health Manpower and the Medical Auxiliary, 65 pages, 1971, £1.80 or

US$4.15 from ITDG.

This book includes an annotated bibliography (19 pages) that is also contained in the larger annotated bibliography **The Training of Auxiliaries in Health Care**. There are also three articles not in the larger book: Oscar Gish points out the necessity of developing non-traditional health care systems in the developing world, if the health needs of these countries are to be met. Kenneth Hill discusses the importance of using health care auxiliaries. He also writes of the changes that need to take place in the training and roles of doctors in the health care systems, particularly in developing countries. Examples of some existing programs training and utilizing health care auxiliaries are provided by Katherine Elliot.

Medical Care in Developing Countries, book, 500 pages, edited by Maurice King, 1967, reprinted 1973, $12.50 ($11.25 to developing countries), from Oxford University Press, 16-00 Pollitt Drive, Fair Lawn, New Jersey 07410, USA; or available possibly at lower cost from Oxford University Press, Electricity House, Harambee Avenue, P.O. Box 72532, Nairobi, Kenya; Spanish edition available (price unknown) from Editorial Pax Mexico, Libreria Carlos Cesarman, S.A., Argentina 9, Mexico City, Mexico.

"A primer on the medicine of poverty." This classic book evolved out of a WHO/UNICEF supported conference on "Health Centres and Hospitals in Africa." In it, Maurice King, David Morley, Derrick Jellife and others come together under King's editorship to create a remarkable, comprehensive handbook for medical personnel. The slant is decidedly towards the doctor or other professional from the developed world, who is working in the developing world. Material covered ranges from the organization of health services and the cross-cultural outlook in medicine to pediatrics, anaesthetics, and the laboratory.

The contents are sophisticated yet understandable to the layman. Recommendations are always realistically within the limits imposed by poverty and a commitment to get basic care to the largest number of people possible.

Pediatric Priorities in the Developing World, book, 429 pages, Dr. David Morley, 1973, ₤1.25 or US$3.20 from TALC.

"This book examines the problem facing child health services throughout the developing world: the urgent need to decide which of all the measures that may be taken to reduce the appalling levels of childhood mortality and morbidity should have the highest priorities when financial resources are so severely limited...The author is responsible for the innovation of the under-fives' clinic and for the design of a weight chart" to quickly identify and combat malnutrition. These two measures have subsequently been adopted by many developing countries.

"The author's objective is to orient the medical student or doctor towards the practical problems he will meet when involved in child care in a rural community. Careful emphasis is placed on the social, economic, cultural and ethical considerations which are ignored by most medical schools. Not only doctors but also nurses and other health workers...will benefit from this book. It is written for the doctor dissatisfied with the type of medical training which is based largely on European systems of health care, much of which may be inapplicable to his own country."

Morley emphasizes low-cost health services, within the means of the people involved, and the need to make extensive use of auxiliaries and villagers themselves. Primary focus is on rural societies because of the large numbers of children and the need for a different type of health care system than that suited to urban areas. Morley also stresses the need for the pediatrician to work on health education, and teach his own skills to his staff.

Morley worked for many years in a rural area of Nigeria. More recently he was instrumental in the establishment of the Tropical Child Health Unit at the Institute of Child Health in London. He also helped create the organization Teaching Aids at Low Cost (see page 245).

Nutrition in Developing Countries, book, 300 pages, Maurice King and others, 1972, Ł2.20 or US$5.00 from TALC; Spanish edition available (price unknown) from Editorial Pax Mexico, Libreria Carlos Cesarman, S.A., Argentina 9, Mexico City, Mexico.

"There are many reasons why children are malnourished. One of them is that people do not know enough about nutrition or how to feed children. This is why we have written this book. Some of the people who might read it have not been long in school, so we have tried to write it in easy English with as few new words as possible. We hope that it will be useful to everyone who can do anything to improve nutrition and especially to medical assistants, medical students, nurses, midwives, agricultural assistants, community development and homecraft workers and also to teachers in schools. All these people can teach other people. This, therefore, is mostly a book to teach what and how to teach."

Chapter headings include: Growth, When Growth Fails, Proteins, Energy Foods, Vitamins and Minerals, Non-Foods and Water, More About Food, The Need for Food and its Cost, Feeding the Family, Artificial Feeding, The Food-Path, Helping Families to Help Themselves, and Helping the Community to Help Itself. The appendix explains how this book can be used in class. There is also a vocabulary-index which explains the unusual terms.

The authors say that this is mostly a book for Malawi, Tanzania, Zambia, Botswana, Rhodesia, and Kenya. It certainly has much that would be of interest anywhere. Includes many drawings.

Doctors and Healers, book, 63 pages, A. Dorozynski, 1975, price unknown, from International Development Research Centre, Box 8500, Ottawa, Canada K1G 3H9.

A good introduction to the rationale and philosophy arguing for the increasing use of health auxiliaries and local people involved in their own health care.

"There is a virtual monopoly concerning health care delivery, and that monopoly does not always serve the best interests of all people. Other methods of health care delivery can be not only more effective under certain conditions, but also much less costly."

The author demonstrates that for the problem of health care delivery there are many practical solutions that are outside the medical monopoly. He cites successful examples from many developing countries.

Health By The People, book, 202 pages, edited by Kenneth Newell, 1975, 36 Swiss Francs or US$12.00, from World Health Organization, Distribution and Sales Service, 1211 Geneva 27, Switzerland; or local WHO distributors.

This is a collection of descriptive articles on 10 successful rural health programs in Indonesia, India, Guatemala, Venezuela, Niger, Iran, Tanzania,

China and Cuba. Focuses on community development and health services that use local people as health workers. The programs described range from national to village scale.

"There is no longer any doubt that a primary health worker can work effectively and in an acceptable manner and that he or she does not need to be a nurse or a doctor as we at present know them."

"The wider issues presented here include...self-sufficiency in all important matters and a reliance on outside resources only for emergencies; an understanding of the uniqueness of each community coupled with the individual and group pride and dignity associated with it; and lastly, the feeling that people have of a true unity between their land, their work, and their household."

"Each country or area started with the formation, reinforcement, or recognition of a local community organization. This appeared to have five relevant functions: It laid down the priorities; it organized community action for problems that could not be resolved by individuals (e.g., water supply or basic sanitation); it 'controlled' the primary health care service by selecting, appointing, or 'legitimizing' the primary health worker; it assisted in financing services; and it linked health actions with wider community goals."

"In no example presented here is there a separation of the promotional, preventive, and curative actions at the primary health care level."

Written by planners, participants, and observers. Follows the origin and evolution of each of the 10 programs.

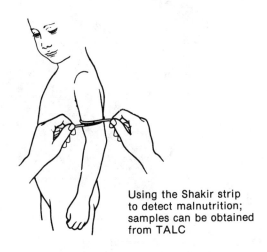

Using the Shakir strip to detect malnutrition; samples can be obtained from TALC

Health Care Publications from Teaching Aids at Low Cost, Institute of Child Health, 30 Guilford St., London WC1N 1EH, England.

The following books and pamphlets are available from TALC (most of the longer publications are reviewed separately):

a) **Paediatric Out-Patient's Manual for Africa**, booklet, 50 pages, by the staff of St. Luke's Hospital in Nigeria, 1975, £0.25 or US$0.50.

For use by senior staff nurses, student nurses and paramedical staff. Includes 5-year weight chart, immunization routine, intravenous fluids. Lists symptoms for common ailments and malaria, malnutrition, pneumonia, polio, anemia, cholera, urinary infections, tuberculosis, whooping cough, tetanus. Dosages of common drugs for newborn infants and young babies.

b) **Care of the Newborn Baby in Tanzania**, booklet, 43 pages, by Dept. of Child Health at the University of Dar es Salaam, 1975, Ł0.40 or US$0.80.

"This manual was written for Tanzanian medical assistants, but nurses, rural medical aids, medical students and doctors should find it useful. It attempts to give an account of the most important aspects of care of newborn babies in this country."

Chapter headings: characteristics of the newborn baby, routine management and abnormalities during the newborn period, and the low birth-weight baby.

Many illustrations.

c) **Memorandum on Tuberculosis in Developing Countries** and **Memorandum on Leprosy Control**, both about 20 pages, Ł0.15 or US$0.30 each.

Standard First Aid and Personal Safety, book, 253 pages, American National Red Cross, 1973, $1.95 from WETS.

A very good basic first aid book. Well illustrated. A good value at the price.

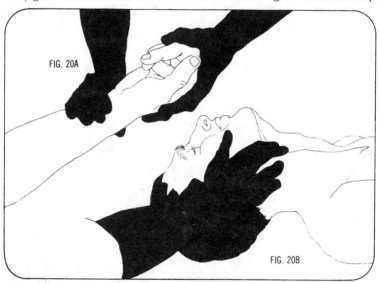

FIG. 20A

FIG. 20B

One of the many drawings in **Standard First Aid and Personal Safety**

Health Care in China—An Introduction, book, 140 pages, Christian Medical Commission, 1974, Ł0.60 or US$1.25 from TALC.

The Christian Medical Commission gathered a group of medical and social scientists in Hong Kong (3 of whom then visited the People's Republic of China). This group was asked to try to answer the question "What in the Chinese experience of rebuilding a health care system might be of value to communities in other cultures and social systems?"

"This booklet is that group's answer. The Christian Medical Commission is publishing this report because we believe that the information will be of value to health workers both in the developing world and in the industrially developed countries where the failures in health care systems stand out so sharply against the technological and economic advancement."

This book briefly examines the following (chapter headings):The relationship of health to national development goals, health care organization, epidemic disease control, population policies, traditional and Western medical practices, and manpower for health care. At the end an interesting list of the contents of a barefoot doctor's bag is provided.
A good overview of the Chinese health care system by an impartial group.

Medicine in China, reprints of 5 articles from the British Medical Journal, 17 pages, Dr. E.M. Adey and Dr. A.J. Smith, 1974, £0.40 or US$1.00 from TALC.

Five articles by Dr. Adey and Dr. Smith, published in the British Medical Journal, and reprinted especially for TALC. These are very good overview articles on a health and health care system that has successfully reached China's enormous rural population—an extraordinary achievement. The articles cover: the relationship of traditional to modern medicine, barefoot doctors and their function within the medical pyramid, public health, population control, and the relationship of the structure of Chinese medicine to the structure of the society.

TALC provides these reprints because "up till recently health workers have assumed that the developing countries of the world would slowly produce a health care pattern not dissimilar to that which exists in Europe and North America. However, many now believe we all may have much to learn from patterns of care developed in countries such as China."

Serve the People, book, 317 pages, Ruth and Victor Sidel, 1973, $4.45 from WETS.

Victor Sidel, a physician specializing in community medical care, and Ruth Sidel, a psychiatric social worker, provide a complete description of the health care system in the People's Republic of China as of 1973. They describe how health care has evolved since the 1949 revolution to meet the needs of the Chinese people from the limited resources available.

"The methods used (in the PRC today) seem extremely well suited to the health problems of today's China, and even more important, they are remarkably well integrated with the social structure the Chinese are trying to build. They are recruiting, training, motivating and employing medical personnel in ways very different from those in the West. Human power is often substituted for technology, but within that context medical personnel appear to be used to their fullest potential. Medical care is considered not only in terms of individual well-being, but in relation to the society and its overall development."

The Sidels' description of the innovative and successful use of medical auxiliaries, integration of traditional and Western medicine, new approaches to mental illness, and revolutionary attitudes toward health care in the PRC make this an inspiring and important book for those interested in new models for health care.

Medicine and Public Health in the People's Republic of China, book, 333 pages, edited by Joseph Quinn for the Fogarty International Center for Advanced Study in the Health Sciences, DHEW Publication No. (NIH) 73-63, free to serious groups, from Office of Nutrition, USAID, Washington DC 20523, USA.

This book is a collection of articles on health and medicine in China, and contains information not found in the other books on China we've reviewed. The section "Chinese Medicine Throughout the Ages" includes articles on acupuncture, surgery, traditional medicine as a basis for Chinese medical practice and the role of the family in health care. The second section, "Health Care Organization and Administration" treats public health laws in China, health care in rural China, the training of medical workers and the Academy of Medical Sciences. The last group of articles describes the health problems that China is struggling to overcome today.

The introduction states: "Inasmuch as the audience for this document is intended to be those persons with a general interest in the subject of Chinese medicine, rather than the biomedical specialist, the lack of confirming evidence by onsite observation or experimentation was not considered a deterrent to the preparation of this document."

A Barefoot Doctor's Manual, book, 950 pages, translation of a 1970 Chinese manual by the United States Department of Health, Education and Welfare, Public Health Service, now reprinted in low-cost paperback form by Running Press, $5.95 plus postage from WETS.

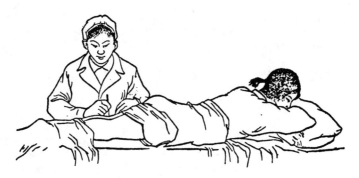

Acupuncture with the patient in the prone position

This enormous paperback was translated by the US Dept. of Health, Education and Welfare, from a manual originally published by the Institute of Traditional Chinese Medicine of Hunan Province, People's Republic of China, in September, 1970. "It focuses on the improvement of medical and health care facilities in the rural villages. The purpose is to integrate the following areas: prevention and treatment, with emphasis on treatment; disease and symptoms, with stress on disease; traditional Chinese and Western medicine, with attention on traditional Chinese medicine; the native and the foreign, with focus on the native; and mass promotion and quality improvement, with mass promotion as the base, and quality treatment as the goal. By following these principles and adapting itself to actual conditions on the rural level, this manual aims to basically meet the working needs of the "barefoot doctors" serving the broad rural population."

The first 6 chapter headings are: Understanding the Human Body, Hygiene, Introduction to Diagnostic Techniques, Therapeutic Techniques (Chinese herbs, folk treatment, Western treatment), Birth Control, Diagnosis and Treatment of Common Diseases. The seventh chapter is an extensive one (400 pages) on Chinese medicinal plants.

The successful integration of traditional with Western medicine serves as a useful model for many other societies.

Donde No Hay Doctor (Una guia para los campesinos que viven lejos de los centros medicos), handbook, 300 pages, David Werner, 1973, $5.00 ($3.50 to local groups in developing countries), from the Hesperian Foundation, Box 1692, Palo Alto, California 94302, USA.

"This medical handbook, written in basic Spanish specifically for the 'campesino' (villager), takes into consideration local beliefs and customs, gives guidelines for determining the usefulness vs. hazard of different folk remedies, and discusses the common misuses as well as correct uses of medications commonly available. It starts with a discussion of traditional concepts of illness and healing, and from there leads into 'modern' concepts. The book, which has hundreds of simple but informative drawings, is also used by health workers to teach patients about their health problems, their causes and prevention." An interesting feature of this book is a colored index that tells the names, uses, and prices of drugs the villagers may come into contact with (many of these drugs are commonly used without any knowledge of their effects).

This handbook is an excellent model of what can be done to entrust literate villagers with some of their own health care. It is a product of more than 10 years' work in the creation of a villager-run health care network in the mountains of Mexico, and uses much of the local campesino vocabulary.

The Spanish edition is now being widely distributed in Latin America. An expanded English version of this handbook is scheduled for late 1977, $5.00.

Sketches in **Donde No Hay Doctor**
illustrating the sewing up of a wound

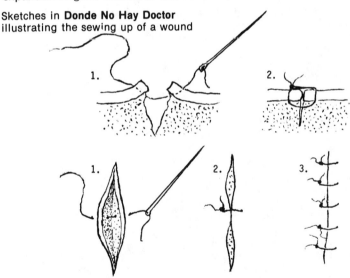

Ponga el primer punto en medio de la cortada, y ciérrela.
Ponga suficientes puntos para cerrar toda la herida.

The Child in the Health Centre—Book One: A Manual for Health Workers (Experimental English Edition), book, 552 pages, Maurice King and staff of Lembaga Kesehatan Nasional, limited circulation edition published in 1974 is to be replaced by a widely-available printed edition in early 1977, price unknown, contact Team Leader of MCH Package, Lembaga Kesehatan Nasional, Jl. Indrapura 17, Surabaya, Indonesia; TALC may distribute the new book.

This text is the key to "a health care package, which defines the minimum standard of outpatient care that we must provide for every child...the first basic language, problem oriented manual of health centre pediatrics." Moderate level of English ability required.

The simple language and careful explanations make this book useful to a wide range of health workers. Portions of it could be presented to beginning primary care workers. The full text could serve as a reference and training manual for more sophisticated experienced workers (this is assuming translation into local language at an equivalent level; only in a few developing countries where English language ability happens to be widespread, e.g., the Philippines and India, could this manual be used for such personnel in its current form). The text can be used for training at a wide variety of levels because it allows a worker to learn as much as he or she is able to learn. Simple scientific explanations.

There is a lesson in simple medical vocabulary and an indexed glossary of some 1200 medical and related terms, explained in simple English.

Subject matter includes mechanisms of infection and disease, health education, drug descriptions and equipment list, immunization and check-ups for the healthy child, records, clinic evaluation, and health care for newborn babies. There is a major section on the problems of sick children (275 pages) covering everything from problems such as malnutrition, diarrhea, and worms to injuries, poisoning, genito-urinary symptoms and children who can't walk or talk.

An extraordinary text crammed full of information and a lot of good human advice.

The Well Body Book, large paperback book, 350 pages, Mike Samuels M.D., and Hal Bennett, 1973, $6.95 from WETS.

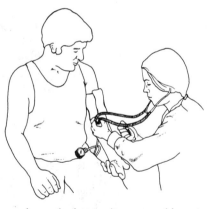

This book comes from the counterculture movement in the U.S., and is an attempt to demystify much of medicine as it is practiced here. The book explains how to perform a simple, basic physical examination, how to take a systematic medical history, and it describes the symptoms, causes and treatment of most common diseases found in the U.S. This enables the reader to do some self-diagnosis and treatment, but serves more to explain how the body works and what is disease and how it progresses. There is much space devoted to exercises that help one to feel health, tension, and disease in one's body, and how to relax and stay healthy.

The more conventional sections of the book (on basic physical examination and diagnosis & treatment—142 pages) are probably of more use outside the U.S. than the other, more culturally-bound sections. The simple language (some American slang, however) means that these more conventional sections might be adapted or serve as a model for manuals to be used with health auxiliaries. However, the lack of coverage of parasites and tropical diseases is a significant shortcoming in this regard.

The Tooth Trip, book, 232 pages, Thomas McGuire (D.D.S.), $3.95 from WETS.

''The Tooth Trip is a book of preventive dentistry. It tells how you can completely prevent cavities and gum disease through self-examinations and home care.''

This is a delightful, well-illustrated, very readable book written by a dentist. It explains tooth decay and gum and mouth diseases, and provides enough information for the reader to determine the likely nature of any mouth problem he or she may have.

The book goes a long way toward demystification of dentistry by explaining the equipment and procedures so that the patient can understand what's happening *and* participate in decision-making about what treatment he or she will get for a particular dental problem.

Highly recommended for Americans. The illustrated simple explanations of preventive dental care will be of interest to health and dental programs in developing countries (though the fancy equipment described in the latter part of the book is not widely available in these countries).

Simple Dental Care for Rural Hospitals, booklet, 26 pages, D. Halestrap, 1970, £0.40 or US$0.90, from TALC.

This booklet came out of the author's experience working with dental workers in rural Africa. Extraction, sometimes without local anesthesia, was usually the only treatment provided in cases of severe toothache or advanced gum disease. ''Consequently, it was considered that the dental workers in many of

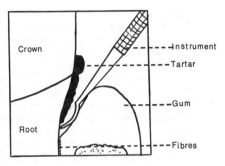

these hospitals would benefit from some further instruction in simple dental work, so the author arranged to provide this by re-visiting some eighteen of them. Any necessary instruments were supplied where needed and an experimental edition of this booklet was used during the work in order to provide a background to, and reminder of, what was being taught. It has now been revised in the light of further experience...Its aim, therefore, is to offer a simple basic textbook for use in rural hospitals in developing countries, it being primarily for the benefit of the para-medical worker whose job it is to treat dental patients.'' It is not intended to replace training, but to reinforce it.

The booklet gives a simple explanation of tooth decay, gum disease, and how to keep teeth clean. The treatment shown is removal of tartar, locating and giving injections prior to extraction, and methods of extracting teeth. Complications are briefly discussed. Sketches of a homemade headrest that attaches to a regular chair are included. The booklet has many photos and drawings. Text is in simple English.

A Medical Laboratory for Developing Countries, book, 330 pages, Maurice King, 1973, original hardback price was $8.00, paperback now available possibly at lower cost, from Oxford University Press, Electricity House, Harambee Avenue, P.O. Box 72532, Nairobi, Kenya; Spanish edition available (price unknown) from Editorial Pax Mexico, Libreria Carlos Cesarman, S.A., Argentina 9, Mexico City, Mexico.

''This book aims to bring the minimum level of laboratory services within the range of everyone in developing countries and is written especially for laboratory and medical assistants who work in health centres and district hospitals. Each piece of equipment needed in a medical laboratory is fully described and illustrated. (These drawings are explanatory only, and are not intended to lead to local production of the equipment.) Every step in the examination of specimens is simply explained and the method of performing it is illustrated; the methods chosen are those that give the greatest diagnostic value at the minimum cost. Ways of obtaining specimens are given, and where it might prove helpful some anatomy, physiology and a brief account of treatment is included. The last chapter contains a detailed equipment list (total cost about $500 in 1973)."

This book should be used by health workers with some basic laboratory science training, who have a good knowledge of English. King attempts to present the material in "easy English" but does not always successfully do this; nor does "easy English" mean that beginning-level English speakers will be able to use this manual. Good drawings may help to offset some language problems.

King covers the following major topics: basic relevant chemistry, sterile technique, descriptions of equipment and chemicals, records and specimens, weighing and measuring, the microscope, blood, urine, cerebrospinal fluid, stools, blood transfusion, and other specimens. There are more than 100 clear color plates of commonly seen slide specimens (in the hardback edition).

This manual is focused on what are certainly 'intermediate' technology and techniques for medical laboratories. Medical technology in the rich countries is rapidly becoming so capital-intensive that progressively fewer people can afford good quality care. Medical personnel are at the same time becoming increasingly dependent on expensive machines and tests to carry out their duties. Compared to this, King's book is a down-to-earth catalogue of relatively inexpensive equipment for basic laboratory tests. However, virtually all of the equipment King mentions would have to be imported (at a cost which in 1973 amounted to $500 per health center—presumably before shipping and taxes). There is a need to develop simple designs for this equipment so that it can be reproduced at least within the country, if not locally. China is one obvious source likely to have the necessary designs.

Highly recommended.

A Model Health Centre, book, 167 pages, by the Conference of Missionary Societies in Great Britain and Ireland, 1975, £3.30 or US$6.60 surface mail from TALC.

"...Offered as a design primer and reference book for those engaged in planning, developing, and operating health services whether at a national or local level."

This manual covers specifics concerning the architectural layout of a model health center, building dimensions, and cost of materials, all with many detailed sketches and diagrams. It also presents clinic schedules, record keeping, number and type of staff, operational policies, potential problems (with possible solutions), programs in immunization, nutrition, maternal-child health, under-fives clinics, oral hygiene, school visits, latrine construction, community involvement and support, and goals and philosophies.

The orientation is towards the community. "Not only are the staff to go out into the community, but also the community is to have facilities within the centre; these facilities being the main new idea generated by this study." The need for medical auxiliaries is also identified, recognizing that they can do an "immensely valuable job extremely well" in promoting community-based preventive medicine. The center ideally would have a staff of eight: two nurses, midwives, or medical assistants working with 4 auxiliaries (with 1-2 years in-service training) and 2 local assistants. The center is expected to be able to refer patients to doctors in a district hospital when necessary, and to receive visits from doctors on a regular basis.

There is an excellent bibliography of reference books, including books recommended for the health center library.

For new health programs this is an excellent guide for planning centers with a community outreach. The book should help lead to efficient and effective health care, especially through the promotion of preventive medicine. Established health centers will also find it valuable as a source of new ideas that could generate improvements in existing programs.

A valuable reference book that all health programs should have on hand.

Design for Medical Buildings, book, 146 pages, 1975, by Philip Mein and Thomas Jorgensen, $5.00 (for the paperback edition) surface mail from The Director, Housing Research and Development Unit, University of Nairobi, P.O. Box 30197, Nairobi, Kenya.

"The manual contains design, construction and cost guidelines for the building of medical facilities with limited resources. It has been prepared primarily for the doctor and his staff who, in rural Africa, must often be their own architects. It should however also be of value to the architect who, perhaps for the first time, is confronted with the special problems associated with the provision of medical buildings in rural areas.

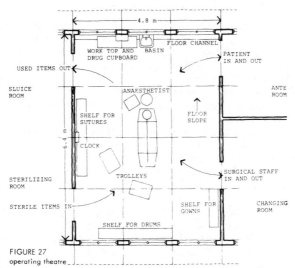

FIGURE 27
operating theatre

"Medical buildings at present tend to be excessively expensive, consuming funds which are sorely needed in other areas such as the primary health sector. The guiding principle of this book is that the expenditure of material, monetary and manpower resources (on buildings) should be reduced to the lowest level consistent with adequate and acceptable medical care."

The book covers everything from initial feasibility studies to supervision of the construction work. "Each building problem requires its own solution according to local needs and benefits from the use of local materials and skills." Design examples are given, but the emphasis is on "providing the tools and methodology for design in the form of standards and guidelines."

Here is an example of the contents: "The best guide to an appropriate type of construction is to study other buildings in the area, for example, their shape, whether they have flat or pitched roofs, and the materials from which they are made. It is generally true that the further one deviates from the local architecture, the more money and time will be used in building."

A remarkable book.

Health Records Systems, booklet, 20 pages, C. Frost and G. Ellmers, $1.50 from VITA.

"The development of this manual grew out of a need for an easy and concise health record system that required little or no experience with filing methods...Because there are so many variables present in each medical application, this manual is not designed as a definitive answer to problems. Instead, it is hoped that the suggested methods can be adopted or modified to meet any situation."

The booklet stresses the need for simplicity and uniformity in a health records system—for easy implementation and local use by workers with minimal training. Several record systems are explained, and sample charts and cards are included for each one.

Mosquito Control—Some Perspectives for Developing Countries, report, 50 pages, National Academy of Sciences, 1973, $4.25 from NTIS (Accession No. PB 224-749/AS; foreign orders add $2.50 handling charge).

"Not a technical handbook, this report aims at arousing interest in some unusual but promising mosquito-control methods that might otherwise be ignored. It is written for administrators or program directors of agencies that fund mosquito-control research and application projects and for scientists working on neighboring topics."

The booklet deals exclusively with biological control of mosquitoes, though the need for simultaneous environmental control (e.g. drainage) is stressed. No pesticide approaches are discussed, in part because "...mosquito resistance to chemical pesticides has caused the failure of many vector-control campaigns."

Particularly successful seems to be the minnow **Gambusia Affinis**, which can destroy large numbers of mosquitoes by feeding on the larvae. This approach is "particularly appropriate for controlling mosquitoes in rice paddies and small water impounds."

Contact, journal, 6 times each year, about 15-20 pages in length, usually one article in each issue and some news notes, available in English, French and Spanish, free from Christian Medical Commission, World Council of Churches, 150 Route de Ferney, 1211 Geneva 20, Switzerland.

"The papers seek to report current innovative and courageous approaches to the promotion of health care. Individual copies are devoted to case studies of comprehensive health care projects, discussions on the churches' role in healing, and address many of the practical concerns and needs of health workers around the world."

Past issues have covered topics such as: community health care in rural Java, family planning to benefit whom?, primary health care and the village health worker, a need for change in medical education, health care and justice, and self-reliance and nutrition. Highly recommended.

HEALTH CARE EQUIPMENT

Health Care Equipment

Most of the items listed in this section are such things as locally-built wheelchairs. Very little published material seems to be available on low-cost designs for the equipment used directly by health care personnel, such as microscopes, dental equipment, and so forth. It is useful to note that refrigerators can be operated using methane gas, and incubators can be heated by a few low-wattage light bulbs or by passing the exhaust pipe of a regularly-used engine-driven generator through the incubator compartment. Solar water heaters can be found in ENERGY: SOLAR, and the list of further references at the end of this section gives some ideas of books where simple designs for other equipment useful in health care can be found. Of particular note is Maurice King's book **A Medical Laboratory for Developing Countries,** reviewed in the HEALTH CARE section.

Intermediate Techniques: Designs for Hospital Equipment, booklet of simple drawings, 23 pages, S. Eaves and J. Pollock, 1973, Ł0.50 or US$1.15 surface mail from ITDG; or Ł0.20 from TALC.

MATERIALS: light metal pipe, sheet iron, angle iron.

PRODUCTION: small workshop needed, some welding desirable.

This booklet consists of 29 simple drawings of hospital equipment that can be produced in a small workshop. Dimensions and actual construction technique are to be decided by the reader.

Of particular interest are: a neo-natal suction pump; a premature baby incubator that used four 40-watt light bulbs; an haematocrit centrifuge for blood tests, that uses an electric sewing machine motor and can be made inside a heavy enamel cooking pot; a hospital water still; and a constant temperature water bath.

There are 9 items for which separate, more complete plans are now available (see the Designs for Hospital Equipment series that follows this entry). In addition to these, **Intermediate Techniques** includes a variety of cabinets, rolling tables, beds and similar hospital and clinic furniture.

All of the designs were developed in hospital workshops and the Zaria Intermediate Technology Workshop (Nigeria). The drawings have been reproduced with the hope that they will "provide ideas and stimulation to those interested in intermediate techniques."

The following Designs for Hospital Equipment are available in the form of dimensional drawings, for Ł0.45 or US$1.05 each from ITDG. Please note the drawings grouped together and reproduced here.

1—Invalid Carriage with Chain-Drive and Brake, 11 pages.

MATERIALS: 3/4" conduit tube or ½" G.I. tube; 1½" and 1¼" G.I. tube;

½'' plywood; bicycle chain, pedal, pedal bearing, front forks, 3'' gear, and 3 wheels.

PRODUCTION: some welding.

The drawings are straight-forward and sufficient for construction, using English units only.

3—Hospital Ward Screen, 7 pages.

MATERIALS: several sizes of tubing, some steel angle, and wire rod.

PRODUCTION: some welding.

Drawings with English units that are simple but sufficient for local construction. The screen has a metal tubing frame, and four rollers for easy movement. The only obvious reason for bothering with these plans is that such a screen might be easier to keep clean than a wood-and-woven-mat screen, if screens were considered necessary.

4—Instrument Trolley, 4 pages.

MATERIALS: metal conduit tubing, steel angle, flat bars, plywood, small wheels, perhaps formica for instrument surface.

PRODUCTION: some welding.

Drawings with English units only. Simple but sufficient for local construction. The trolley is just a metal cart. It has a metal tubing frame that supports two trays, and moves on four rollers.

5—Hospital Wheelchair, 6 pages.

MATERIALS: metal conduit tubing, steel angle, flat bars, plywood, small wheels, 6'' rubber rim wheels.

PRODUCTION: some welding.

Drawings with English units that are simple but sufficient for local construction. The wheelchair has a metal tubing frame, plywood seat, and ground-level wheels (thus it cannot be self-operated).

A similar wheelchair appears in **Intermediate Techniques**, under the name "Patient's Pushchair." The latter is only a simple drawing without sufficient information for construction.

6—Bush Wheelchair, 7 pages.

MATERIALS: conduit tubing, plywood, steel angles, two bicycle wheels.

PRODUCTION: some welding.

Dimensional drawings with English units that are simple but sufficient for

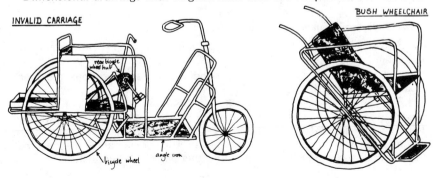

local construction. It has a metal tubing frame, plywood seat, and two bicycle wheels. These large wheels would enable it to handle relatively rough terrain, for which there is presently no other equipment. It appears that the wheelchair would have to be pushed by a second person in order to remain balanced and avoid tipping over backwards.

7—Bush Ambulance, 9 pages.

MATERIALS: conduit tubing, steel angle, plywood, bicycle wheels.
PRODUCTION: some welding.
Dimensional drawings with English units only. Simple but sufficient for local construction.

The bush ambulance is a kind of wheelchair with a tow-bar that can be attached to a bicycle with a chain or simple U-joint. It has a metal tubing frame, plywood seats, plywood foot-rest, and two bicycle wheels. It can travel over terrain that is rough, or along narrow tracks. It may also be drawn by a man on foot or an animal. The same piece of equipment appears in **Intermediate Techniques**, but is entitled "Bicycle Ambulance," and consists of a simple drawing only.

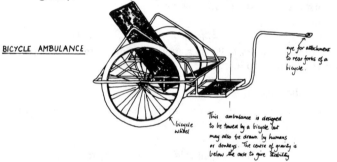

BICYCLE AMBULANCE

eye for attachment to rear forks of a bicycle.

bicycle wheel

This ambulance is designed to be towed by a bicycle but may also be drawn by humans or donkeys. The centre of gravity is below the axle to give stability.

8—Hospital Blood Transfusion Drip Stand, 5 pages.

MATERIALS: conduit tubing, iron tubing, steel rod, iron rod, rubber bushing, 4″ diameter rubber tires (3).
PRODUCTION: some welding and brazing.
Dimensional drawings with English units. Simple but sufficient for local construction. The blood transfusion drip stand is made of tubing, with rods bent to hold the bottles. The height is adjustable after construction. The stand rolls on three wheels—these may be unnecessary. The same piece of equipment appears in a single simple drawing in **Intermediate techniques**, but is entitled "Transfusion stand."

10—Paraplegic Turning Frame, 13 pages.

MATERIALS: galvanized iron water tube, mild steel angle sections and flat bars, standard bicycle hub wheel bearings, 4″ diameter rubber tires (4).
PRODUCTION: some welding, metal-bending; the specifications are more critical for this unit than most of the others.
Dimensional drawings with English units. Simple but sufficient for local construction. This particular set of drawings is somewhat more sophisticated than the others, and demands closer attention to the details given, so that the moving parts will operate smoothly and have sufficient clearance. It seems that a good rural workshop could still produce this piece of equipment.

12—Hospital Patient's Trolley, 5 pages.

MATERIALS: galvanized iron tube; mild steel strips, angles and rods; metal hinges; 4″ diameter rubber tires.

PRODUCTION: some welding.

Dimensional drawings with English units. Simple but sufficient for local construction. This particular set of drawings is less clear than most of the others. It requires more imagination on the part of the builder—though the trolley itself is not really of complicated design.

The trolley keeps a patient flat on his back while being rolled along. A stand with attachments to hold transfusion bottles is part of the trolley. The same trolley appears in **Intermediate Techniques**—some of the fittings are perhaps more understandable in that single drawing than in this set of production plans.

PARAPLEGIC TURNING FRAME   PATIENT TROLLEY

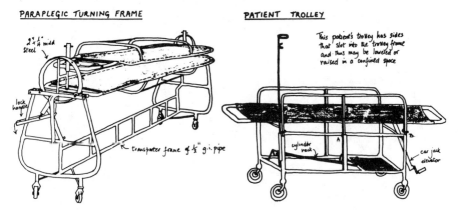

Bandages Impregnated with Plaster of Paris, booklet, 19 pages, Dr. Louis Navias, $1.50 from VITA.

MATERIALS: cotton gauze, plaster of paris, a binder material that can be made from a variety of local resources, denatured alcohol, glycerine.

PRODUCTION: simple, both for making plaster of Paris from gypsum, and later producing the bandages with a metal trough and locally-made roller.

This is a fairly complete booklet for the local production of bandages (casts) for support of weak limbs and broken bones. It follows the process from the production of plaster of paris from gypsum, the production of organic binder substance from a variety of local resources, mixing, and finally to the production of good bandages. Numerous charts and descriptions of short tests and experiments are included to facilitate local adaptation.

Although thorough and fairly simple, the use of some technical terms and particularly the need for local adaptation/selection of a particular organic binder (whose chemical composition must be known), mean that this booklet is not directly useable at the local level. However, a simplified version with specific amounts of particular ingredients locally available could easily be produced.

FURTHER REFERENCES ON HEALTH CARE EQUIPMENT

Medical Laboratory for Developing Countries has a good presentation of the low-cost commercially available basic equipment for a medical laboratory; see review on page 251.

Build Your Own Science Laboratory and **The New UNESCO Source Book for Science Teaching** both have information on simple microscopes, slide apparatus, and other equipment for a science teaching lab that might be useful to rural health care workers; see reviews on pages 52 and 53.

PRINT, COOPERATIVES, BEEKEEPING, SOAP-MAKING

Print, Cooperatives, Beekeeping, Soap-Making

Print

These materials will give an idea of some of the low-cost uses of print for communication. **Rural Mimeo Newspapers** looks at one particularly promising low-cost print technology. **Print: How You Can Do It Yourself** gives an overview of the low-cost print technologies as they now exist in the developed countries (we have not seen enough examples of low-cost print technologies currently being employed in the developing countries). **Basic Bookbinding** provides the necessary information for small-scale hand bookbinding; also useful to a library or information center. **How to Do Leaflets, Newsletters and Newspapers** gives some valuable guidelines for newspaper writing, editing, and organization (**Rural Mimeo Newspapers** also does this well). And **The Organization of the Small Public Library** can be valuable for any group with an information center or local appropriate technology library.

We have not yet found a book that we like on silk-screen printing (an extraordinarily low-cost technique for printing posters and putting designs on clothing). However, it should be noted that there is a very good section with drawings of the equipment in the VITA **Village Technology Handbook.** The subject is also introduced by **Print: How You Can Do It Yourself** (with drawings) and **Liklik Buk** (without drawings)—see review on page 50. For North Americans, we suggest referring to the series of illustrative drawings on page 359 of the **Whole Earth Catalog.**

Rural Mimeo Newspapers, booklet, 42 pages, Robert de T. Lawrence, 1965, $2.00 from UNESCO, 7 Place de Fontenoy, 75700 Paris, France; or WETS.

This is a low-cost printing scheme for small communities in developing areas. Describes a successful project in Liberia, in which 30 mimeo papers grew up within a year, a number of them spontaneously. Small mimeograph machines are lightweight and easy to repair. They can be purchased for as little

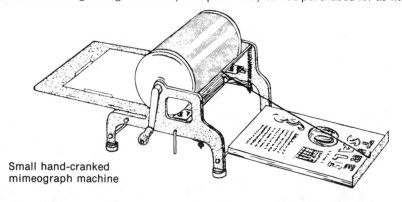

Small hand-cranked
mimeograph machine

as US$40-50. ''On the basis of the Liberian experience, it is estimated that a paper could be established with an initial outlay of as little as $100, and that it could provide a living for its owner/editor from the outset.''

Part II, on organizing a rural newspaper program, gives suggestions on how to plan, staff, publish, and assist low-cost newspapers in rural communities of developing countries.

Part III, on how to publish a low-cost community newspaper, gives hints on writing, editing, printing, and distributing a rural newspaper. It is suggested that sponsoring agencies adapt this section to fit local conditions and publish it in pamphlet form.

Print: How You Can Do It Yourself, booklet, 56 pages, J. Zeitlyn, 1975, Ł1.00 or US$2.00 from Interaction Trust Ltd., 14 Talacre Road, London NW5, United Kingdom.

This is a good overview of low-cost community-level print technologies. While most relevant to groups in developed countries, it does give a good idea of the operation of spirit and stencil duplicators, offset presses, and silkscreen techniques.

How to do Leaflets, Newsletters, and Newspapers, booklet, 44 pages, Nancy Brigham, 1976, $1.25 plus postage from The New England Free Press, 60 Union Square, Somerville, Massachusetts 02143, USA.

This booklet provides guidelines for the small community or neighborhood newspaper. Includes suggestions for the effective design of leaflets, the scheduling of a newsletter or newspaper, how to determine the ''look'' of the newspaper, the techniques of layout and paste-up, obtaining and presenting information, and editing. Briefly covers the low-cost print technologies.

While this booklet is intended for use in the United States, the language is quite easy to understand and it may be useful in other areas.

Basic Bookbinding, book, 136 pages, A. Lewis, 1957, $1.75 from Mother Earth News.

This book provides step-by-step instructions with many illustrations for the essential operations involved in the binding of books by hand in cloth and in library style. ''Sufficient detailed information is given to enable a student, working on his own, to do so with success.''

Materials used are carefully explained. All the tools necessary are relatively simple ones. The descriptions and illustrations of the tools needed are sufficient for the craftsman to make them himself.

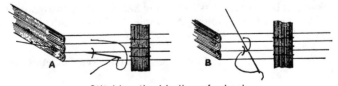

Stitching the binding of a book

The Organization of the Small Public Library, booklet, 66 pages, I. Heintze, 1963, $1.75 from META.

This booklet ''has been written specifically for people without previous training in librarianship who are faced with the task of running small public libraries and need guidance. Explains the rudiments of public library work in a simple and practical way, with many illustrations, and gives the reader the basic information he needs...Intended primarily for the rapidly developing countries" but the principles and procedures are nearly the same everywhere.

Might be useful in the acquisition and organization of a small library of materials on appropriate technology.

Cooperatives

Cooperatives are essential to the successful development and spread of appropriate tools and techniques. The cooperative, if properly structured, represents an appropriate scale and kind of organization for many purposes. We have not been able to pursue this important subject, in part because we feel that information on the formation and operation of cooperatives is better known than almost any of the information on other small-scale technologies and techniques. Therefore, in this section we include only some information on simplified accounting systems for cooperatives.

In the future we would appreciate being notified of particularly good practical publications on the subject of cooperatives.

The following teaching handbooks in booklet form are available from ITDG (see address listing). They cost $1.95 for a complete set, or $0.80 each. "Each of the individual pamphlets on accounting is complete in itself, dealing with a particular type of co-operative business, but, together, they constitute a comprehensive manual on accounting for primary co-operatives." The series presents a particular, simplified system—a double-entry book-keeping system based on a single working ledger. The authors have attempted to meet "a real and widespread need for a system which is both effective and straight-forward enough to be taught to rural-based secretaries in a relatively short time."

Generally, these handbooks all seem to be excellent. They do, however, assume that the economic system has already moved considerably away from local self-sufficiency in food production.

The booklets are:

Co-operative Accounting #1, Thrift and Credit Co-operatives, 20 pages, ITDG, 1970.

This is a booklet for small thrift and credit co-operatives that do not yet have an efficiently working accounting system. In addition, it can be used to form such co-operatives. Such organizations serve to encourage members to save, and provide a locally-controlled mechanism to grant loans to members.

This booklet has been written as a teaching handbook, so the points made are illustrated by practical examples. A simple table for calculating interest payments is included and explained in the appendix.

Co-operative Accounting #2, Consumer Co-operative Societies, 38 pages, ITDG, 1971.

''The main function of a consumer co-operative is to buy goods and re-sell them to its members. It raises capital from its members" for rent and an original stock of goods, by selling shares to them.

This booklet is for creating buying co-operatives, or for the use of any buying co-operative that does not yet have a simple but effective accounting system. There is an appendix with an information table for calculating interest and dividends to be paid on members' shares.

Co-operative Accounting #3, Marketing Co-operative Societies, 31 pages, ITDG, 1972.

This booklet is for any small group marketing the same kind of product, especially produce—but within a larger system (not simply in a village market). The example used involves 150 members. This booklet claims that marketing co-operatives have more possible forms than the two previous kinds of co-ops. "A marketing co-operative is primarily concerned with marketing the goods that its members produce. Cattle, coffee, cotton, fish, handicrafts, rice, and wheat are examples. These goods can be sold in many different ways: to a marketing board, to wholesalers, through co-operative unions, direct to individual retailers or consumers, or by auction."

The advantages of a marketing co-op are: producers can get a better price than the individual; they can often sell directly to consumers; they can spread the transport costs; and they can establish a reputation for grading and reliability.

"What all marketing co-operatives have in common is that they provide a service to their members in helping them market their produce and to obtain a fair price for it...Many marketing co-operatives encourage the use of modern techniques by selling seeds, fertilizers, and tools to their members." Often these can be purchased much more cheaply in quantity.

Beekeeping

One major unresolved problem with the literature on beekeeping is that it is written from the point of view of developed countries. It is assumed that such specialty items as prepared comb foundation can be purchased (not made) by the beekeeper. These pressed foundations when fitted into the frames assure that there will be a 'bee space' of 5/16-inch-between frames, in which bees will not build solid combs but leave as passageways. Comb foundations are important, as they reduce the amount of beeswax required for building comb, enable the beekeeper to control where the comb will be constructed, provide a solid starting point for comb on both sides, and are usually made of worker-cell bases, which reduces the number of unwanted drone-cells.

Several options are available to prospective beekeepers in areas where the equipment to make the comb foundations is not available. These were recommended to us by an old, experienced beekeeper who began long before the time of the commercially available comb foundations. One approach from that time period also relied on movable frames. The top portion of each frame has pieces of comb cut from a natural hive and tied in place with string. The bees will extend the comb to fill each frame. The string should be cut within the first few days as soon as they are no longer necessary, or the bees will waste considerable effort in cutting it themselves.

Another approach would be to acquire a sheet of the commercial comb foundation, and make a mold from it to be used with a hand-operated press for the production of additional foundations. This first sheet should be chilled so that it hardens, and then an impression of both sides can be obtained by applying a thick layer of some kind of hardening material.

This discussion illustrates a major drawback to much of the literature in appropriate technology categories. Somewhere along the line between pre-industrial modes of production and mechanized operations the vital elements of control over the process and developments of technology were lost to the user. Critical steps have been bypassed or forgotten, making it difficult to come up *with simplified systems that still employ the most current knowledge.*

First Lessons in Beekeeping, book, 127 pages, C. Dadant, 1917 (reprinted 1975), $1.00 from Dadant & Sons, Inc., Hamilton, Illinois 62341, USA.

An excellent primer for the beginning beekeeper, this inexpensive book is a reliable source of information about bees, hives, producing honey, and other subjects. This is a condensed version of the more exhaustive text, **The Hive and the Honeybee** also by Dadant.

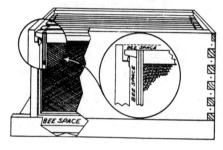

The hive is constructed so that there is a bee space (5/16 inch) in which bees will not build combs and which they will reserve as passageways for themselves. (from **First Lessons in Beekeeping**)

The Hive and the Honey Bee, book, 740 pages, Dadant & Sons, Inc., 1974, $9.95 from Dadant & Sons, Inc., Hamilton, Illinois 62341, USA.

"A collection of world famous beekeeping authorities contributed to produce this classic reference book on all phases of bees and beekeeping. Twenty-two chapters cover all the aspects of beekeeping from history of beekeeping through equipment, management, anatomy and behavior, pollination, disease, honey and honey processing, honey plants, beeswax and pesticide poisoning."

Those willing to make the major investment in this expensive text will not be disappointed. The format is more readable than **The ABC and XYZ of Bee Culture**, although the content is essentially the same.

The ABC and XYZ of Bee Culture, book, 726 pages, A.I. Root and Company, reprinted 1974, $9.75 from A.I. Root and Company, Medina, Ohio, USA.

This is a complete encyclopedia on the art and science of beekeeping, arranged alphabetically and well illustrated. A.I. Root and Company are pioneers in beekeeping enterprises in the United States, and have enjoyed an international reputation since the first edition of this volume was published in 1877. They cover all innovations to the present, and an extensive glossary helps the reader to understand the more technical portions of the book. Recommended to those interested in large-scale bee cultivation.

"Some cover of boards or other shade material (trees, bushes) should be provided to protect the hives from the severe heat of the summer sun. In very hot climates, sheds are built to shelter the hives. It is not uncommon in hot climates for the combs to melt from excessive heat." (Under such circumstances the bees do their own airconditioning of the hive. They gather small droplets of water to be evaporated inside the hive, cooling it down. The beekeeper can cooperate by placing nearby a pan of water filled with pebbles, so that the bees can land without falling in and drowning—editors.)

Bee-Hive Construction (Leaflet CL/AT5), 5 pages, free from CCPD, World Council of Churches, 150 Route de Ferney, 1211 Geneva 20, Switzerland.

Sketches with a short description of the fabrication of a simple bee-hive from wood, using handtools.

A Homemade Honey Extractor, plans, 3 pages, Larry McWilliams, 1974 in Countryside Journal, reprinted in **Cloudburst 2** (see page 44).

MATERIALS: ½-inch rod, ½-inch bolt (3), a 3-inch and 10-inch pulley (wood), water pipe cap, wire mesh, short pipe for drain, belt, plywood or wood planks.

PRODUCTION: hand tools.

This is a simple unit made mostly of wood, which holds honeycombs in wire baskets and spins them with the use of a hand crank. This motion forces the honey out of the comb, and it flows down to a drain at the bottom of the barrel or wooden box in which the spinning unit is housed. You get clear honey with a minimum of effort. The empty wax honeycombs can be reused by the bees, who will concentrate on filling them with honey rather than having to build them again.

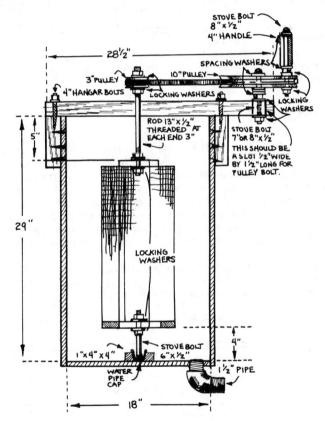

Cross-section of the honey extractor

Plans for a Complete Bee-Keeping System, dimensional drawings, 20 pages, 1975, $5.00, from Garden Way Publishing, Dept. 50027, Charlotte, Vermont 05445, USA.

MATERIALS: wood, 20-gallon steel drum, nuts and bolts, steel shafts, pipe nipples, netting, glue and nails.

PRODUCTION: some metal drilling, but mostly use of hand tools.

This is a full set of plans for small-scale honey production. Included are the bee-hive with all components, honey extractor, smoker, gloves, and protective veil. The dimensional drawings (English units) are clear. The equipment can be easily constructed of locally available materials in most places.

The information is complete and detailed, but the price is quite high for such a short leaflet, and may keep many people from ordering this set of plans.

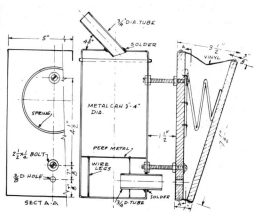

Smoker for temporarily driving the bees out of the hive

Soap-Making

Soap-making is a very simple process, for which there are a variety of good informative leaflets available (see below). There is no reason that a country should be dependent upon multi-national corporations for such a basic item as household soap; surprisingly, this is increasingly the reality in many places. The well-advertised soap of the multi-national corporations is not as good as homemade soap for many uses, such as removing grease from clothing. And the chemical additives such soap contains are destructive to plants. Homemade soap on the other hand contributes to lush plant growth wherever used wash water is dumped.

Soap-making is the basis for small-scale cottage industry in many areas. At the Bangli mental hospital in Bali, coconut oil soap is made in large blocks. The blocks are cut using simple wire and wood frames (see sketches below). Each of

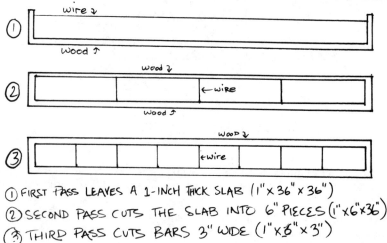

① FIRST PASS LEAVES A 1-INCH THICK SLAB (1"x 36"x 36")
② SECOND PASS CUTS THE SLAB INTO 6" PIECES (1"x6"x36")
③ THIRD PASS CUTS BARS 3" WIDE (1"x6"x3")

the three dimensions is cut simply and accurately by pushing the soap through the frames. The bars are then stamped with a heavy press that gives them an attractive, imbedded design, and then wrapped in colorful locally-printed paper. The soap is marketed in the community. Jobs are thus created and money kept within the community.

In some countries, all lye (caustic soda) is imported. A report on the local manufacture of caustic soda has been produced in a limited number of copies by the Technology Consultancy Centre, University of Science and Technology, University Post Office, Kumasi, Ghana, West Africa. This describes a small scale industrial process for the production of sufficient quantities of caustic soda to lead to production of 1,000 bars of soap per day.

Introduction to Soap Making (A.T. Unit Report #9), reprint of a VITA paper, leaflet, 26 pages, small charge for postage, from Appropriate Technology Unit, Christian Relief and Development Association, P.O. Box 5674, Addis Ababa, Ethiopia.

An excellent description of the process of home or village-level soap-making. Recipes for soaps made of different materials and with different uses. Explains how to make your own lye from hardwood ashes, and how to measure the strength of this lye solution.

We think this is the best paper available on soap-making in village circumstances. Recommended.

How to Make Soap (Reprint #43), 4 pages, $0.25 from Mother Earth News Reprints, Box 70, Hendersonville, North Carolina 28739, USA.

This is quite good; it tells both how to obtain lye from hardwood ashes and general soap-making hints when using purchased commercial lye. It does have a recipe that uses coconut oil instead of animal fat (mineral oil cannot be used to make soap).

The Preparation of Soap, leaflet, 6 pages, $1.00 from TOOL.

This leaflet includes a method for determining the concentration of lye through the use of a float; it also covers vegetable oils other than coconut oil, which are mixed with lye in different proportions. Sometimes a bit confusing.

Instructions for Making Soap, single page, free from The Pennwalt Corporation, Pennwalt Building, Three Parkway, Philadelphia, Pennsylvania 19102, USA.

These instructions are quite good for U.S. residents (based on the use of Pennwalt lye). Only to be used with lye in U.S. commercial concentrations.

Make Your Own Soap, small paperback book, $1.95 from WETS.

This is one of a number of paperback books on soap-making. It gets into the finer points of elegant soaps, coloring and perfuming.

FURTHER REFERENCES ON SOAP-MAKING

VITA Village Technology Handbook has a very good section on village-level soap-making—essentially a condensed version of the material included in the Introduction to Soap Making listed on this page; see review on page 41.

Dick's Encyclopedia of Practical Receipts and Processes has a wide variety of recipes for different kinds of soaps; see review on page 54.

2,000 Down Home Skills and Secret Formulas for Practically Everything also has many different soap recipes; see review on page 55.

Liklik Buk, the Papua New Guinea rural development catalogue, has some very general directions for making soap; see review on page 50.

VILLAGE INDUSTRIES
AND OTHER SUBJECTS

Village Industries
and Other Subjects

The books included in this section cover a wide variety subjects important for village and small community self-reliance, ranging from soy bean processing to pottery.

Simple Methods of Candle Manufacture, compiled by the Industrial Liaison Unit of ITDG, 19 pages, 1975, Ł0.70 or US$1.60 from ITDG.

"The technology of candle making is very old and despite the introduction of mass production methods, candles can still be made by well-established methods which require only simple equipment. Much of this equipment can be made by rural craftsmen." Different waxes and wicks are discussed. Illustrations and descriptions are given for each of four methods of small-scale production.

Chalk Stick Making, booklet, 19 pages, Dr. Louis Navias, French edition also available, $1.50 from VITA.

MATERIALS: plaster of paris, hydrated flour, hydrated lime with talc or clay, and corn starch

PRODUCTION: simple tools

"Chalk sticks and blackboards are as basic to the business of education as teachers and classrooms. In some parts of the world, however, chalk sticks are difficult to obtain...imported, costly, and in short supply. The booklet provides a brief outline and simple introduction to the small-scale manufacture of chalk sticks." Five methods are included, using a variety of ingredients: flour, cornstarch, hydrated lime with talc or clay, plaster of paris and others. Diagrams are included for each of the simple chalk stick making techniques, including dimensional drawings for some simple molds and other equipment that can be locally produced or adapted.

The book presents a straight-forward approach, and sufficient information to go ahead with the production of chalk sticks, thus reducing dependence on imported chalk and creating local jobs.

Chemicals from Biological Resources, booklet, 24 pages, Alan Dalton, 1973, Ł0.50 or US$1.15 from ITDG.

This is a general survey, especially useful in identifying chemicals from renewable resources that can be produced economically in areas of labor surplus. The author mentions processes that cheaply produce chemicals that might otherwise have to be imported. No details are given on the processes themselves, however.

"This survey represents an attempt to stimulate those people surrounded by abundant and renewable natural resources to see them as raw chemical materials, which, by simple processing often suitable for cottage industries, may enable them to overcome some of their other economic and social needs."

Rural Tanning Techniques, book, 250 pages, FAO Development Paper #68, 1974, $2.50 from Distribution and Sales Section, Food and Agriculture Organization of the United Nations, Via delle Terme di Caracella, 00100 Rome, Italy; or from regional distributors of FAO publications.

MATERIALS: compounds such as potash alum, salt, hard water

PRODUCTION: the necessary sharp tools are illustrated in the book, and can be locally made; many of the tannin compounds can be produced locally also; the emphasis is on single-family or village-level operations.

This is a very detailed, thorough book on rural tanning techniques. It covers the preparation of hides and skins for tanning, various tanning methods and processes for different types of hides and skins. There is a section on setting up a rural tannery and checking for suitable water supplies, and a section on the tanning process as performed in rural India, using improved techniques from the Central Leather Research Institute in Madras. As written, the book describes very labor intensive techniques, taking extensive examples and illustrations from Kenya. It does, however, proceed with the assumption that labor should eventually be replaced by machinery and more "modern" facilities and methods.

A very useful aspect of this book is that it aims at less developed areas where all of the materials and chemical compounds might not be readily available. Thus, there is discussion of how to obtain the ingredients and make these different compounds, such as vegetable tannins, from barks, trees, and nuts. This orientation to rural, self-reliant areas makes this book very useful in non-industrialized areas where there is a premium on materials that can be found and used locally. Many photos.

Home Tanning and Leather Making Guide, book 176 pages, A.B. Farnham, 1950, $2.00 from WETS.

MATERIALS: knives, other sharp tools, soap, water, salt, tannin compounds.

PRODUCTION: suited to single person operations, but access to available tannin compounds is necessary.

It has been said that this book "contains absolutely everything you need to know—old time techniques." In fact, that's not quite true, and **Rural Tanning Techniques** has several advantages over this book. Farnham covers the various aspects of tanning, including how to skin an animal, curing the hides, preparing hides for tannin, and the actual tanning and leather-making process. Also included are descriptions and illustrations of the simple sharp tools that are needed, and other considerations such as how to check for hard water, which tanning chemicals to use, etc. It is assumed that the tanner will be able to obtain the necessary potash and other solutions, and does not cover how to make these materials locally (see **Rural Tanning Techniques**).

The last three chapters of the book deal with the marketing of hides. Much of the information is directed at rural American towns, but there is good information on the preparation of hides for shipping and marketing, as well as how to make hides into leather in this section.

This book would be useful in teaching tanning techniques, or as a reference for someone who is already familiar with the processes.

Yay, Soybeans!, pamphlet, 36 pages, The Farm, 1976, free from The Farm, Summertown, Tennessee 38483, USA.

Soybeans are converted into a wide array of nutritious and exotic foods in the recipes of this stimulating booklet: soymilk, soycheese, soy ice cream, soy yogurt, and many others. Recipes and techniques are detailed, delicious, and simple. The information comes straight from the mouths and stomachs of The Farm, a rural community of young American vegetarians living on a solid rice and beans diet in Tennessee.

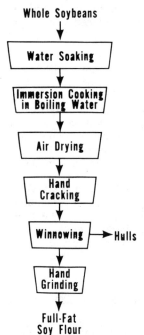

Full Fat Soy Flour by a Simple Process for Villagers, leaflet, 11 pages, 1975, free from Agricultural Research Service, U.S. Dept. of Agriculture, Peoria, Illinois 61604, USA.

This useful leaflet presents all the needed information for converting raw soybeans into flour with a high nutritional value.

"One part of this research was to find a simple hand process for villagers where skilled labor, electric power, and steam cannot be had. A process that uses only simple equipment was developed. With this equipment six men can make 136 kg. (300 lbs.) of soy flour in an 8-hour day. Operation can be changed from hand to mechanical by wind, water, animal, or other available power source. A production of 136 kg. per day will supply half the daily need for protein of more than 1,600 adults."

The equipment required appears to be available in a village setting, or easily manufactured locally, such as a hand grain winnower (see page 98) and a hand grinder (usually commercially available). This process could be used in many circumstances.

Village Soy Protein Texturizer, information from Meals for Millions Foundation, P.O. Box 680, Santa Monica, California 90406, USA.

This group has a unique machine which processes soy beans to produce a textured soy protein product. This final product is similar in texture to meat and is aiding the spread of soy bean consumption for low-cost protein. The texturizer costs about $50.00. Meals for Millions cooperates with groups from 20 countries, providing training in the use of the machine.

The Homesteader's Handbook for Raising Small Livestock, book, 242 pages, J. Belanger, 1974, $3.95 (paperback) from WETS.

This is a handbook on raising small livestock on a small scale. Easy to understand, non-technical language. Many drawings and photos, often of build-it-yourself cages, pens, water devices, etc. Covers goats, rabbits, chickens, sheep, geese, hogs, turkeys, guinea fowl, ducks, and pigeons. Written for North Americans moving from the cities back to small farms. No information on vaccinations or shots. Does include a list of further references.

There is a good section on rabbits. Rabbit meat tastes like chicken. France and Italy together produce 200 million pounds of rabbits each year. Rabbits reproduce quickly and have high labor and small space requirements. The fur can be used (tanning instructions are given). Hutches (rabbit cages, usually raised off the ground) can be easily built out of bamboo. This chapter also tells how to make a well-balanced rabbit feed.

The Backyard Dairy Book, book, 86 pages, Len Street and Andrew Singer, 1975, L1.55 or US$3.55 from ITDG.

This book was written to encourage small-scale home dairy production in England, using goats and cows. Briefly looks at breeds, feed and housing requirements, and milking. Most of the book is on home production of dairy products from milk: cream, butter, cheese and yogurt.

Automotive Operation and Maintenance, large paperback manual, 200 pages, E. Christopher Cone, 1973, $6.50 from VITA.

This book grew out of the author's experiences in Liberia, West Africa. He began as a "mechanically inclined novice" working with a church mission. "It was largely through experiment and occasional disaster that much of the material for this book was assembled."

"The intent is to offer suggestions to the driver or mechanic who operates in an area where service facilities and technical assistance are not readily available. In such areas he must be his own advisor on every problem which may arise.

"The first section concerns operation of a car in an area served by pioneer roads. The section is intended to assist the driver with temporary repairs to his vehicle so that he can get home in the event of mechanical trouble.

"The second major portion of the book is devoted to maintenance suggestions. These are intended for use in a frontier shop or repair center, no matter how ill-equipped this may be. This book should be used as a supplement to the vehicle's shop manual, and as a source of guidance. The shop manual will tell how to reline the brakes, for example, but this book is intended to indicate when relining is needed."

Chapter topics are: mechanical emergencies while driving, operating on pioneer roads, avoiding road hazards, extricating the vehicle, procedures when stranded, winches and towing, field expedients (on the spot temporary repair suggestions), check lists (for problem-locating and solving), tests and testing equipment, shop techniques, body repairs, a shop building, diesel engines, tools and equipment (for the car and shop), vehicle modification, parts and supplies, storage facilities, preventive maintenance, selecting a vehicle (a look at four-wheel-drive vehicles available), miscellaneous formulas, definitions, and an index.

The manual includes many large, simple drawings and diagrams that provide ingenious solutions (along with the text) to difficult problems; e.g. freeing a car stuck between logs on a bridge; extricating a vehicle stuck in mud or snow; temporary repair of broken brake or fuel lines. There are diagrams for homemade hoists and tire removers as well as general shop hints and a very handy index.

The **Whole Earth Epilog** calls this book "an experienced list of disasters that can befall you and your vehicle...solutions that require only rudimentary skills and primitive resources." The language is not difficult; closer to standard English than almost any automobile shop manual.

The emphasis is on imagination and improvisation. An excellent book.

Ceramics: Techniques and Projects, book, 80 pages, by the editors of Sunset books and Sunset magazine, 1973, $2.45 surface mail, from Mail Order Department, Lane Publishing Co., 85 Willow Road, Menlo Park, California 94025, USA.

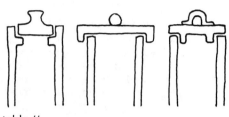

"Designed for the beginning potter as a general introduction to working with clay, this book features discussions of basic techniques and suggestions for projects that can improve skills or be starting points for other ideas... Much can be accomplished with only a few simple tools and a work table."

Covers the basic characteristics of clay, simple tools (photos and descriptions, but not including a potter's wheel), hand-building and the coil method, working on the potter's wheel, making spouts and handles, glazes, and effects of firing.

The low price and large number of photos (more than 100) make this an excellent introductory book on pottery.

Kilns: Design, Construction, and Operation, book, 240 pages, Daniel Rhodes, 1968, $9.95 from WETS.

"This book is written from the point of view of one who has built and fired kilns, rather than that of a theorist...The principles and methods involved in kiln design and construction receive a thorough and authoritative treatment. The information which applies to the structure and size of any kiln, be it gas-fired, oil-fired, wood burning, or electric, updraft or downdraft, is the basis for discussion of methods and procedures required by specific kilns. Thus, all aspects—masonry construction, fuels, burners, combustion, refractory materials, heat retention, and transfer—are covered."

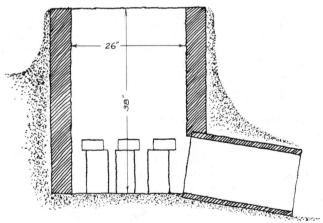

174. *Rudimentary wood burning kiln.*

Thoroughly illustrated and detailed with photographs, sketches, tables, and dimensional drawings, this authoritative book is written in easily understandable English. Included are various original designs, accompanied by step-by-step instructions and diagrams, enabling the reader to construct a kiln with confidence. Firing theory and techniques, temperature measurement and control, and safety precautions are presented effectively for proper maintenance.

We find this book a valuable asset, although its high price may limit its circulation in developing nations.

A Potter's Book, book, 283 pages, Bernard Leach, 1940 (reprinted 1973), $15.00 from WETS.

This book is to the whole subject of ceramics what Daniel Rhodes' book is to kilns—thorough, but a bit expensive. This is a book on "the workshop traditions which have been handed down by Koreans and Japanese from the greatest period of Chinese ceramics in the Sung Dynasty. It deals with four types of pottery: Japanese raku, English slipware, stoneware, and Oriental porcelain. The student of pottery learns how to adapt recipes of pigments and glazes, and designs of kilns, to local conditions. A vivid workshop picture is given of the making of a kiln-load of pots from start to finish..."

Includes basic recipes for glazes and descriptions of different kinds of kilns and firing methods. Many illustrations. There is a glossary of pottery terms. Highly recommended.

FURTHER REFERENCES ON VILLAGE INDUSTRIES

VITA Village Technology Handbook has plans for a potter's wheel; see review on page 41.

Making Do has drawings of a potter's wheel; see review on page 46.

Cloudburst 2 has drawings of a potter's wheel and two kinds of pottery kilns; see review on page 44.

PERIODICALS

Periodicals

Appropriate Technology, journal, 4 times each year, Ł3.00 or US$7.00 (for surface mail) and Ł4.50 or US$10.50 (for airmail) for one year, from ITDG.

This is the journal of the Intermediate Technology Development Group. It is intended as a medium of communication for people involved in the development and dissemination of intermediate-level appropriate technologies in developing countries. Problems, ideas, and solutions are shared. Readers are encourage to contribute. Each issue includes news, notes, and book reviews. There are typically thirteen 2-page articles on a wide range of subjects in each issue. If you are working in a developing country and can afford only one journal, this is the one to get. Highly recommended.

Some of the most interesting articles from each issue are:

Vol. 1, No. 1

Education, Training, and Development (and Appropriate Technology);
Intermediate Food Technology in Tanzania;
Rural Technology in China;
Village Aluminum Project, Oporama River State, Nigeria;
Problems of Developing Appropriate Technologies in India;
Appropriate Agricultural Mechanization Technologies for Asian Development;

Vol. 1, No. 2

Large-Scale Solar Steam Cooker (Brace Research Institute—plans);
Water Pipes from Bamboo in Mezan Teferi, Ethiopia (drawings of drill bit design and joints);
The Cassava Grinder (plans);
Better Maize Handling in Southern Nigeria (plans for oil-drum dryer);
The Cycle Rickshaw (describes a back-axle differential for pedi-cabs);
Simple Methods of Building Low-Cost Roads (drawings);

Vol. 1, No. 3

Laurie Baker and the Technology of Low-Cost Building (some drawings);
Pitcher Farming (drawing);
Medicine in China;
Solar Water Heater from Bardoli (drawing);
Nepalese Water Mill;
Rock Bits from Scrap;
Rasulia Bladed Roller Thresher (plans);
Simple Foundry Methods for Village Use;

Vol. 1, No. 4

Reducing Nepal's Grain Losses;
A Machine for Preparing Pounded Yam and Similar Foods in Nigeria;

A Design for a Medium-Span Wooden Bridge in Kenya;
Appropriate Technology, Poverty, and Unemployment—The ILO Program;
The Hydraulic Ram;
Roofing with Low-Cost Corrugated Asphalt Sheets;

Vol. 2, No. 1

Ferrocement Boatbuilding in a Chinese Commune;
Animal Power Boosts New Crop Production;
A Simple Manual Maize-Shelling Device (plans);
An Efficient, Cheap Incinerator (plans);
New Agricultural Machines from International Rice Research Institute;
Fence Post Driver;

Vol. 2, No. 2

A Foot-Powered Thresher for Rice and Other Small Grains;
Irrigation and Self-Reliance;
Water Jars from Cement Mortar (photos);
The Generation of Methane from Waste Materials;
The Concept of Village Technology in Eastern Africa;
Indigenous Building Methods.

Vol. 2, No. 3

The Cretan Sail Windwheel as a Power Source;
Starting a Workers Cooperative;
Educational Equipment: An Appropriate Technology?;
Ferro Cement Barge Project in the Sudan;
Some Developments in Tropical Timber Technology;
An Introduction to Methods of Rainwater Collection and Storage;

Vol. 2, No. 4

Low Cost Tube Wells;
Food from Wind (an excerpt from the book of the same name);
Oil Soaked Wood Bearings (a reprint of the AGL leaflet of the same name);
Aquaculture in Resource Development;
Health Auxiliary Training in Papua New Guinea;

Vol. 3., No. 1

A Low Cost Rice Storage Bin of Non-Reinforced Cement for Rural Farmers;
A Simple Low Maintenance Water Filter Suitable for Village Use;
Wooden Jolley to be used on Adapted Kick Wheel;
Nethouse Horticulture in Botswana;
Intermediate Technology Suburban Style in Africa;
The Chain and Washer Pump (an excerpt from the book of the same name);

Vol. 3, No. 2 (August 1976)

Low Cost Oil Palm Mill Project in Sierra Leone
Hand-Dug Water Wells Lined with Reinforced Concrete
Portable Hand Planter for Grains
Practical Fish Farming: Making a Start
A Maize Sheller for Every Household
Farming and Ranching the Green Turtle
A Solar Oven From Yantra Didyalawa

Alternative Sources of Energy, magazine, quarterly (4 times each year), 70 pages average length, U.S.—1 year subscription for $5.00, foreign—1 year subscription for $6.00 (foreign airmail $15.00), from Alternative Sources of Energy, Route 2, Box 90A, Milaca, Minnesota 56353, USA. Back issues: #11-16 are $1.25 each; #17 & 19 are $2.00 each, #18 & 22 are $1.50 each; and #20 & 21 are $1.75 each.

Alternative Sources of Energy is a quarterly magazine for people concerned with the development of alternative technologies for a decentralized society. Emphasis is on alternative environmental technologies in energy sources, agriculture, architecture, transportation, and communications; and the synthesis of old and new technologies. It attempts to provide a communication link between those who are exploring ideas for individual and small community energy self-sufficiency. This is a magazine for experimenters—there are very few plans for finished and tested products presented. ASE is aimed primarily at people in the U.S.; we feel, however, that there are occasionally articles of interest to those in developing countries who are experimenting in somewhat the same areas. Each issue contains articles, experiments, book reviews, letters, and feedback from readers. Highly recommended.

The articles listed below are some of the highlights from the first 22 issues (numbers 14-22 have more practical projects than do the earlier issues). Note that issues 1-10 are now available as a single book.

Issues #1-10, $5.00 in U.S., $6.00 foreign.

This a collection of many different articles from ASE's first 10 issues. There are many theoretical but simple discussions, philosophies and some interesting project ideas, although they are just that: ideas, not specific construction plans. Articles on solar, wind, methane, water power, agriculture and architecture. It is written in a generally rambling text, and is useful for an experimenter who wants to know what is happening with alternative energy sources in the U.S.

Issues #11-22 contain the following articles of possible interest in developing countries:

New Alchemy Institute's Sail Windmill in Madurai India—description (#12);
Bio-dynamic Gardening (#12);
Wave Power—energy for pumping from ocean waves (#12);
Chimney Heat Exchangers (#13);
Rewinding a Car Generator for 110 volts AC (#13);
Underground Hydroponic Greenhouse and Fish Tank (#13);
.75 Kilowatt Windmill—some drawings and text (#14);
A Graphical Method for Designing Windmill Blades (#14);
Water Power—overview (#14);
Natural Water Cooling and Freezing Using Night Sky Radiation (#14);
Algae Research in India—very extensive (#16);
Baking Bread in a Solar Oven (#16);
Hybrid Windmills (#16);
Recycling Auto Batteries (#16);
Alternative Energy Equipment Guide—mostly U.S. manufacturers (#17);
Greenhouse Design (#18);
Geodesic Parabola—for making solar focusing collectors (#18);
Kilowatt Counter: A Consumer's Guide to Energy Concepts, Quantities, and Uses (#19);
Intermittent Absorption Refrigerator—the icy ball system (#20);
Solar Oven (#22).

RAIN Magazine—Journal of Appropriate Technology, 10 issues a year for $10.00, from RAIN, 2270 N.W. Irving, Portland, Oregon, 97210, USA.

This magazine continues to be the most significant American voice calling for the development of appropriate technology that fits North American circumstances. The journal serves to encourage communications among groups in the Pacific Northwest of the United States (that area beginning to be known as 'Ecotopia'). Includes news and notes on groups, books, and other publications along with a few articles on subjects of broader American interest. A dedicated good-humored staff is committed to unearthing the best, serious documentation supporting arguments for environmentally-sound, decentralized, human-scale technology in the U.S. Not directly relevant to developing countries. RAIN is essential reading for anyone in the U.S. interested in the above approach. The magazine has a 'living lightly' subscription rate for people with low incomes.

Highly recommended.

The Mother Earth News, magazine, 6 issues per year, $10.00 per year in U.S. and Canada, $12.00 per year foreign, from The Mother Earth News, P.O. Box 70, Hendersonville, North Carolina 28739, USA (they also sell books from this address—see publisher's listing).

This is a leading magazine among Americans dissatisfied with the high-polluting, fast pace of American life, who are interested in living closer to the land. It has articles on farming, organic gardening, alternative sources of energy, and a variety of simple techniques and equipment. There are many ideas and personal stories by people who have designed, built, and used a variety of equipment and techniques in North American rural settings; but the articles are rarely in depth and tend to overlook the problems encountered.

The limitations (as we see them) of this magazine for readers in developing countries are the following: 1) the text is often not in standard English, 2) few thorough detailed plans are presented—most articles are short idea pieces and brief descriptions, 3) the vast amount of other information (such as classified ads and specifically U.S.-oriented articles) tends to overwhelm the one or two items of relevance to developing countries that appear in each issue.

Organic Gardening and Farming, magazine, monthly, $7.85 for 1 year for U.S. residents, $9.35 for 1 year for foreign residents, from Organic Gardening and Farming, Rodale Press, 33 East Minor St., Emmaus, Pennsylvania 18049, USA.

This is a magazine on small-scale agricultural techniques that do not use chemical fertilizers or pesticides. Also includes information on appropriate technology tools for agriculture and home use. They have begun to include articles on pedal-powered equipment, for example (see review of a reprint from the May 1976 issue, on page 192).

Undercurrents magazine, 6 issues per year, $7.50 per year in U.S. and Canada ($6.50 surface mail to all other countries; airmail rates vary), from Undercurrents Subscriptions, 11 Shadwell, Uley, Dursley, Gloucestershire, England.

A journal of people's technology in the United Kingdom, full of news notes on groups and events, and information on small-scale 'alternative' technology that fits conditions in that country. They try to keep ITDG honest by continually pointing out how intermediate technology can be taken over by the powerful members of the community unless the poorer members are somehow organized politically. While most of the subject matter is not of direct interest to people in developing countries, this magazine should prove to be of considerable interest to alternative technologists within other developed countries. A delightful, humorous, irreverent style.

Rural Development Network Bulletin, free from Overseas Liaison Committee, American Council on Education, Washington DC 20036, USA.

"The RDN Bulletin is designed to facilitate an exchange of information about the design, planning, and implementation of rural development projects and programs in the developing world. It is published three times a year in English, French, and Spanish."

Self-Reliance Newsletter, 6 issues per year, $6 for individuals and $12 for institutions, from Self-Reliance Newsletter, The Institute for Local Self-Reliance, 1717 18th Street N.W., Washington D.C. 20009, USA.

This is the newsletter of the Institute for Local Self-Reliance. Addresses problems facing the United States, particularly urban problems. Articles, news notes, book reviews. Not very relevant to problems of developing countries, but essential reading for Americans interested in self-reliance as part of the development of small-scale technology suitable to the conditions in the U.S.

Compendium, Wind and Solar Energy for Water Pumping, short newsletter, published occasionally, from TOOL.

This is a limited distribution newsletter for people actively doing work on wind and solar energy uses for water pumping in developing countries. Notes on organizations and experimental results from all over the world.

TAICH News, 4 page newsletter, 5 or 6 times a year, free from Technical Assistance Information Clearing House, 200 Park Ave. So., New York, N.Y. 10003, USA.

Contains information on American and foreign international agencies doing technical assistance work in developing countries. Book reviews, notes on conferences and workshops also included. Increasingly has information on the subject of appropriate technology.

TRANET, c/o William Ellis, 7410 Vernon Square Drive, Alexandria, Virginia 22306, USA ($15.00 for four issues).

TRANET is a quarterly newsletter-directory which gives descriptions of AT centers around the world. The intent is to help develop a network so that centers with similar experience can make direct contacts. Some literature reviewed. Started following the UN HABITAT conference. From what we have seen of TRANET, it is both valuable and expensive for such a short newsletter. There may be discounts for Third World appropriate technology groups.

FURTHER REFERENCES FOR PERIODICALS

Contact, a journal on health care in developing countries; see review on page 254.
Wind Power Digest, see review on page 151.
Pedal Power News Notes, see review on page 196.
World Neighbors Newsletter, see review on page 49.
CoEvolution Quarterly, features a 'soft technology' review section; see notes with Whole Earth Catalog publications reviewed on page 51.

GLOSSARY:
TECHNICAL TERMS

Glossary

The following words are defined as they are used in the text.

abrasives—substances used for grinding, polishing, sanding, etc., such as sandpaper.

acetate plastic—a clear plastic sheet that can easily be marked with a pen or other writing instrument.

acidity—the degree to which a substance has the properties of an acid.

acupuncture—the traditional Chinese art of healing and eliminating pain through the use of needles and pressure points.

adhesive (solder, glue)—a substance used to permanently join two objects.

adobe—unburnt sun-dried brick.

aeration—contact with oxygen or air.

aerobic composting—process of decomposition while oxygen is present.

aerodynamics—the study of the motion of air and the forces acting on bodies in motion (such as windgenerator blades).

agitator type washing machine—a machine in which the dirt is loosened from clothing through the up-and-down motion of one or more pistons or other part, which serve to move the water.

agribusiness—a term describing highly-centralized agriculture operations in developed countries, where agriculture is a business rather than a way of life.

airfoil—the shape of an airplane wing or a windgenerator blade; designed for high-speed movement through air.

algae—small water plants, valuable as a protein source and animal feed or raw material for a methane digester.

alkaline—having a high level of soluble salts; this can make agriculture difficult.

alkali-puddled clay—a building material; clay is mixed with water and lime to create an easily-shaped material that is durable.

alloy—a metal made of a mixture of two or more common metals.

alternator—a machine for changing mechanical energy into electrical energy; a kind of generator that initially produces alternating current.

aluminized Mylar—a very strong thin sheet of plastic material coated with aluminum.

amenities in the workshop—special tools in the workshop.

ammeter—an instrument which measures the strength of an electric current in the form of amperes (amps).

anemometer—a simple device that is used to measure wind speed.

angle iron—pieces of iron or steel with a cross-sectional shape like the letter "L".

animal husbandry—a branch of agriculture concerned with the production and care of animals.

anvil—a blacksmith's tool; a heavy steel block on which metal is pounded for shaping.

apparatus—equipment.

appliance—a small device for performing a specific task; in the U.S., especially household devices that use electricity.

aquaculture—fish farming or the cultivation of other organisms that live in water.

arc welder—a kind of welding machine that uses an electric current passing across a gap to produce the necessary heat.

Archimedes screw—a water lifting device that has a screw-shaped rotating blade and axle inside a cylinder.

arid—dry.

armature—the iron core with wire wound around it, in a generator, alternator, or electric motor.

auxiliary generating equipment—additional electric generating equipment; for example, a unit that can be used during periods when there is no wind to operate a wind generator.

bagasse—the part of sugar cane that is left after the cane has been crushed and the juice has been removed.

baled hay—hay that has been compressed into bundles and tied.

band saw—a saw that has a long narrow continuous band for a blade; the band travels in one direction only, rotating around several wheels.

barefoot doctors—local health workers doing preventive medicine and basic health care without lengthy medical training or expensive equipment; originated as a description of local health workers in China.

barrel staves—narrow, curved strips of wood which form the sides of a wooden barrel.

batch process (methane digester)—a system in which the digester is loaded only at the beginning of a digestion cycle; gas production varies considerably during the digestion period.

BB shells—pieces of metal which serve as a case for steel balls in ball bearings.

bearing—any part of a machine on which another part revolves.

bellows—a blacksmith's device for forcing air into a fire to increase the rate of fuel consumption and thus the temperature.

belt sander—a machine with a long abrasive belt that travels around two or more rotating cylinders; the belt is used for sanding and smoothing rough pieces of wood.

bicycle caliper brake—a bicycle hand operated brake, that has two arms that can be forced to rub on the rim of the wheel to slow the bicycle.

bicycle hub—the center of the wheel which revolves around the axle.

bicycle sprocket—a gear.

bio-dynamic—a principle of agriculture stressing the relationships between different kinds of plants, the soil, and nutrients.

bio-gas—see methane gas.

bio-gas plant—see methane digester.

biological control—control of insects and other pests using natural means (predators, competitors, bacteria); non-chemical methods.

bio-mass energy—energy from biological sources.

bit—the cutting edge of a tool.

bow saw—a saw operated by a foot treadle with an overhead bow which acts as a spring mechanism; together they pull the saw blade up and down.

brackish—water with a heavy salt content, such as in inland seas.

brazing—to bond two pieces of metal using a metal rod with a lower melting temperature than either of the pieces to be connected; usually uses copper wire, and can be done with a small propane torch.

breastshot (breast) water wheel—a water wheel driven by water entering near the mid-point of the wheel.

broadcast sower—a device which spreads seeds over a small area by throwing them through the air.

BTU—British Thermal Unit; a measure of heat energy; specifically, the amount of heat required to raise the temperature of one pound of water one degree

Fahrenheit.

buffer—a machine for polishing metal.

bunsen burner—a simple gas burner.

burlap—coarse material used to make sacks and bags, usually made out of jute; also called 'gunny sacks'.

bushing—a round lining for an opening, used to limit the size of the opening, resist wear, or serve as a guide.

butyl rubber basin liner—a kind of plastic sheet used to prevent liquid from leaking through a basin.

calcium chloride—CaCl2.

capital—money; or equipment that represents an investment in money.

capital-intensive—techniques that have a high equipment-to-labor ratio to accomplish a particular task; an automobile is a much more capital-intensive form of transportation than is a bicycle.

carbonized plant material—dry plant matter high in carbon content that will make a building material; straw, thatch, palm leaves.

carbon/nitrogen ratio—the proportion of carbon to nitrogen in the material being placed in a methane digester; there is a proper ratio that allows maximum gas production and a proper chemical reaction.

carding machine—a machine used to prepare cotton or wool for spinning.

cash crop—a crop grown for sale outside the area, often not a food crop; for example, rubber, quinine, cloves, coffee.

casting (verb)—the process of making products from a mold usually using hot molten (liquid) metal.

casting (noun)—a product made from a mold; the result of the above process.

catalyst—something which acts to help a process take place.

caulking—a filling material used to make a boat or other object 'water-tight' so that water cannot enter or escape.

chaff—the seed coverings and other material separated from the grain during threshing.

chaff cutter—a tool which is used to chop dry vegetative materials such as straw into small pieces.

chain pump—a pump with an endless chain passing over a wheel at the top and entering a pipe below the water; it is fitted with discs which lift the water through the pipe.

chainsaw—a portable power saw that has teeth linked together to form an endless chain.

channel iron—pieces of iron or steel which have the cross-sectional shape of a channel.

churn—a container in which milk or cream is beaten to form butter.

circular sump—a circular pit lined with bricks, cement, or other material to hold wet material without losing the moisture.

clods—large dried pieces of soil that must be broken up before planting.

coefficients of transmission of heat—generally accepted statistics about the rate at which heat will move through different materials.

cogs—the teeth on the rim of a wheel, for transmitting or receiving motion by fitting between the teeth of another wheel.

color patina—surface color of metal, caused by the hardening proces in black-smithing or long exposure to air.

commutator—in a generator or electric motor, a revolving part that collects the electric current from, or distributes it to, the brushes.

compacted—something that is compressed and packed firmly together.

composting—a method for breaking down organic solids (such as leaves, straw and manure) into easily used fertilizer.

condensation—the process whereby water vapor in the air changes its form into a liquid.

conduit tube—lightweight metal tube usually used for protecting electrical wires.

connecting rod—a rod connecting by back and forth motion two or more moving parts of a machine; for example, the connecting rod between the crankshaft and piston in an automobile engine.

contacts (electricity)—metal points which when touching allow electricity to flow through a circuit.

continuous process (methane digester)—a system in which the digester has a small amount of material added each day; gas production remains fairly constant.

converter—a device employing mechanical rotation for changing electrical energy from one form to another.

cooper—someone who makes or repairs wooden barrels.

copra—coconut meat dried for storage and transport; used to produce coconut oil.

corn (maize) sheller—a tool used to remove the kernels (seeds) from pieces of corn.

corrosive—causing the wearing away of metal or other material by rusting or the action of chemicals.

counterweight—a weight equal to another, to balance it.

crankshaft—a shaft used to transfer rotational motion into up-and-down motion; or the reverse.

crop diversification—the practice of growing a variety of plant crops within a particular area; opposite of 'monoculture.'

crop duster—a device for spreading pesticides or herbicides in the form of dust or spray.

crop rotation—a practice of changing the kind of crop grown on a particular plot after each harvest, to protect the soil from becoming exhausted.

crucible—a container used to hold metal while it is being melted.

cultivator/cultivating—an implement to loosen the soil and remove weeds while crops are growing/the process of doing this.

culture plates—glass microscope slide plates used to observe blood samples and other very tiny materials.

culvert—a drain that passes under a road, railroad, footpath, etc.

curing (cement)—physical processing with water to help the cement reach its maximum strength.

curing (fish)—to preserve by chemical or physical processing.

curing (hides or skins)—to preserve by chemical or physical processing, for future use.

current regulator—an electrical device which controls the level of current (amperes) passing through an electrical circuit.

currier—a worker who treats leather.

cutout—a switch which cuts the electric circuit to a windgenerator under two conditions: 1) windspeed too low to charge the batteries, and 2) windspeed so high that electical output threatens to damage the system.

Darrieus rotor—a vertical-axis windmachine that has long thin blades in the shape of loops, connected at the top and bottom of the axle; often called the 'eggbeater' windmill because of its appearance.

data processing—a method for evaluating and using information, usually by means of a computer.

decomposition (bacterial)—the chemical breakdown of organic matter by micro-organisms.

decoy—a plant which attracts insects away from other, more valuable plants.

defecation—the act of passing human waste out of the body.

dehydrate—to remove water from fruits and vegetables, for preservation (drying).

demystify—to remove the mystery from; to make something understandable.

detention time—the time period that incoming material is retained in a methane digester for processing.

diaphragm pump—a pump which moves water through the alternating expansion and contraction of a chamber.

die—a metal-working cutting tool, e.g. for cutting screw-threads in a steel rod.

differential—an arrangement of gears connecting two axles in the same line and dividing the driving force between them, but allowing one axle to turn faster than the other when necessary; it is used in the rear axles of automobiles to permit a difference in the speeds of the two wheels while turning corners; also has the characteristic that the shaft comes in at a 90-degree angle to the axle, and does not turn at the same rpm.

digestion—the process by which organic materials are decomposed by the action of bacteria, producing gas and fertilizer.

distilled water—water that has been evaporated and condensed so that all chemicals and salts have been removed; pure H_2O.

drag (aerodynamics)—the slowing force acting on a blade or wing moving through air.

drainage—the removal of surface water.

draught chain—a heavy chain used to pull objects, such as a harrow.

drill press—a machine for drilling holes in metal or wood.

drive shaft—a shaft that transmits motion or power, as from the transmission to the rear axle of an automobile.

dry cell battery—a battery that uses dry chemical activity for storage of electricity; cannot be recharged.

dung—animal waste, manure, shit, excreta.

dynamo—see generator.

earth auger—a device for drilling narrow diameter holes for wells.

ecologically-sound—any approach which fully considers and does not affect the natural balance of the environment and ecosystem.

ecosystem—a system made up of a community of people, animals, plants and bacteria, and the physical and chemical environment with which it is connected.

electro-magnetic device—a core of magnetic material surrounded by a coil or wire through which an electric current is passed to magnetize the core; used in switches.

emulsified asphalt—asphalt in liquid form, containing some kind of solvent which breaks it into tiny drops.

energy-gobbling American homes—homes built in North America that consume enormous amounts of energy in the form of gas and electricity.

environment—the physical and biological surroundings.

environmentally-sound—see ecologically-sound.

erosion—the wearing away of land, soil, and other earth formations by wind, water, or ice.

escapement mechanism (clock)—the special gearing inside a clock that allows a sprocket to turn one notch at a time.

evaporation—the process whereby water changes from a liquid to a vapor and disappears into the air.

excreta—human or animal waste matter; shit.

eyebolt—a bolt which has one circular end through which a piece of wire or rope can be passed.

farrier—a blacksmith that makes horseshoes (metal bands) and attaches them to horses' hooves.

feathering mechanism—a mechanism on a windmill which in strong winds turns the blades increasingly out of the wind; this slows the windmill and protects it from damage.

feed grinder—a tool used to grind food into very small pieces so that fish or other animals can eat it.

ferrocement—cement-sand concrete reinforced by wire mesh.

fiberglass—glass in the form of small fibers (similar to hairs), used in making insulation and harder structures such as boats.

fibrous insulation (local)—insulation made of local plant or animal materials such as coconut husks or animal hair.

field (electricity)—magnetic forces created by an electric current; important in the operation of a generator or alternator.

flametrap device—a unit to prevent the flame from backing up along a gas pipeline towards the source.

flange—a rim for attachment to another part, usually on a pipe or a wheel.

flat plate collector—a glass or plastic-covered metal panel which traps the solar energy that falls on it; this heat is then transferred by a water or air system for hot water heating or home heating.

flow—the amount of water that moves past a point in a given amount of time; often measured in liters per second.

flue—a pipe through which smoke or hot air passes.

flue duct—an opening to a flue which can be regulated to affect the amount of air passing through; this has an effect of regulating the rate of fuel consumption and the temperature in a fireplace or kiln.

fluorescent tube—an electric light bulb that uses a tube of fluoride gas instead of a wire filament; usually 2½ times as efficient as a standard electric light bulb—this means that a 40-watt fluorescent tube provides as much light as a 100-watt electric bulb.

flywheel—a heavy, rotating wheel used to moderate any variations in the speed of the machinery with which it revolves.

foam composite—an industrialized lightweight material.

forage crops—crops valuable as animal feed.

forge—a blacksmith's furnace for heating iron and steel hot enough so that it can be shaped by pounding.

formica—rigid plastic product.

foundation (building)—the base on which a structure rests; usually of concrete, stone, or blocks, and positioned partially underground.

foundry (iron)—a workshop where iron is melted and poured into molds to make tools.

freewheel (bicycle)—an arrangement in the rear hub which allows the rear gear to either drive the wheel or rotate freely when not being pedaled.

funnel—a device with a large opening on one end and a smaller opening on the other; used to pour liquid into a bottle, for example.

furrow—a shallow channel made in a field by a plow.

fuse—a wire or strip of easily melted metal, placed in an electrical circuit; if the current becomes too strong, the metal melts, cutting the circuit before the entire wiring system is destroyed.

gabled roof—a roof with two sloping surfaces that meet at a line along the top in an inverted "V" shape.

galvanized—coated with zinc for protection from rust and corrosion.

gas compression—gas must be pressurized so that it can be burned effectively.

gear down—to arrange gears or pulleys so that the original speed of rotation of a pedal-power unit, windmill, or water wheel is decreased; for example, to operate a winch.

gear up—to arrange gears or pulleys so that the original speed of rotation of a pedal-power unit, windmill, or water wheel is increased; for example, this would be necessary to generate electricity.

generator—a machine for changing mechanical energy (such as the rotation of a windmill rotor) into electrical energy; has a stationary field and rotating armature, and produces direct current electricity.

glaze—in ceramics, the coating given before the final firing (placement in the kiln for heat treatment); helps to seal the clay and adds color to the object.

glazing—on a flat plate collector for solar water heating—the plastic or glass covering.

gobar gas—methane gas (CH_4).

grain silo—a long-term storage chamber for grains; usually water- and air-tight to prevent spoilage and insect damage.

grass wilderness—a name for rain forest land which has had all of the trees and cover vegetation removed the soil can only support the growth of hardy grasses, and is very difficult to restore to fertility; sometimes called a 'green desert.'

green manure—a crop which is plowed back under into the soil while still green, for its beneficial nitrogen-adding effect on the soil.

greenhouse—a glass or plastic covered building used to trap solar energy and protect plants from bugs, wind, rain, cold, evaporation of moisture; allows a controlled environment.

greenhouse effect—heat from sunlight is trapped inside any closed container with a glass or plastic cover.

grindstone—a hard stone for grinding grain; or a revolving stone for sharpening tools or shaping and polishing objects.

ground water—water found underground, for example, in a well.

guy wires—wires attached to a tower, for example, so that it cannot move or shake due to the wind.

hacksaw—a handtool used to cut metal.

handyman skills—general maintenance and repair skills.

hardware store—a kind of store in the United States which sells small tools, nuts and bolts, wire, plumbing parts, and miscellaneous metal parts with a wide variety of uses.

head—the total usable height water falls when used in a water wheel, turbine, or hydraulic ram; or the distance water is lifted by a pump.

health auxiliaries—health workers that have undergone a short training period, but are not among the categories normally thought of as 'professionals.'

heat exchanger—any unit which is designed to pass heat from one fluid or material to another.

heat pump—a device that extracts heat from one location and distributes it to another, by expanding and contracting a fluid; one unit of energy used to operate the pump can allow 4 units of heat energy to be captured; due to the unique characteristics of this kind of a pump, heat energy can actually be extracted from a cold area (such as the inside of a refrigerator) and distributed to a warmer area (which seems to defy the normal laws governing the movement of heat energy).

heater duct tape—a wide, strong variety of tape that serves to prevent heat loss in hot air pipes.

herbicide—a chemical substance used to kill or control weeds or other undesirable plants.

hermetic storage—air-tight storage.

high carbon steel—steel that has a relatively high carbon content and can be hardened for this reason.

high-tech—complicated technology that requires a specialized industrial base to produce and service it.

hinges—metal pieces that connect doors and windows to walls.

hipped roof—a roof with four sloping surfaces coming to a point at the top.

hoist—a device for raising another object; a kind of winch.

hollow block mold—a mold used to make hollow building blocks that maintain the strength of solid blocks but are lighter in weight.

horticulture—the science and art or growing fruits, vegetables, and flowers.

huller—a machine used to remove the outer coverings (hulls) from rice, peanuts or other agricultural product.

humus—black or brown decomposed organic matter.

hybrid—a new variety created by plant breeding, often producing higher yields but genetically sterile (the crop cannot be used for seed).

hydraulic—using water or other liquid.

hydraulic ram pump—a device used to pump water with no other power source; uses the impact of the water itself to pump a small portion of the water to a higher level than the original source.

hydraulics—the study of the properties of water and other liquids within engineering.

hydroelectric unit—a unit that generates electricity from falling water.

hydroponics—the cultivation of plants without the use of soil.

impacted soil—soil which has been compressed to make it firmer.

incubator—a special compartment used to keep chicken eggs or premature babies at a warm temperature.

indigenous—originally from the area.

input—what is put in.

insolation—the amount of solar energy falling on an area, usually measured in BTU's per unit of area.

insulation—material used to reduce the transfer of heat through a wall, a roof, the back of a solar water heater, or the walls of a fireless cooker.

intake—the place where water enters the pump.

intensive methods—gardening techniques used on small plots to obtain high yields; the productive potential of the soil is increased through composting, aeration, and other techniques.

intermittent—an activity that starts and stops irregularly.

invertebrates—spineless organisms.

inverter (electricity)—a device for converting direct current into alternating current by mechanical or electronic means.

jacks and lifts—devices for raising objects using teeth or threads or a hydraulic system.

khadi—a word used by Mahatma Gandhi, referring to hand-spun cloth made by small cottage industries or individuals; also used to describe a policy based on village self-reliance stressing local production of food, clothing and other things to meet local needs.

kiln—a structure for the high-temperature treatment of bricks, or pottery for hardening; or for the conversion of limestone to lime, used as a cement-like material in building.

labor bottleneck—a period during the season when total output is limited by the fact that all available labor is being used; under these circumstances, labor-saving equipment will not destroy any jobs.

labor-intensive—techniques or projects that have a low capital to labor ratio.

laminated blade—a blade made of thin sheets of wood glued and pressed together.

lattice—pieces of wood interwoven together with spaces in-between.

latrine—a device for depositing and isolating human waste.

leaching—the draining away of important soil nutrients by water action.

leap-frog—to jump over.

legumes—plants that add nitrogen to the soil, such as soybeans or any other beans.

lift (aerodynamics)—the part of the total aerodynamic force acting in a direction perpendicular to the relative wind; opposes gravity in an airplane.

lift (water-pumping)—the height water is raised by a pump.

lime—calcium oxide; a cement-like substance used in building (for mortars and plasters).

lime kiln—a furnace used to make lime from coral or limestone.

limestone—a rock that is formed mainly by the accumulation of organic remains (such as shells or coral); consists mainly of calcium carbonate and is used extensively in building; yields lime when burned.

linkage mechanisms—connecting mechanisms.

litmus paper—paper which is used in a simple chemical test for acidity or alkalinity of water or soil.

load (electricity)—the amount of power moving through an electrical circuit at any moment; or the device which is using this power; or the amount of power that a generator is producing.

loading rate—the amount and timing of loads of material being placed in a methane digester; important in obtaining an optimum concentration of solids.

low-impact technology—technology that fits into the human and biological environment with very little disruption or consumption of resources.

lye (caustic soda)—a strong alkaline solution rich in potassium carbonate, leached from wood ashes; used in making soap.

machining—precision work on metal.

machete—a large knife, used for chopping brush and other heavy cutting.

malnutrition—inadequate nutrition.

manure—animal excreta; shit; dung.

masonite—thin board made from compressed wood fibers.

masonry—the fitting together of cut or formed blocks or bricks.

mechanization—replacing hand tools with machines.

metal primer—a first protective layer of paint; usually to combat rust and build a base for additional layers of paint.

methane gas—a naturally-occuring gas (CH_4) that can be produced using a methane gas digester system; this gas burns at about 2/3 the level BTU (British

Thermal Units) of natural gas.

methane (or bio-gas) digester—a device which through biological activity produces methane gas and fertilizer from animal manures and crop residues (such as straw and leaves).

Michell water turbine—a turbine with curved vanes and hollow center; water passing through it propels the turbine both when entering and leaving; considered by many people to by the most practical easily constructed water turbine; operates well under a range of head and flow rates.

microbiological action—activity by tiny organisms; for example, decomposition in the soil.

micro-organism—a very tiny organism that can only be viewed through a microscope.

mild steel—low carbon steel; easily shaped but cannot be hardened.

modes of transport—types of transport; bicycles, cars and buses are all different modes of transport.

mold—a container in the shape of a desired product, used to form building blocks or for casting metal parts.

monoculture—the practice of using only one crop variety in a given area; the crop tends to be more vulnerable to attack by pests and diseases than in a diversified crop area.

morbidity—the level of disease (incidence of disease) among the population.

mulch—a top covering of the soil consisting of organic materials (grass, compost, dead weeds) that serves to keep moisture in the soil.

multi-blade (fan) windmills—a windmill design, common on American farms, which has a large number of blades and is usually used for water-pumping.

Mylar—see aluminized Mylar.

networking—the process of making people with similar interests aware of each other, to increase communication and cooperation.

neutralize (magnetic field)—to stop the action of a magnetic field.

nipples (bicycle)—small threaded pieces of metal which serve to attach the spokes to the rim of a bicycle.

nitriding—a process used in hardening forged steel.

novice—beginner.

nutrients—substances vital for growth and development of organisms, such as vitamins, fertilizers, protein, etc.

oil press—a tool used to crush oil-bearing vegetable material to extract the oil.

optics—having to do with the properties of light.

organic—of, related to, or coming from living organisms.

organic agriculture—a form of agriculture that uses only natural materials and techniques.

organic manures—waste material from natural sources, such as animal dung and decaying plants.

output—what is produced.

overhaul—to check thoroughly and make needed repairs.

overshot water wheel—a water wheel driven by water entering near the top.

panacea—a cure for all problems.

parabola—a shape commonly used in solar cookers to focus sunlight on a small area so that it becomes very hot.

parabolic cylinder—a solar energy device with a cross-sectional shape of a parabola; sunlight is focused all along the length of a pipe or tube.

parabolic dish—a solar energy device shaped like a dish or bowl, having the characteristics of a parabola and focusing sunlight on a point or a very small area.

parboiling (or para-boiling) rice—a preliminary cooking process which serves to seal the outer surface of the rice.

patent—a license giving the inventer or patent owner the exclusive right to make, use, or sell a particular invention for a period of years.

paternalistic—resembling the relationship a father has with his children.

pathogens—dangerous and harmful micro-organisms, such as bacteria and viruses; found in human and other wastes, responsible for spreading diseases.

pedal thresher—a lightweight machine operated by foot power, that is designed to be carried easily into the fields for use in threshing; mainly a wooden drum revolving at about 450 rpm, driven by a pedal and gearing system.

pelton impulse wheel—a kind of water-power device which is driven by the impact of a jet of water; can be used to generate electricity.

perennial crops—crops in which individual plants continue to produce each season for a period of years.

pesticide—a chemical substance which kills plant pests (insects and rodents).

pipe nipple—a pipe connector with threaded fittings.

piston pump—a pump which raises water by the up-and-down motion of a rod with a valve, on the inside of a cylinder.

planned obsolescence—a deliberate attempt by manufacturers to produce an item that will be rapidly out of style or no longer used.

plowshare—the cutting blade of a plow.

plumbing float control valve—a valve commonly used in flush toilets, which allows water to slowly fill a tank until the floating ball reaches the desired water level, and the valve is closed; can also be used in a variety of other systems such as an oil-drum storage tank for a solar water heating unit.

pole saw—a saw operated by a foot treadle with an overhead pole which acts as a spring mechanism; together they pull the saw blade up and down.

polythene—a kind of plastic.

potable water—safe drinking water.

potter's kick wheel or **potter's wheel**—a tool used to form cups, bowls and other round objects; a heavy flywheel on the bottom allows smooth work on the clay.

poultry—chickens and similar birds raised for meat.

power co-efficient—the percentage of the total available power in the wind that a windmachine can capture at any specific windspeed.

power output—the amount of mechanical or electrical power produced.

precision file guide—a tool that aids in sharpening chain saw blades.

privy—a kind of latrine; usually a platform with a hole over a pit, for isolation of human waste.

propane torch—a hand-held torch that burns propane gas; used for workshop activities.

protective canopy—a plant cover, in the form of shrubs or trees, which protects the soil from the harsh effect of sun, wind and rain; particularly important in tropical forests that receive heavy rainfall.

pvc pipe—polyvinyl chloride (plastic) pipe, made from petroleum products.

radiating plate—a metal plate which serves to pass the heat from a fire underneath to the area or substance being heated; prevents direct contact with the flames and smoke of the fire.

ravine—a small narrow valley with steep sides, created by a stream.

reaming—work using a tool called a 'reamer' to smooth out or enlarge the inside of a pipe.

recycling—reusing; processing in order to reuse material.

refractory materials—heat resistant materials.

reinforcing rod or **rebar**—metal rod used to increase the strength of concrete.

relay—an electro-magnetic device for automatic control that is operated by variation in conditions of an electric current; used to operate other devices (such as switches).

rendering fat—melting fat until it becomes a liquid.

ripping chain—a tool used on a chainsaw for cutting along the length of a log, instead of across it.

riveting—binding of metal to metal using small pins (rivets) pounded on both sides.

root crops—the roots are the parts that are eaten; for example, potatoes and carrots.

rotating wooden drum washing machine—a machine that loosens the dirt in clothing by the rotating action of a drum or barrel inside a tub of water.

rpm—revolutions per minute.

rudiments—the elementary steps or information.

runoff agriculture—a form of cultivation totally dependent upon water which can be channeled onto the fields during and immediately following rains.

sail cloth—cloth normally used on sailing ships.

sail windmill—a kind of windmill that uses removable cloth sails (usually 4-8) as the blades.

sailwing windmill—a kind of windmill that has a small number (usually 2 or 3) of blades that are usually made of cloth and are shaped like an airfoil (the shape of an airplane wing).

saline water—water with a high level of salts.

savannah—a treeless plain found in tropical and subtropical regions; a transition zone between rain forest and desert.

Savonius rotor—a windmachine with a vertical-axis, usually made from split oil drums.

sawyer—someone whose job is to saw wood.

scum controlling device—a mechanism that is used to break up the thick layer of materials that rises to the surface in a methane digester; this layer tends to prevent the production of gas.

sealant—a substance such as wax, plastic or silicone used for sealing, to make a substance air-tight or water-tight.

seed drill—a tool which places seeds into the ground.

seed propagation—to produce seeds for future use.

sewage—human waste material carried away by water.

shanty—substandard crude shelter.

shingles—overlapping pieces of wood or other material used in roofing.

shop tools—tools that are commonly found only in small workshops; usually mechanized.

short out (electricity)—to allow the electric current to go in a shorter path, thus preventing the normal action of a circuit, by connecting two wires that are not normally connected.

shrouded windmill—a windmill with a funnel around the outside edge of the swept area which forces wind from a larger area to pass through the blades.

sieve—a device with small holes or screen to separate larger particles.

silicone sealant—a plastic compound used to seal a container so that water cannot enter or escape from it.

silk-screen printing—a printing process in which ink is forced through a cloth screen that has some parts of it blocked to create the design.

sizing—determining the proper size; or separating according to size (for example, 'sizing peanuts').

skilsaw—a hand-held electric saw with a circular blade.

skylight—a glass or plastic piece of a roof which allows light to enter a house or a room.

slash and burn shifting cultivation—the practice of cutting and burning forest vegetation to open land for subsistence agriculture in tropical countries; usually by small farmers; the soil is exhausted within 5 years and the farmers must move on to clear more forest.

sludge—the outflow of a digester or sewage treatment plant.

sludge treatment ponds—basins in which sewage, animal manures, and other wastes are broken down.

slurry—diluted waste material as it is placed into a digester.

small holder—someone who owns only a small amount of land or some product.

smoker—a device used in beekeeping—a hand-bellows with some burning material which produces smoke to force the bees to move out of or into the hive.

soil cement—a mixture used to make blocks without sand and with a low proportion of cement.

soil-conservation—a policy of maintaining and promoting the health and fertility of the soil; for example, by planting trees to prevent erosion.

solar distillation—a process in which solar energy is trapped and used to evaporate water, which then condenses as pure water that can be used for drinking.

soldering—a technique of lightweight metal bonding, by melting a soft metal at a lower temperature than in brazing.

soldering iron—a small tool used in lightweight metal bonding.

solvent—a liquid substance capable of dissolving or dispersing another substance.

sowing—planting seed, especially by throwing (broadcast sowing) or use of a mechanical metered device.

space heating—heating the air in a house, room or small area.

spinning wheel—used to make cloth thread.

spokes—the bars or wires extending between the hub and rim of a bicycle or cart wheel.

spoon-tilt hammer—a device that has a hammer at one end, a balancing point, and a bucket-shaped (spoon-shaped) hollow at the other end; the bucket end is slowly filled by a continuous flow of water from a pipe or stream; as the water fills this end it begins to drop down, which raises the hammer end; the water is able to escape when the bucket tilts too far, and the hammer then falls; the hammer can be used in a blacksmith's shop, and the same principle has been used to pound rice to remove the hulls.

spring leaf—high carbon steel, tempered to be very hard and respond like a spring; used in automobile springs.

squatter settlements—areas where poor people have moved in to live on previously unoccupied land.

stabilized soil—soil that has had emulsified asphalt, cement or other material added; used to make blocks.

stabilizing agent—a substance that binds or makes firm, such as cement or lime; usually used in making building blocks.

staves—see barrel staves.

stroboscope—a revolving disc with holes around the edge which allow flashes of light to pass through it at regular intervals.

stryrofoam—an industrially-created material that is used for insulation, floating objects, and packaging.

subsistence agriculture—a system of farming in which the family produces all or almost all of their own goods, including food, tools, cloths, etc.; there is usually not a significant surplus for sale.

suction pump—a pump which lifts liquids only by creating a vacuum above the liquid level; used to lift water but only to about 20-25 feet (33 feet is the theoretical maximum).

sugar cane crusher—a tool used to flatten sugar cane stalks and extract the juice which contains the sugar.

superphosphate—a synthetic chemical fertilizer; a combination of rock phosphate and other chemicals.

symptoms—evidence of disease.

synthetic—man-made; non-natural.

synthetic fertilizer—an artificial substance which helps plants grow and develop.

swampy areas—land that is always wet.

swelling soils—soils that expand and shrink under conditions of changing pressure, water content, or temperature.

table saw—a saw with a rotating circular blade that has a flat surface built around it like a table.

tanner—someone who tans (preserves) animal hides and skins.

tarpaper—a thick paper product soaked in asphalt; used for water-proofing in roofs and walls.

tempering steel—hardening steel.

thermosiphon principle—heated liquids tend to rise; in a solar water heater, this principle can be used to enable circulation of water from a flat plate collector to a storage tank located above it, without the use of a pump.

thresher—a machine used to separate grain or beans from the unwanted straw or other plant material.

tie-ridging—a technique of field preparation in Africa, in which channels between ridges are periodically blocked by earth, to trap rain water and prevent drainage.

tiller—a device for plowing the soil; a cultivator.

tin snips—a tool similar to scissors, for cutting sheet metal.

tines—the teeth on a rake, harrow or cultivator.

tinkerer—a person who likes to make gadgets and inventions, but not in a serious manner.

tip-speed ratio—the ratio of the speed of the tip of a windmachine blade to the speed of the wind; a low tip-speed ratio (such as 1:1 in the Savonius rotor) at a moderate wind speed means the windmachine is better adapted to mechanical applications such as water-pumping; a high tip-speed ratio (such as 5:1 in a two-bladed windgenerator) at a moderate wind speed means the windmachine is better adapted to generating electricity.

tongs—a tool used by blacksmiths to pick up hot pieces of metal.

toolbar—a frame to which different tools can be attached for various land preparation activities, such as plowing or cultivating.

topography—the surface features of a region.

torque—the force that acts to produce rotation.

toxic chemicals—poisons which may be harmful to plants, animals and humans.

trailer chassis—the frame of a trailer.

trap—a plant which can eliminate harmful insects.

treadle-power or **treadle-mechanism**—a use of foot power in which an up-and-down motion of the foot on a board produces a rotating motion on a machine.

trowel (verb)—to apply mortar using a trowel (a flat hand tool).

truss—a rigid framework of beams or bars for supporting a roof or bridge.

tubers—plants such as sweet potatoes which can be reproduced by planting pieces of the roots.

turbulence (wind)—wildly irregular motion of air.

turnbuckle—a metal sleeve with opposite internal threads at each end; by turning it, one can tighten or loosen two threaded rods coming together at that point.

twist bit—the cutting edge of a wood drill; has a twisted blade.

undershot water wheel—a water wheel that is turned by water flowing underneath it; for example, by a small river.

updraft and downdraft kilns—the adjective refers to the direction of air movement through the kiln.

urea—a high nitrogen fertilizer made from animal wastes or natural gas using a high-technology, energy-intensive process.

vane—a thin flat or curved object that is rotated about an axis by a flow of water or wind; for example in a windmill or water turbine.

vaulted roof—a roof in the shape of an arc.

ventilation—the circulation of air through a room or enclosed space.

vertical-axis—an axle or axis which runs in a vertical (up and down) direction.

vertical-axis water wheel—a water wheel driven by water coming through a channel and hitting in on one side; has a vertical-axis instead of the usual horizontal axis found on water wheels.

vertical-axis windmill—a windmill such as the Savonius rotor which always faces the wind, regardless of what direction it comes from; this differs from the more common horizontal-axis windmills which must turn to face the wind.

vise—a workshop device used to clamp or hold objects.

voltage—the electric potential between two points, expressed in volts; can be understood as the 'pressure' forcing electricity through the lines similar to pressure in a water system.

voltage regulator—a simple electrical instrument that controls the voltage level of the current from generator to battery (as in an automobile or windgenerator system).

voltmeter—an instrument for measuring voltage.

water-proofing—applying a substance to protect an object from contact with water.

water hammer—see spoon-tilt hammer.

water seal toilet—a human waste disposal system that has a passageway filled with water which prevents odors, gases, and disease organisms from returning through the passageway.

water turbine—a device powered by the reaction or impulse of a current of water subject to pressure; usually has curved blades; is used to generate electricity because it has a higher rpm than a water wheel.

water wheel—a wheel with buckets or paddles which allow it to be turned by falling water or water moving underneath.

welding—high temperature heavy duty metal bonding; arc-welding uses heat created as an electric current passes across a small gap; oxy-acetylene (carbide) welding uses the heat created by burning a mixture of oxygen and acetylene gas.

welding jig—a device used to hold metal that is being welded.

well rings—metal or concrete cylinders placed inside a well to prevent material from the walls from collapsing inward.

wheelwright—someone whose job is the making or repairing of wheels or wheeled vehicles.

winch—a device for hauling, pulling, or raising another object, that allows the operator to slowly move something that he would normally not be able to move at all, through a system of pulleys.

windgenerator—a machine which used wind power to generate electricity.

winding (wire)—a coil of wire; when electricity is passed through this coil a magnetic field is created, which can be used to operate switches.

windmachine—any kind of machine which gets its motion from the wind.

windmill—originally a machine which uses the wind to drive the grinding stones of a mill to make flour from grain; often used to refer to any kind of windmachine, particularly wind-powered machines for water-pumping.

windwheel—any kind of windmachine which has blades or arms in the shape of the spokes of a wheel.

winnower—a machine used to separate grain from hulls or straw.

wire mesh—wire or steel reinforcing bars in a woven pattern; used as reinforcement in ferrocement construction.

workplace—a job, in this context including a calculation of all supporting capital costs for tools.

Yurt—a traditional Mongolian dwelling.

Appendix

A page from an Indonesian village technology booklet. Shows how to make a device for killing rats using gas from burning sulphur. See review of these booklets on page 48.

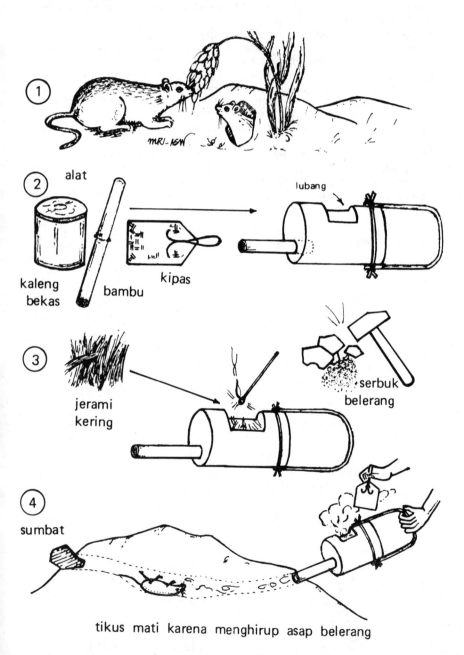

tikus mati karena menghirup asap belerang

Conversion Table

Metric

Length
1 mm = .039 inch (.003 foot)
1 cm = .39 inch (.033 foot)
1 meter = 39.4 inches (3.28 feet)
1 kilometer = 0.62 mile

Area
1 square cm = .155 square inch
1 square meter = 10.8 square feet
1 hectare = 2.47 acres

Volume
1 cubic cm = .061 cubic inch
1 cubic meter = 35.3 cubic feet
1 liter = .264 U.S. gallon

Weight
1 gram = .035 ounce (avoirdupois)
1 kilogram = 2.2 pounds

Temperature
$°C. = 5/9 \times (°F. - 32°)$
Example: How many °C. = **77 °F?**
$5/9 \times (77 °F. - 32°) = $ **25 °C.**

Energy
100 calories = .396 BTU
100 watts = .134 horsepower
  1 kilowatt-hour = 3413 BTU

Common Abbreviations
millimeter (mm)
centimeter (cm)
meter (m)
kilometer (km)
gram (gm)
kilogram (kg)

English

Length
1 inch = 2.54 cm (25.4 mm)
1 foot = 30.5 cm (.305 meter)
1 mile = 1.60 kilometer

Area
1 square inch = 6.45 square cm
1 square foot = .093 square meter
1 acre = 0.4 hectare

Volume
1 cubic inch = 16.4 cubic cm
1 cubic foot = .028 cubic meter
1 U.S. gallon = 3.78 liters

Weight
1 ounce (avoirdupois) = 28.3 grams
1 pound = 0.45 kilogram

Temperature
$°F. = (9/5 \times °C.) + 32°$

Energy
1 BTU (British Thermal Unit)
               = 252 calories
1 horsepower = 746 watts (.746 kw)

Common Abbreviations
inch ('')
foot (ft. or ')
ounce (oz.)
pound (lb.)
horsepower (hp)
British Thermal Unit (BTU)

Additional copies of the **Appropriate Technology Sourcebook** are available at the following prices:

Individuals and organizations in the developed countries including those operating programs overseas: US$4.00 (surface mail) or US$6.50 (airmail).

Individuals and local organizations in developing countries: US$2.00 (surface mail) or US$4.50 (airmail).

A special low-cost edition of Part 1 of the OECD Development Centre book **Appropriate Technology: Problems and Promises** is being offered by us to people in the U.S. and in developing nations. (We are not allowed to offer this to people in any of the 23 industrialized member nations of the OECD.) This 100-page reprint is available from us for US$2.50 in the U.S., and US$2.00 in developing nations. Price includes surface mail postage (add $1.50 for airmail). See review of this publication on page 31. The full 344-page edition is available to anyone, from the address given on page 31, for US$12.50.

We accept UNESCO coupons.

All orders should be sent to: Appropriate Technology Project
Volunteers in Asia
Box 4543
Stanford, California 94305
USA